D0629791

PRACTICAL SURVEYING

PRACTICAL SURVEYING

A TEXT-BOOK FOR STUDENTS PREPARING
FOR EXAMINATIONS OR FOR SURVEY WORK
AT HOME AND OVERSEAS

BY

G. W. USILL,
Assoc.-M.Inst.C.E.

Fifteenth Edition

REVISED BY

K. M. HART, F.R.I.C.S., M.I.Mun.E.
Chartered Surveyor, Chartered Municipal Engineer

LONDON
THE TECHNICAL PRESS LTD.

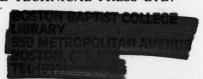

Second Edition, Revised 1888
Reprinted 1889, 1890
Third Edition, Revised 1893
Fourth Edition, Revised 1895
Fifth Edition, Revised 1897
Sixth Edition, Revised 1899
Seventh Edition, Revised 1901
Eighth Edition, Revised 1904
Ninth Edition, Revised 1907
Tenth Edition, Revised 1911
Eleventh Edition, Revised 1915
Twelfth Edition, Revised 1919
Thirteenth Edition, Revised 1926
Fourteenth Edition, Revised 1932
Reprinted 1936, 1938, 1942
1946, 1947, 1949
Fifteenth Edition, Revised 1960

THE TECHNICAL PRESS LTD., 1960

Printed by Willmer Brothers & Haram Ltd., Birkenhead

PREFACE

THE continuing demand for this practical text-book demonstrates how well and truly the late Mr. Usill laid the foundations, and how subsequent Editors have added to the structure, each contributing from their personal experience to the goal of producing a carefully balanced yet comprehensive elementary text-book for practical surveyors and students alike.

Despite the past popularity of the work, however, a great deal of revision has been necessary in order to bring it into line with the requirements of modern practice. At the same time, the opportunity has been taken of tidying up some of the nineteenth-century phraseology (but retaining the 'Usill' touch) and of rearranging the chapters in more logical sequence.

Much new material has been added. In particular, the chapter on Traversing has been expanded, and should now be of assistance to students reading for their professional examinations. Chapter 12 deals briefly with Geodesy—the higher and specialised sections of the profession. This chapter has had, of necessity, to be short, for each heading provides material for whole volumes; but I hope enough has been said to make it an intelligent introduction to an absorbing subject.

A selection of past examination questions set by important professional bodies has been included at the end of many of the chapters, and I am indebted to the Senate of the University of London, the Royal Institution of Chartered Surveyors, the Institution of Civil Engineers, and the Institution of Municipal Engineers for permission to reproduce these questions. I also wish to acknowledge the kindly co-operation of the numerous instrument makers and manufacturers who have provided much valuable information and have lent blocks for the various illustrations. Finally, I am indebted to Mr. K. P. Money for a number of new drawings.

My object has been to enhance the value of this popular text-book by presenting it with a 'new look'; and if I have been successful in adding anything, however small, to its usefulness, my task will not have been in vain.

K. M. HART.

CONTENTS

Chapter 1

OFFICE WORK

"Surveying is the art of ascertaining, by measurement, the shape and size of any portion of the earth's surface, and representing the same, on a reduced scale, in a conventional manner, so as to bring the whole under the eye at once."

Preliminary remarks – Before attempting to describe the various instruments with which the surveyor must be acquainted to enable him to carry out surveying operations in the field, a description of the office work, together with some practical hints on the use of drawing instruments, will be dealt with.

Invariably the student will find that before he would be allowed to handle expensive scientific instruments a certain amount of basic drawing office experience will need to be acquired. He will probably be given some tracing to do or some small plans to draw in order that he can begin to learn the art of draughtsmanship. It is, therefore, logical that this book should commence where the student is likely to begin – in the office.

Next to proficiency in all field operations, office work is of great importance. Accuracy in the field is an essential requirement, but no less important is the ability to portray the results

1

of observations graphically so that it can be easily understood
by all except the uninitiated.

Necessity for system – System is very important in all branches
of surveying, especially draughtsmanship. The beautiful
Ordnance Plans in various scales are the result of accuracy in
the field and methodical elaboration in the office. Even the
small scale 1-inch maps speak for themselves; while the large
scales enable the Ordnance Survey authorities, by their perfect
administration, to delineate the most minute features, of which
these plans are faithful representations.

George Stephenson, in the early days of railway enterprise,
was wont to express the opinion that a map or detailed drawing
should be so executed as to enable either to be read "like a
book," and there is no reason whatever why a survey should not
be so as well.

Drawing boards – The modern drawing board, on its own or
mounted complete on a drawing table, usually consists of $\frac{7}{8}$-in.
timber of well seasoned yellow pine with grooved back and
slotted ledges to withstand warping in changing climatic conditions. One edge of the board has a metal or ebony strip or

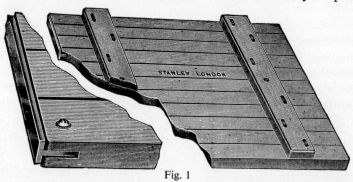

Fig. 1

straight-edge inserted against which the stock of the tee-square
is placed. Sizes range from the Half-Imperial (23 x 16 in.) to
Antiquarian (54 x 33 in.) and extra large sizes can be obtained
up to 8 ft. 4 in. x 2 ft. 7 in. Those in general use in most offices
are the Imperial (31 x 23 in.), the Double Elephant (42 x 29 in.)
and the Antiquarian.

The Double Elephant and Antiquarian size is the normal size for drawing tables. Figures 1 and 2 illustrate a standard drawing board and drawing table (showing the tee-square) respectively.

Fig. 2

Scales – A box of six boxwood scales, 12 in. long, with the accompanying offset scales, is indispensable. These scales are, one, two, three, four, five, and six chains to one inch on one side and corresponding feet on the other side – that is to say, the full length of the 1-chain scale of 12 in. represents 12 chains on one side and 792 ft. on the other; the 2-chain scale, 24 chains and 1,584 ft.; the 3-chain, 36 chains or 2,376 ft.; the 4-chain, 48 chains or 3,168 ft.; the 5-chain, 60 chains or 3,960 ft.; and the 6-chain, 72 chains or 4,752 ft. The offset scales are 2 in. long, representing 2, 4, 6, 8, 10, and 12 chains, or 132, 264, 396, 528, 660, and 792 ft. Boxwood scales are more reliable than ivory, but are more easily damaged. Always wipe them well before and after use, as the moisture of the hands encourages them to collect dirt.

Besides these chain or survey scales and offsets it will be necessary to have Ordnance Survey scales and, in addition, a selection of engineer's and architect's scales are really indispensable. Modern scales are engine divided which ensures extreme accuracy.

Pricker – All surveys should be plotted with a pricker with as fine a point as possible, and care should be taken to avoid making either too many or too large punctures. Round those required for further reference always mark lightly with a pencil thus ⊙.

Pencils – Only the best quality of lead should be used to plot work, 3H or 4H are the best; and don't lean too hard upon the pencil, as by so doing you make an indentation as well as a line.

Points of pencils – As to the best form of point for a pencil, the chisel-shape marks well against the straight-edge and for mechanical drawing is much the best; but for plotting a survey, if (as it always should) the pencil be held perfectly vertical, a fine point is easier and better to manipulate.

Drawing and tracing material – It is advisable to select a good quality drawing paper; inferior paper is not conducive to neat, accurate work and can often completely spoil an otherwise excellent drawing. The hand-made Whatman's "Not Hot Pressed" of medium thickness is the best but it is expensive and would be used only for important drawings. It has the advantage, like most hand-made papers, of expanding evenly in both dimensions on damping or adverse atmospheric conditions, unlike the machine made detail or cartridge drawing papers which are inclined to expand unequally, the expansion being greater in the cross direction of the paper machine than in the machine run direction. However, the cost of drawing paper is high and the machine made cartridge drawing paper is more often used.

Tracing paper should not be used for important ink tracings as it is easily damaged and quickly loses its transparancy in storage; on the other hand it is less prone to expansion and contraction than tracing linen. A good tracing linen will keep indefinitely if protected from dampness and maintained in an even temperature. Tracing linen will not take pencil well; it will stretch and lose its nature if damped; it must always be well rubbed over with french chalk or an impregnated cloth before it will take ink; it is usual to work on the glossy side, although some draughtsmen prefer the matt face.

Protractors – The best form of protractor is circular, of as large a diameter as possible. Electrum or brass protractors are best, of which there are various kinds (see Figs. 3 and 4).

Fig. 3

Fig. 4

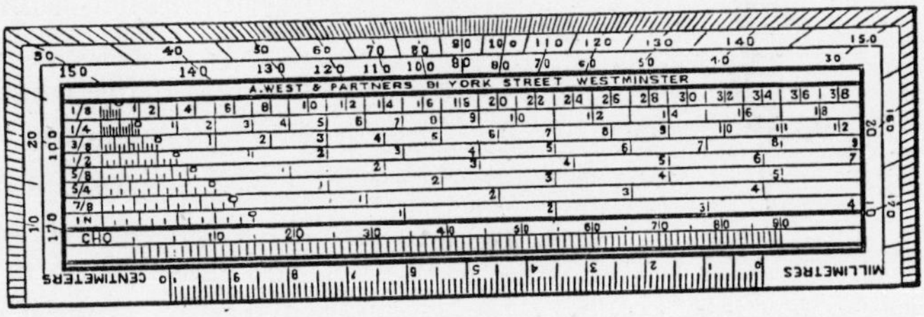

Fig. 5

Another form is the rectangular protractor (Fig. 5) which also combines a selection of scales, but neither this nor the other forms of protractors should be used for plotting. The most accurate method of plotting and setting out triangles is by trigonometry which is explained in Chapter 6.

Beam compasses – For striking arcs of large radii, such as are often required in plotting a chain-survey, ordinary compasses are useless even with the lengthening bar. For such purposes these arcs should be described by means of beam compasses or trammels (see Fig. 6). This excellent instrument consists of two brass boxes, each having a movable plate parallel with its vertical side, which is actuated by screws *a a*, so that it can be clamped tight against the mahogany* beam A. One of these brass boxes has a slow-movement screw D which enables the point C to be slightly moved at pleasure, whereby it may be adjusted to a hair's-breadth. The points may be removed at either end, and a pen or pencil one substituted.

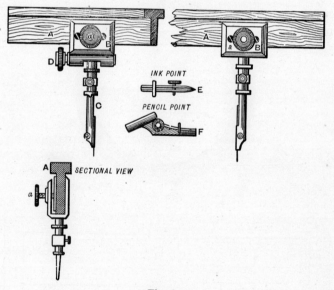

Fig. 6

* These beams are made in any length from 10 to 48 inches of well-seasoned mahogany, or metal, having a "T" head to stiffen them.

How to use the beam compass – The best way to manipulate the beam compass is to draw a pencil line, and upon this to carefully measure the required length with a scale; then to apply the compass by moving the boxes approximately along the beam so that the points are near the mark, then clamp the screws *a a*, and with the slow-motion screw D get the exact position.

Great care in striking an arc – Great care is required in striking an arc with beam compasses, as at first, until one is accustomed to their use, they appear clumsy. Place the point of one end upon the station, holding the box lightly with the left hand, whilst with the right guide the other box in the direction required, taking care to keep vertical the arm carrying the points, and not to press heavily upon the box. Thus if upon the line A B (Fig. 7), which is 1,260 links long, we wish to determine

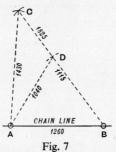

Fig. 7

the point C, we must measure on a pencil line the length A C=1,430 links, and placing the point at A describe an arc at C. And again with the length B C adjusted in the compasses, viz. 1,825 links, we describe an arc intersecting the other arc at C, and from A and B we draw the lines A C, B C respectively. Should there be a check- or tie-line, as from A to D, on B C we must strike the arc whose radius is 1,115 links, corresponding with the distance which the station D is from B, and draw a line A D, which when scaled should correspond with our measurements in the field, viz. 1,040 links.

Parallel rules – Parallel rules are exceedingly useful in plotting a survey, and for traverse work they are indispensable. Those made to work upon rollers (as in Fig. 8) are the most reliable, and should be from 15 to 24 in. long, brass or gun-metal being preferable to ebony.

Fig. 8

Set-squares, etc. – For setting out right angles and to facilitate plotting, celluloid or mahogany set-squares are necessary, similar to those illustrated in Figs. 9 and 10, those in Fig. 10 being framed in mahogany and edged with ebony: the former

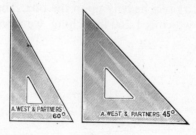

Fig. 9

are less liable than the latter to get "out of square," but are more apt to soil the paper. Perspex is now largely used in place of transparent celluloid.

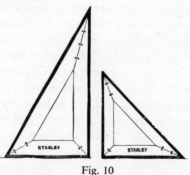

Fig. 10

Offsets – In plotting offsets or any of the features of a survey the greatest care is required. Place the edge of the scale accurately on the line, as in Fig. 11, and place two weights on *a* and *b*, then gently draw the offset scale *c* along the edge of the

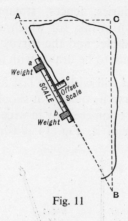

Fig. 11

other scale to the point where it is required to make a lateral measurement, and prick off the length of the offset. It will be seen that a portion of a triangular field has been already plotted.

Curves – No office should be without a box of curves, such as Fig. 12, which are made of pearwood, and are of regular radii from $1\frac{1}{2}$ to 150 in.

Fig. 12

French architectural curves – These useful curves can be obtained in many forms some of which are illustrated in Fig. 13. They may be obtained in transparent celluloid or in pearwood.

Fig. 13

B

Drawing-pens – A survey should be distinguished by good draughtsmanship, equally with accuracy in execution.

The various boundaries, fences, streams, buildings, etc., should be neatly drawn in ink, for which a good drawing- or ruling-pen is indispensable; and the survey-lines – the basis of the whole work – require to be drawn with a clear but fine line.

A good drawing-pen will with care last for years, and like a fountain pen, to preserve its quality, it should not be loaned to others. Much depends upon the way in which a pen is used and the care that is taken of it. Fig. 14 illustrates the right and

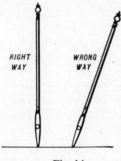

Fig. 14

wrong way of holding a drawing-pen. In the former case not only do you wear the point equally, but you have perfect command over the pen, whilst in the latter you wear the points at one angle, and you cannot manipulate the pen with the same facility or neatness as if held vertical. The various types of drawing-pens are shown in Fig. 15. A is the ordinary pen; B has a hinged nib **a** which enables it to be cleaned better than A, and also is easier to sharpen; C is a double or road pen, its chief advantage being assumed to be the possibility of drawing lines straight or curved parallel to each other at one stroke. D and E are dotting- or wheel-pens, the latter of which has at the head a small receptacle for wheels of different lengths of dot. These instruments are neat as pieces of workmanship, but, without great care, are apt to make a smeared instead of a dotted line. If you are the draughtsman you should be – and there is no possible excuse why you should not – you can draw parallel and dotted lines far more neatly and effectively without such contrivances than you can with them.

Dividers – Fig. 16 illustrates the usual form of dividers. A is the ordinary sector type, as is B, only with double joints. C and D are hair-dividers, with outside and inside screws respectively.

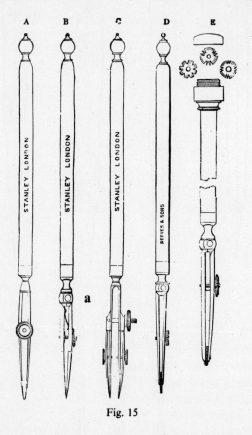

Fig. 15

These instruments will be found exceedingly useful for accurate measurements. The student should be warned against applying the points of the dividers upon the scale for the purpose of measuring on a plan; it is wrong and slovenly, and spoils the scales. Mark off the distance you require on paper, and apply your dividers thereto.

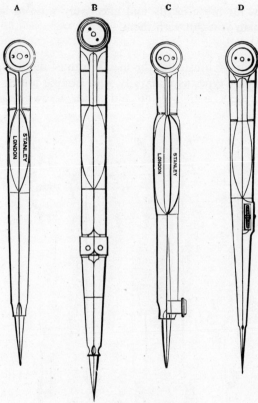

Fig. 16

Spring-bows – Needle spring-bows (Fig. 17) are indispensable for plotting a survey: the other kind make too large holes in the paper.

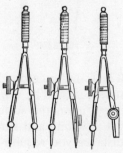

Fig. 17

The equipment of a surveyor would be quite incomplete without a set of ordinary drawing instruments such as is shown in Fig. 18. A is the ordinary cheek compass; the point may be removed, and in the slot may be substituted either the pencil or ink point, or if the sweep is not sufficiently long a lengthening bar may be made to intervene.

A

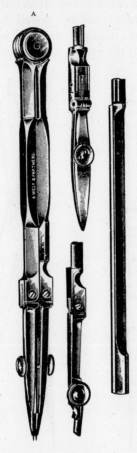

Fig. 18

Proportional compasses – For enlarging and reducing plans, of which I shall have something to say presently, I recommend the proportional compass, of which Figs. 19 and 20 are illustrations

– the former when closed, the latter when open for use. On the one face of the divider (as in Fig. 20), on the left of the groove, is a scale of lines, whilst on the right side is one of circles; and on the other face (see Fig. 19), on the left side of the groove is a scale of plans and on the right one of solids.

To set the instrument, it must first be accurately closed (as in Fig. 19), so that the two legs appear as one; the nut **c** being then unscrewed the slider may be moved until the line across it coincides with any required division upon any one of the scales. Now tighten the screws and the compasses are set.

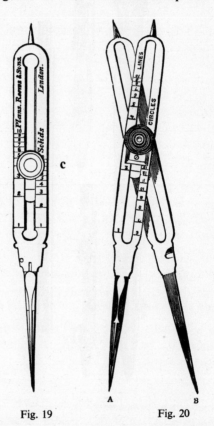

Fig. 19   Fig. 20

To use the proportional compasses – To enlarge or reduce a plan, once, twice, thrice, or up to ten times, bring the line on the slider opposite the scale of lines to a mark represented by 2, 3, 4, 5, 6, 7, 8, 9, or 10, and at the short end you will have that much less than the other, and *vice versa*.

Horn centre – A thin transparent disk of horn about $\frac{9}{16}$in. in diameter, having three small needle-points to keep it steady. Placed over the centre from which an arc is to be struck with compasses, it prevents their point from making a hole in the paper.

India rubber – This useful aid to erasure should be resorted to as little as possible, for good work and workmanship should not require to be obliterated. Yet, if it is necessary at times – and it must be, of course – the best kind is the soft white india rubber; only use it gently, taking care not to damage the surface of the paper, or you will regret it when you commence putting the tints on your plan. On no account should a knife be used for erasing.

Indian ink – For all purposes of draughtsmanship the best is the only ink to be used, and the extra cost of good quality, as compared with that of inferior, is so slight as to be hardly worth discussing.

Bottled ink is now almost invariably used, the most useful size is probably the 1 oz. bottle which contains the patent filler top. Inks tend to thicken if exposed to the atmosphere and the bottle should, therefore, be tightly corked when not in use.

Only the best quality waterproof brands should be used; this is particularly essential in the case of coloured inks which otherwise have a tendency to "run."

Colours – For colouring plans, I prefer the hexagonal sticks, as in mixture you get a better tint without risk of foreign matter getting in. Of course, in the case of mixture, each colour must be separately rubbed up, and any incorporation must take place afterwards.

The following is a list of the chief colours required by the surveyor:

Brown Madder	French Blue	Raw Sienna
Burnt Sienna	Gamboge	,, Umber
,, Umber	Hooker's Green	Scarlet Lake
Carmine	Indian Red	Sepia
Chinese White	,, Yellow	Vandyke Brown
Cobalt Blue	Indigo	Venetian Red
Crimson Lake	Neutral Tint	Vermilion
Chrome Yellow	Payne's Grey	Yellow Ochre
Emerald Green	Prussian Blue	Ultramarine

For mixing up any large quantity of colour, the nest of saucers (Fig. 21) is most useful as, fitting one on the other, they virtually keep the colour hermetically sealed. For colouring

Fig. 21   Fig. 22

plans in great variety the round slant and basin (Fig. 22) is extremely useful, as you may have occasion to wash your brush frequently, whilst for ordinary variety of tints the ordinary straight slant (Fig. 23) is convenient.

Fig. 23

Conventional signs and colours – The following are some of the conventional colours used to illustrate the principal features of a survey. Fences are shown by a firm line; post and rail thus: —I—I—I—I—; walls by parallel lines; paled fences thus: T T T T T T.

Roads are tinted in light burnt sienna. Footpaths of macadam or gravel by a darker tint of the same colour. Pavements by neutral tint.

Buildings are sepia or tinted lake, whilst outbuildings are shown by light indian ink. In some cases existing buildings are shown by neutral tint or light indian ink, whilst new or proposed buildings are tinted lake. Churches or public buildings are generally delineated by some special method, such as hatching.

Water is shown by Prussian blue or ultramarine. There are various ways of doing it, the most effective being by what is termed rippling; or it may be coloured dark at the edge, and led off by a fairly dry brush, called shading. Trees are either sketched in indian ink or are coloured. Pasture-land is tinted green, or if uncoloured is marked *Pas.*, in distinction to *Ara.* for arable land. Marsh-land and heath or gorse are shown as on page 35.

All buildings when inked-in and coloured should be back-lined on the right-hand side and bottom, bearing in mind that light falls over the left shoulder at an angle of 45 deg. And here let me say that, if possible, a plan should not be coloured for at least twenty-four hours after it has been inked-in, as a preventive against the ink running; this is more important when coloured inks are used on the plan as these are more likely to run. When this happens a plan can be completely spoiled as little can be done to remedy the trouble.

If there are large areas to be coloured it is advisable to go over the surface with clear water or add some oxgall to the tint to ensure a more uniform flow. Care should be taken in colouring and inking in plans and the following precautions will prove to be useful:

Commence inking-in from top – In commencing to ink-in a plan, it is always best to begin working from top to bottom, taking care to keep the lower part well covered over, so as to prevent dirt or grease getting on the paper.

Always work from left to right – In all operations, field or office, it will be found most convenient to work from left to right, and in all cases the top and bottom, left and right sides of the paper should represent north, south, west, and east respectively.

Place work in centre of the paper – Great care should be taken so that the plan is in the centre of the paper, from the sides, leaving as much space as possible for the title, and should any

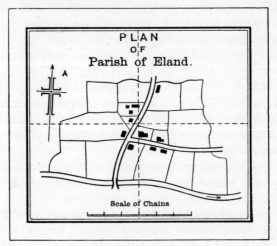

PLAN
oF
Parish of Eland.

A

Scale of Chains

Fig. 24

of the ground be irregular in shape, as in Fig. 24 at A, it is as well to place the north point in such a spot as will keep the plan symmetrical.

Boundaries of different properties – Boundaries of different property may be shown by an edging of different colours; if for

REFERENCE.

THE VARIOUS BOUNDARIES OF PROPERTY
SHEWN ON THIS PLAN ARE INDICATED THUS

T. JONES ESQ.	Pink
H. MORRIS ESQ.	Green
EXORS OF LATE J. SMITH ESQ.	Blue
LORD NOWHERE.	Yellow
MRS GREENE.	Bt.Sienna
TRUSTEES OF SION COLLEGE.	Neu. Tint
THOS. BLAKE & OTHERS	Lt.Indian Ink

Fig. 25

one only, lake or green is most usual; but when there are a variety of owners, the boundaries are generally indicated by lake, green, blue, yellow, burnt sienna, neutral tint, light indian ink, with a schedule of colours as reference in the corner, as in Fig. 25. The name of the colour should be tinted in the block to correspond with the edging of the boundaries.

Paint brushes and pencils – With regard to paint brushes or pencils, especially coloured pencils, I need hardly say that the best are the cheapest in the long run. To leave brushes in water, or to neglect to cleanse them after use, is unpardonable—and very expensive.

Precautions in colouring – In colouring take care to mix sufficient. A less quantity makes it sometimes difficult to match. Colours should be mixed light. If the tints are not dark enough, they can be easily strengthened by an extra coat, thus avoiding blotched colouring. It is best to colour towards you, taking care not to go over the same place a second time if possible; the colour in parts wants to be floated towards the draughtsman. Do not take too much colour in your brush, and always have a small clean brush handy to finish-off an edge. It is most convenient to have a piece of clean white blotting-paper to rest the wrist on when colouring, also to take up colour that oversteps the boundary. Be very careful not to go over the edge, as it makes a plan look very ragged. Colouring is best done by a slow and regular stroke, extra care being observed at boundaries. For shading, a brush at each end of the handle is required, the one to put the colour on, and the other clean and slightly moistened to lead off the colour. The process is best done from left to right. Sable brushes are preferable to camel's hair.

North points – North points are shown in various ways, some ornamental and others quite plain. Both types are illustrated here, but the practical surveyor of to-day has little time to adorn his plans with out-of-place decorations, and I recommend the adoption of a neat and simple figure, such as the example in Fig. 28. In all cases the magnetic north should be shown.

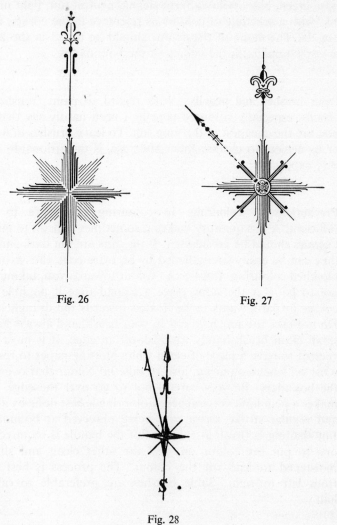

Fig. 26

Fig. 27

Fig. 28

Borders – Every plan should have a border round it, with a margin of from 1 to $2\frac{1}{2}$ inches. A simple line is very neat for an ordinary plan, and where greater elaboration is necessary, then either a thin line on the top and left, with a thick line bottom and right, as in Fig. 29, or as in Fig. 30, with a thick line in the midst of two fine lines. Sometimes a very fine and large plan will bear a line of neutral-tint, say three-eighths thick, and strongly black-lined in indian ink.

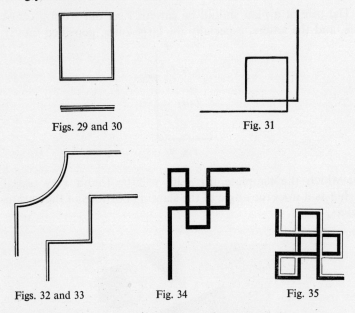

Figs. 29 and 30   Fig. 31

Figs. 32 and 33   Fig. 34   Fig. 35

Some plans are finished with ornamental corners, such as are shown in Figs. 31, 32, 33, 34, and 35, which are as simple and effective as possible. A good survey does not require much adornment, and the neater it is finished off the better it will commend itself.

Printing on plans – One of the last and most important things in connection with a plan is the printing, to which too much attention cannot be paid. A plan may be perfect so far as draughtsmanship and colouring are concerned, but entirely spoilt by reason of bad printing. Here again simplicity should govern the work.

There are many forms of printing that can be adopted and it is better to select one or two styles best suited to the student's individual taste and practice these styles on every possible occasion. A useful form of lettering to adopt in these days when speed is often essential is the single stroke capital and single stroke small (upright or slanting). For more elaborate headings the Modern Roman or Commercial Gothic are both useful.

The title of a plan should be carefully set out from a centre line, and the letters, especially the large ones, pencilled faintly,

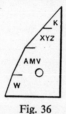

Fig. 36

for which the template, Fig. 36, will be found very useful, giving as it does the angle of the slanting portions of the various letters.

Fig. 37

Stencils – Pen stencils are now in general use and these may be obtained in various sizes and styles complete with pen and holder. Figure 37 illustrates one type and shows the stencil in action. Both alphabet and figures are available in upright or sloping styles. It will be observed that the stencil body is raised above the work by two shoulders at top and bottom which enables the whole stencil to be moved along a straight-edge without smudging the letters already made.

No draughtsman, however, worthy of the name would be prepared to use stencils in preference to hand printing; it is essential that the art of hand printing is mastered as early as possible – and long before the student intends sitting for his professional examinations.

Enlarging and reducing plans – It is often necessary to enlarge or reduce either whole or portions of surveys. For reliable purposes, the most satisfactory method is to replot the work to a larger or smaller scale from your field notes. But this may not always be possible, consequently in these days of "labour saving," we have appliances for expeditiously accomplishing these results. As this work would be incomplete without a description of the pantograph and eidograph, I quote from an excellent authority upon the subject.

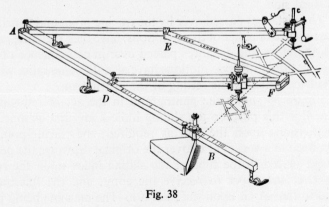

Fig. 38

Pantograph – "The Pantograph (Fig. 38) consists of four rulers, A B, A C, D F, and E F, made of stout brass. The two longer rulers, A B and A C, are connected together by, and have a motion round, a centre at A. The two shorter rulers are connected in like manner with each other at F, and with the longer rulers at D and E; and, being equal in length to the portions A D and A E of the longer rulers, form with them an accurate parallelogram, A D F E, in every position of the instrument. Several castors support the machine parallel to the paper, and allow it to move freely over it in all directions. The arms, A B and D F, are graduated and marked $\frac{1}{2}$, $\frac{1}{3}$, etc., and have each a sliding index, which can be fixed at any of the divisions by a milled-headed clamping-screw, seen in the engraving. The sliding indices and the ruler at C have on each of them a tube, adapted either to slide on a pin rising from a heavy weight called the fulcrum, or to receive a sliding holder with a pencil or pen, or a blunt tracing-point, as may be required.

"When the instrument is correctly set, the tracing-point, pencil, and fulcrum will be in one straight line, which may be proved by stretching a fine string over them. The motions of the tracing-point and pencil are then each compounded of two circular motions, one about the fulcrum, and the other about the joints at the ends of the rulers upon which they are respectively placed. The radii of these motions form sides about equal angles of two similar triangles, of which the straight line B G, passing through the tracing-point, pencil, and fulcrum, forms the third side.

"The distances passed over by the tracing-point and pencil, in consequence of either of these motions, have then the same ratio, and, therefore, the distances passed over in consequence of the combination of the two motions have also the same ratio, which is that indicated by the setting of the instrument.

"Figure 38 shows the pantograph in the act of reducing a plan. For this purpose the sliding indices are first clamped at the divisions upon the arm as required; the tracing-point is then fixed in a socket at C, over the original drawing; the pencil is next placed in the tube of the sliding index upon the ruler D F, over the paper to receive the copy; and the fulcrum is fixed to that at G, upon the ruler A B. The machine being now ready for use, if the tracing-point at C be passed delicately and steadily over every line of the plan, a true copy (but at a scale less than the original) will be marked by the pencil on the paper beneath it. The fine thread represented as passing from the pencil quite round the instrument to the tracing-point at C, enables the draughtsman at the tracing-point to raise the pencil from the paper, whilst he passes the tracer from one part of the original to another, and thus to prevent false lines from being made on the copy. The pencil-holder is surmounted by an adjustable weight to vary the pressure of the pencil on the paper, as found necessary.

"If the object were to enlarge the drawing, then the tracer must be placed upon the arm D F, and the pencil at C."

The Eidograph – "The pantograph just described requires four supports upon the paper, and from this cause, and from its numerous joints, its action is apt to be unsteady. An instrument to avoid these defects was invented by Professor Wallace in 1821. This instrument (Fig. 39), called the eidograph, is more regular in its action than the pantograph, as will be readily understood from the following description of its construction, by which it will be seen that there is only one point of support upon which the entire instrument moves steadily and regularly; and the joints, if we may so term them, consist of fulcrums fitting in accurately ground bearings, the motion round these fulcrums being capable of adjustment for regularity as well as accuracy. It also possesses the further advantage over the pantograph, that it may be set with equal facility to form a reduced copy bearing any proportion whatever to the original, while the pantograph can only be set to vary the relations between the original and the copy in the few proportions which are specifically marked upon it.

"The point of support of the eidograph is a heavy weight, H, formed exteriorly of brass and loaded internally with lead, and having three or four small needle-points to keep it steady on the paper. The pin, forming the fulcrum upon which the whole instrument moves, projects from the centre of this weight on its upper side, and fits into a socket attached to a sliding-box, K. The fulcrums are ground to fit very accurately. The centre beam, C, of the instrument fits into and slides through the box K, and may thus be adjusted to any desired position with respect to the fulcrum, and then fixed by a clamping-screw attached to the

C

box. Deep sockets are attached to each end of the centre beam, into which are accurately fitted the centre pins of the two

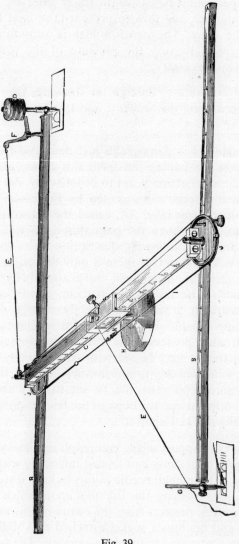

Fig. 39

pulley-wheels J J. These pulley-wheels are made most exactly of the same diameter, and have two steel bands, I I, attached to

their circumference, so that they can move only simultaneously, and to exactly the same amount. By means of screw adjustments these bands can have their lengths regulated so as to bring the arms of the instrument into exact parallelism, and, at the same time, to bring them to such a degree of tension as shall give to the motions of the arms the required steadiness, which forms one of the advantages of the instrument over the pantograph. The arms, A and B, of the instrument pass through sliding boxes upon the under side of the pulley-wheels, these boxes, like that for the centre beam, being fitted with clamping-screws, by which the arms can be fixed in any desired position. At the end of one of the arms is fixed a socket with clamping-screw, to carry a tracing-point, G, and at the end of the other is a socket for a loaded pencil, D, which may be raised when required by a lever, F F, attached to a cord which passes over the centre of the instrument to the tracing-point. The centre beam C, and the arms, A, B, are made of square brass tubes, divided exactly alike into two hundred equal parts, and figured so as to read one hundred each way from their centres. The boxes through which they slide have verniers, by means of which these divisions may be subdivided into ten, so that with their help the arms and beam may be set to any reading containing not more than three places of figures. A loose leaden weight is supplied with the instrument to fit on any part of the centre beam, and keep it in even balance when set with unequal lengths of the centre beam on each side of the fulcrum.

"The pulleys, J J, being of exactly equal size, when the steel bands, I I, are adjusted so as to bring the arms of the instrument into exact parallelism, they will remain parallel throughout all the movements of the pulleys in their sockets, and thus will always make equal angles with the centre beam. If, then, the two arms and the centre beam be all set so that the readings of their divisions are the same, a line drawn from the end of one arm across the fulcrum to the end of the other arm will form with the beam and arms two triangles, having their sides about equal angles proportionals, and being, therefore, similar; hence any motion communicated to the end of one arm will produce a similar motion at the end of the other, so that the tracing-point being moved over any figure whatever, an exactly similar figure will be described by the pencil."

To adjust the Eidograph, and examine its accuracy – "Set the indices of all three verniers to coincide with the zero divisions on the centre beam and arms, and make marks at the same time with the tracer and with the pencil; then move the pencil-point round until it comes to the mark made by the tracer, and if the tracer at the same moment comes into coincidence with the mark made by the pencil, the arms are already parallel, and the instrument consequently in adjustment; but if not, make a second mark with the tracer in its present position, and bisecting the distance between this mark and the mark made by the pencil, bring the tracer exactly to this bisection by turning the adjusting screws on the bands. The instrument being now in adjustment, if the zero division be correctly placed on the arms and beam, the pencil-point, tracer, and fulcrum will be in the same straight line, and they will still remain so when the instrument is set to give the same readings on the three scales, whatever those readings may be, if the dividing of the instrument be perfect.

"The instrument being adjusted we have next to set it so as to make the dimensions of a copy, traced by its means, bear the desired proportion to the original. It must be borne in mind that the divisions on the instrument are numbered each way from the centres of the beam and arms up to 100, and that the verniers enable us to read decimals or tenths of a division; so that if the indices of the verniers were a little beyond any divisions, as 26, and the third stroke of the verniers coincided with the divisions marked 29, the reading would be 26·3. Now suppose it were required to set the instrument so that the proportion of the copy to the original should be that of one number, a, to another number, b. Suppose x to represent the reading to which the instrument should be set, then the centre beam and arms are each divided at their fulcrums into portions whose lengths are $100-x$ and $100+x$ respectively, and consequently $\dfrac{100-x}{100+x} = \dfrac{a}{b}$, from which we find that the required reading $x = \dfrac{100\,(b-a)}{b+a}$; thus if the proportions are as 1 to 2, we have $x = \dfrac{100\,(2-1)}{2+1} = \dfrac{100}{3} = 33·3$, and the instrument must be set with the third divisions of the verniers beyond the indices on the third divisions of the instrument beyond the 33rd. We have, therefore, the following simple rule: subtract the lesser term of the proportion from the greater, and multiply it by 100 for a dividend, add together the two terms of the proportion for a divisor, and the quotient will give the reading to which the instrument is to be set.

"The following readings are thus obtained:

Proportions	Readings	Proportions	Readings
1 : 2	33·3	2 : 3	20
1 : 3	50	2 : 5	42·9
1 : 4	60	3 : 4	14·3
1 : 5	66·7	3 : 5	25
1 : 6	71·4	4 : 5	11·1

"When the copy is to be reduced, the centre beam is to be set to the reading found, as above, on the side of the zero next to the arm carrying the pencil-point, and this arm is also to be set to the same reading on the side of its centre or zero nearest the pencil-end, while the tracer-arm is to be set with the reading furthest from the tracer. When the copy is to be enlarged, these arrangements must of course be reversed: thus 50 being the reading for the proportion 1 : 3, Fig. 40 will represent the setting to make a copy having its linear dimensions three times those of the original; where p represents the position of the pencil-point, t that of the tracer, and F the place of the fulcrum.

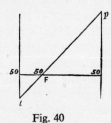

Fig. 40

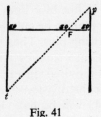

Fig. 41

Fig. 41 represents in the same way the setting to make the linear dimensions of the copy one-third of those of the original."

Enlarging and reducing by squares – Failing the replotting of the work for the purpose, the only satisfactory and accurate method of enlarging and reducing plans is by means of squares and proportional compasses. This method is illustrated by the following example:

Let Fig. 42 represent the plan of an estate which it is required to copy on a reduced scale of one-half. The copy will therefore be half the length and half the breadth, and consequently will occupy but one-fourth of the space of the original. Take a sheet of tracing-paper and draw two lines at perfect right angles to

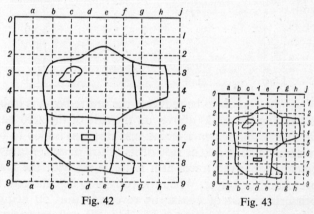

Fig. 42   Fig. 43

each other, as 0 *j*, 0 9, at the top and left of the sheet; now very accurately and carefully divide these lines into spaces of some convenient length, say, 1½ to 2 ins., as *a*, *b*, *c*, *d*, *e*, *f*, *g*, etc., and 1, 2, 3, 4, 5, 6, etc., and draw the squares formed by the intersections in fine blue lines. Now place this piece of tracing-paper over the plan to be enlarged or reduced, and fasten it well down with drawing-pins. Then take another piece of tracing-paper and divide it into squares larger or smaller according to the proportions required: in Fig. 43 they are half the size, consequently whatever the divisions 0 *a*, 0 *b*, 0 1, 0 2, etc., are (Fig. 42), those in Fig. 43 will be half. Beside the plan to be reduced, on the right-hand side lay down a piece of drawing-paper, upon which shall be laid a piece of transfer-paper, and upon this is laid the sheet of smaller squares, all of which are then firmly secured by weight or drawing-pins. In the proportional compasses fix the line across the slides to be coincident with the line opposite the 2 on the left side of the groove (Fig. 20), by which means A B is twice C D, to test which upon a line pick off any length A B, then if the points C D accurately bisect this length you have the

right proportion. And as a further test, try your squares in the
same way, A B being fixed at one of the subdivisions in Fig. 42,
then if the sheets of squares have been accurately drawn, C D
will exactly measure the length on the reduced sheet of squares.
To reduce the plan, mark those points on the large squares
where the fences, etc., intersect, and measure vertically and
horizontally the distance from the nearest intersection of the
horizontal and vertical lines with the A B end of the compass.
At similar points on the small squares mark the same
distances with the C D end of the compasses and make marks;
then if with a fine pencil you draw the lines connecting these
points, you will not only have a record of the work you have
accomplished, but it will be transferred to the paper beneath.

Many responsible commercial firms will enlarge or reduce
plans from an original to whatever scale is desired by photograph or other methods but these are never so satisfactory as
the method of re-drawing, as described. In particular it should
be remembered that if a plan is to be photographically enlarged
the original lines will also be enlarged in the same proportion as
the other details which can effect the accuracy of the plan very
considerably.

Fig. 44

Plan copying – The old method of copying a plan by placing
the original over a clean sheet of drawing paper and either
pricking through all fences, buildings etc. and connecting the

punctures or by tracing over the plan through a carbon sheet is now almost completely outdated by the universal use of photographic reproduction or plan printing and developing machines. Many offices posses such machines either in the form

Fig. 45

Fig. 46

of a simple daylight printing apparatus shown in Fig. 44 or the efficient electric copiers one type of which is illustrated in Fig. 45 with the developing machine in Fig. 46.

Commercial firms now reproduce copies from originals or tracings so cheaply and quickly that the laborious task of hand copying is a thing of the past and is seldom resorted to except in emergency or in parts of the world where such services are not available.

General hints – In plotting, draughtsmanship or in a survey the following hints may be useful:

1. Dust your table, and well cover that part of the paper upon which you are not working.

2. Do not have an inkstand or your colour-pans on the same table.

3. Always clean your scales, tee-square, set-squares, straight-edge, etc., before use.

4. If possible, do not colour over work recently inked-in.

5. Do not make calculations upon slips of paper, but always have a foolscap scribbling-book at hand in which enter all your calculations and the dates upon which they are made.

6. Tracings made for the purpose of copying plans should always be made on tracing paper if the tracing is not to be retained for long periods and should be kept in an evenly balanced office temperature if at all possible. Tracing cloth expands and contracts very much with changes in the weather.

7. Large plans can be made of any length, but their width should not exceed 54 in., otherwise they get so badly damaged in the constant use to which they are subject that their life becomes unreasonably short.

Conventional signs – It may be well at this point to refer to conventional signs which are usually adopted by surveyors to indicate special features:

1. Ditch and hedge are shown by a straight line, the line

represents the centre or root of hedge, the **T**, showing on which side the ditch belongs.

2. Where a change of position of ditch and hedge occurs, it should be carefully noted as in the sketch, which shows that at a certain point the ditch passes to the other side of the hedge, so that on the left the hedge belongs to A and on the right to B.

3. When a hedge alone separates two properties and on neither side is there a ditch, it is called a "foot-set" fence, and is shown in the third illustration above.

4. In most cases it is desirable to show gates, and they may be delineated in either of the ways indicated.

Gates thus:

5. Post-and-rail fencing is shown thus:

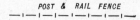

6. Close-paling thus:

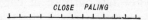

7. Walls by a double line.

8. Footpaths are shown by either a single or double dotted line.

9. Cart-track or bridle-path by a double dotted line; but in measuring upon the ground it is usual only to take the centre of the track, and allow twelve to fifteen links for the width.

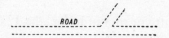

10. Trees are shown thus, and may be described:

TREES

Oak   *Chesnut*

11. Orchards are sketched thus:

12. Woods.

13. Brushwood.

14. Marshy ground.

15. Heath or gorse.

16. Railways, or preferably by a strong blue line.

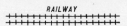

RAILWAY

17. Railway embankment.

18. Railway cutting.

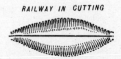

19. Broken ground or cliff.

20. Parish boundaries.

· · · · · · · · · · · · ·

21. County boundaries.

— — — — — —

22. Surveying stations.

23. Direction of line.

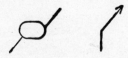

Chapter 2

SURVEYING INSTRUMENTS

Mistakes and errors—Steel band chains—Perambulator—Cross-staff—
Optical square—Sitesquare—Prismatic compass—Box sextant—Clinometers—Abney level—Hand level—Indian clinometer—"Bruton"
pocket transit—Mining dial—Cross sections by clinometer—Plane
table—Telescopic alidade—Microptic alidade—Plane table stand—
Resection—Sun compass—Theodolite—Theodolite stand—Centring
plates—Levelling screws—Parallel plates—Parallel plate screws—
Three-screw theodolite—Ball and socket arrangement—Base or lower
plate—Upper or vernier plate—Vernier—Micrometer—Tavistock
theodolite—Clamps and slow motion screws—Spirit-levels—A frames—
Vertical arc—Telescope—Magnification—Eye-piece—Diaphragm—
Universal theodolite—Theodolite adjustments—Lower levels—Parallax
—Telescope axis—Collimation in azimuth—Collimation in altitude—
Vertical circle—Photo-theodolite—Subtense measurement—Repetition of angles—Rangefinder—Stadia measurements—Stadia—Telescope
constant—Fieldwork—Reduction—Tacheographs—Correlation of
height level—Tacheometer—Tacheometry with staff tilted—Direct
reading devices—Redta tacheometer—Levelling—Setting up—Adjustment of a dumpy level—Reversible level—Tilting level—Precision levelling—Self-aligning level—Level staff—Cowley automatic level—
Aneroid barometer—Ascensional currents—Selection of instrument—
Geodetic and specialist surveying—Examination questions.

THE primitive instruments used in the early days of surveying
have been developed into very highly efficient and very compact
forms. It is hardly possible for colleges to place these highly
developed forms in the hands of students, one reason being the
very high cost of such instruments, which may be ruined by
inexpert handling. In this Chapter, therefore, the types of
instruments in common use will receive particular attention,
and their practical use will be described, so that a good ground-
ing will be obtained. The more highly developed forms will be
mentioned in less detail, with indications of the slightly different
methods of handling which have been evolved. (See also
Chapter 12).

Mistakes and errors – In the course of the description of the various instruments, and of their uses, every endeavour will be made to point out the possibility of mistakes and errors. There is a real difference in the meaning of these two words from a surveyor's point of view.

Mistakes arise, not necessarily through carelessness, but through inadvertence, want of familiarity with the instrument, want of practice, or, at all events, of recent practice. It is almost a certainty that mistakes will be made in levelling if none has been done for some months. It is possible, while taking great care to read a vernier or a micrometer, to book wrongly the large divisions. Such cardinal sins must be avoided by routine in reading, by second reading, or by the application of carefully thought out checks, even at the cost of time and trouble. It is wise practice to commence a series of observations slowly and with every precaution, working up to speed and accuracy, instead of attempting speed on the first day of the operations. Arithmetical work is a fruitful source of mistake.

Errors also must be avoided as far as possible by a routine and checks, but they are more or less elusive. There is the personal error, hardly any two observers being able to agree always on the precise reading of an instrument. In levelling, for example, one surveyor may always have a tendency to read on the low, and another on the high, side, if the wire cuts a graduation necessarily wider than the cross-wire. Many errors arose in the past through imperfect graduation of the circles of a theodolite, which is one reason for providing means for reading at opposite ends of the diameter. Slight errors in levelling the instrument lead to wrong calculation of height, unless reciprocal observations are taken from both ends of a line between two stations. Even then atmospheric conditions may not be the same, so that the refraction varies. The elimination of errors is usually attempted, as far as possible, by double or more numerous observations, and by taking the mean, but a mean may be a departure from the truth by reason of one faulty observation. The surveyor should consider carefully what effect particular methods will have on the results required. For example, in railway surveying it would be wrong to adopt methods which would lead to an under-statement of the height to be surmounted on a grade. In every class of work the methods should be designed so that errors may cancel out rather than have a tendency to cumulate. Errors can be distributed, but consideration must be applied to the method of distribution, so as to avoid too great a weighting of the correction at any one point, especially if that point has particular importance. Apart from the dishonesty of the practice, "faking" usually involves a great deal more trouble than an honest distribution of error.

Steel band chains – The ordinary land chain of steel wire is very apt to become shortened by bending of one or more links, or to become lengthened by the pull when dragged over ploughed or rough ground. A band chain (Fig. 47) will run with much less

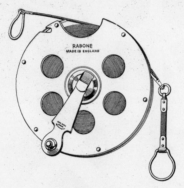

Fig. 47

trouble through rough grass or over debris in scrub or forest, and will retain its accuracy. These chains are made of a strip of blued or bright steel, about half an inch wide, divided into links or feet by brass studs, the first and last lengths being sub-divided into tenths. Metric band chains are made in lengths of 20, 25 or 30 metres, and subdivided into fifths or tenths of a metre. A metre is 3·281 feet. The chain, when not in use, is coiled on a steel cross. It is important to ensure that the band is not coiled wet, so that it will rust, being first rubbed with an oily rag. Should a chain be broken by mischance, clips can be obtained to make a join. It is possible to obtain bands of rustless steel, but these have not such resistance to tension and are rather brittle, being also more expensive by about 50 per cent.

For special purposes much longer chains are used, up to

300 feet. They may be made of Invar (steel and nickel) metal, which is much less susceptible to variations of temperature, but a certificate of accuracy should be obtained with the tape, while the accessory of a tape thermometer is a necessity (Fig. 48). It

Fig. 48

is important, in careful measuring with these tapes, to ensure that they are invariably stretched to the same tension, usually in a catenary, and therefore a spring balance, measuring to 20 lb., should be used at one end (Fig. 49) (see Chapter 12).

Fig. 49

For the very accurate measurement necessary for the base-lines of a trigonometrical survey Invar bars may be used. Another method of measuring a base-line, such as was necessary for the Sydney Harbour Bridge, is to use a length of wire, with straining trestles and index tripods, while there are further forms of apparatus for transferring the ends of the base-line to the ground at either end, referred to further – Chapter 12.

Perambulator – This (Fig. 50) is, to all intents and purposes, a bicycle wheel with handle bars, the diameter of the wheel being 26 inches, or the circumference being 2 yards 9⅔ inches. One, or preferably two, trocheameters, or revolution counters, record the revolutions in yards up to 14 miles or more.

In use, these instruments can only be regarded as giving approximate results, mainly as a check. It is difficult to keep the

D

instrument in a straight line, and if it runs over a stone it will
record an excessive length. It is desirable to calibrate the
trocheameters by occasional runs over known distances, and to

Fig. 50

carry one or more spares, say one for every 100 miles to be
traversed. The solid rubber tyre will wear and be liable to
come off, so that at the start the tyre may be bound to the rim
of the wheel by wire at intervals. It is of use principally to the
explorer, especially if his mapping is done by the plane table.

Cross-staff – In the following chapters I refer to the process of
taking offsets with an offset staff, which for short lengths may
generally be relied upon. Although I am bound in this division
to refer to the cross-staff, I have no hesitation in condemning its
use upon nearly every ground. I look upon such appliances as

Fig. 51   Fig. 52

only an excuse for long offsets, against which I am very strongly
opposed.
  The cross-staff is made either cylindrical, octagonal or open

in shape, about three inches in diameter (see Figs. 51 and 52) and five inches deep. It has slots placed at right angles to each other, in which are contained fine wires strained very true and vertical. In the octagonal staff there are also slots on the other four faces, which may be used for approximating an angle of 45 deg. The staff is fixed upon a rod (spiked at the end), and being placed perfectly perpendicular at a point on the line A B (Fig. 53), at which it is desired to set out a right angle, the slots *a* and *b* are adjusted so that, looking from *a* to B and back from

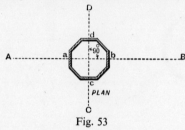

Fig. 53

b to A, the wires are coincident with the points B and A. Many cross-staves have a compass fixed at the top, as in Fig. 51, which – provided the staff is accurately adjusted in a truly vertical position on the line – may serve to take the bearing of the line with magnetic north. There is a form of cross-staff, as in Fig. 52, which is so constructed that the upper part of the cylinder may be moved round upon the lower portion with a rack and pinion movement actuated by a screw. A ring on the lower member is divided into degrees and sub-divisions, and, with a vernier attached to the upper cylinder, it is possible – with the greatest care – to obtain the angle of one or more points, but this can only be regarded as approximate.

Optical square – This is a most accurate and useful little instrument for its purpose, but it also must be used with great

Fig. 54

caution. All appliances of this character are liable to be used to save trouble (i.e. they facilitate long offsets). The optical square (Fig. 54) consists of a metal box of from $1\frac{1}{2}$ to $2\frac{1}{2}$ in.

diameter, formed by an outer and inner tube working one within the other, so that by a slight movement right or left the slots upon the outer tube are made identical with similar slots on the inner one. The cases are so placed in fixing the two together that although capable of a slight movement they are held in position by a screw. This enables the instrument to be protected from dust or dirt when not in use. Within this circular box are contained two mirrors (one of which is only half silvered, the lower portion being plain) placed at an angle

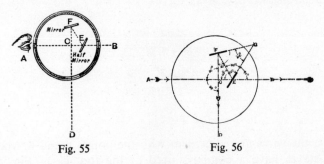

Fig. 55   Fig. 56

of 45 deg. with each other. Referring to Figs. 55 and 56 it will be seen that the glass E is placed at an angle of 120 deg. with the line of sight or diameter of the box, and the mirror F is at 45 deg. with this. Now, by a well-known law, a ray of light in direction of A B falling on E will be reflected on to F at an angle of 60 deg. (F E C), which will be again reflected in the line F C, whereby F C is 90 deg. with A B. Thus, a person wishing to establish a point on his chain-line A B at right angles with some particular

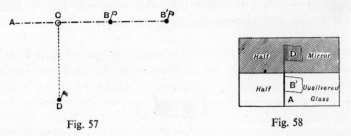

Fig. 57   Fig. 58

point, right or left, has simply to walk along the line in direction of B until the object at D becomes coincident with the forward station B. Thus, supposing a white flag is placed at B, Fig. 57, and another flag at some distance further ahead, say B' (for this is most important, as will be explained hereafter), and at the point D a red flag is fixed; then, provided the observer is in absolute line with B and B', when D appears coincident on the upper half of the mirror E, the red and white flags will be as on Fig. 58. Again, if at any point on the chain-line, as C, Fig. 57, it is necessary to establish a point at right angles, as D, instruct an assistant to move backwards and forwards until his flag is coincident with the points B and B'.

An improved form is shown in Fig. 59.

Fig. 59

The sitesquare – This little instrument, based on the principle of the cross staff, finds a more ready use on building sites than in surveying proper but it has a number of uses as long as its limitations are appreciated. The illustration (Fig. 60) reproduced by courtesy of the makers, Messrs Hilger & Watts of London, shows the instrument centred over the station from which the right-angle is required. It will be noted that the exact centring of the sitesquare is very simply performed. First the tripod is erected in close proximity to the station; the datum rod with the extended clamp arm is now centred exactly over the station point and, when properly adjusted, clamped into position. The instrument is screwed to the top of the datum rod and levelled. It is now ready for use. The telescope head is turned towards the established mark on the base line and clamped; the cross hairs are brought into exact coincidence by means of the fine-setting screw. Now by looking through the second telescope the right-angle can be set out. A feature of the sitesquare is that the instrument may be tilted on a horizontal axis without upsetting the adjustment. Instrumental errors are easily tested by observing carefully through each quadrant of a circle so that when the

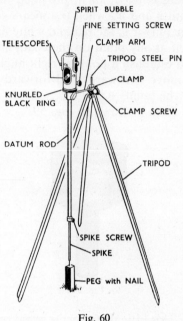

Fig. 60

final reading is taken on the original starting point exact coincidence should be found.

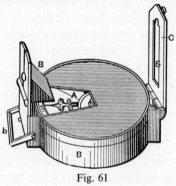

Fig. 61

Prismatic compass – No surveyor should be without this instrument (Figs. 61 and 62), since, apart from the fact that it is extremely useful for observing bearings, and even traversing, it is, in the absence of a theodolite, the only reliable means of determining the magnetic north in connection with a survey. It consists of a magnetic needle balanced on an agate centre or pivot, and carrying a card A, or metal ring, divided into 360 degrees and subdivisions of one-half or one-third of a degree, according to the size and manufacture of the compass. This is contained in a brass or bronze box, from $2\frac{1}{2}$ inches diameter and upwards, at one end of which is a sight-vane C, and at the other is a magnifying prism B, enclosed in a metal case, having a slot for observation, so arranged that whilst the eye sights

Fig. 62

through the slot – towards the wire contained in the vane – the prism, by means of being silvered on its slope, reflects the reading on the card at the same time. When in use the prism is turned by a hinge over the card, and similarly the vane is fixed in a vertical position; but for portability, when not in use, the vane folds on to the glass of the compass, and in doing so it presses a knob which throws the needle off the bearing to save undue wear. While the prism is turned back on to the ring of the box, and is held in position by the movable strap b, the whole is covered with a lid (which may be attached to the bottom during use) to protect it from injury. It should be stated that a knob is arranged in the ring under the vane to enable the operator to steady the needle, by pressing the card, to avoid undue swinging. The best kind of prismatic compasses are fitted with green and red glasses (Fig. 62) for azimuth observations of the sun. The

prismatic compass gives the bearing of a line, or in other words, the angles formed by that line and the magnetic meridian.

I have explained that the card or ring is divided into 360 deg., but whereas in ordinary cases this 360 deg. on north would point in the direction of the vane, in the case of the prismatic compass to simplify reading the angle during observation the order is reversed, so that the north on the card is marked 180 deg., south 360 deg., east 270 deg., and west 90 deg. By this means the 360 deg. is brought under the prism as at A in Fig. 63,

Fig. 63

when a sight is being taken due north, so that in directing the vane towards the point to which the bearing is required the operator is enabled to simultaneously read the angle and cut the point of observation with the vertical wire of the vane.

It should be observed that the prismatic compass cannot be used in places or under any circumstances where there is the slightest metallic attraction, as the needle is so sensitive that the least thing will cause a variation. Again, the compass must not be relied upon for extensive triangulation. From local and other causes slight errors are certain to occur. An examination of any good map will show that the magnetic variation differs in various countries, and in various parts of any large country. It will also probably be noted on the map that there is a steady annual change in the direction of the magnetic pole, so that by reference to the date of the map a correction may have to be applied. In the class of surveying for which the prismatic compass may be used this matter may be of little importance, but the student should be informed of it, and should acquaint himself of the facts. A further reference to the matter will be found in Chapter 6. The change of magnetic variation becomes important in long distance flights.

A good size of instrument is $4\frac{1}{2}$ inches in diameter, but an instrument of this size is best used on a stand, being screwed on to a pivot attached to the stand by a ball-and-socket joint for quick and easy levelling. This is essential if the ring is to revolve easily and to come to rest in the proper position.

The mirror shown on the sight vane (Fig. 62) is intended primarily to bring the sun down to the line of sight, before undertaking which operation the dark glasses must be brought in front of the reading prism. This mirror will also be useful if a sight is to be taken to points considerably above or below the line of sight, such points as have often to be observed in mountainous country.

The prismatic compass is a useful instrument for running traverses in forests, where trees are apt to fall on the traverse line. The compass can be set up on the far side of the tree, and the traverse line taken up again on the same bearing. For the methods of carrying the chainage past the obstacle consult page 169.

Box sextant – This instrument cannot be said to find a widespread use, but may be useful to obtain relative angles of rather more accuracy than can be obtained with most prismatic compasses. It usually requires more rod-holders, and circumstances may make it unreliable owing to the tilting of the plane of observation. The maximum angle of observation is limited to about 120 deg.

The box sextant is about 3 in. in diameter and $1\frac{1}{2}$ in. deep, and has a lid which completely covers it when not in use, but which can be screwed on to the bottom and serves as a handle when taking observations. Fig. 64 shows the chief features of the instrument and Fig. 65 gives an idea of its internal arrangements. A graduated scale from 0 deg. to 120 deg., with subdivisions, is engraved on a silver arc, and along this moves the vernier attached to the arm A to which is fixed the index glass I. This arm is moved by a milled-head screw O acting upon a rack and pinion with the box. In the line of sight, but fixed, is another mirror called the horizon glass, C, the upper part of which only is silvered, the lower and transparent portion being opposite the opening. This glass is fixed perpendicular to the plane of the instrument. These two mirrors, when the vernier is adjusted to zero, should be parallel.

There are two levers s connected with coloured glasses which may be interposed when solar observations are taken, but when not required can be depressed into the box. Many sextants are

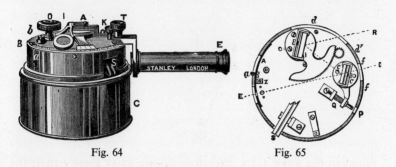

Fig. 64   Fig. 65

provided with a telescope which can either fit into a socket within the instrument, to be pulled out when wanted, or can be attached at the top by means of a screw as T in Fig. 64. But for general use the naked eye is quite sufficient, for which purpose a sliding shutter pierced with a small hole is made to cover the telescope aperture, with the sight hole in the direct line of vision.

The principle upon which the sextant acts is as follows: "When a ray of light, proceeding in a plane at right angles to each of the two plane mirrors which are inclined to each other at any angle whatever, is successively reflected at the plane surfaces of each of the mirrors, the total deviation of the ray is double the angle of inclination of the mirrors." For, let I i and H h (Fig. 66) represent sections of the two mirrors made by the plane of incidence at right angles to each of them, and let S I represent the course of the incident ray, then the ray S I is reflected into the direction I H, making with I i the angle H I A equal to the angle S I i, and is again reflected at H into the direction H E, making the angle E H A equal to the angle I H h. Now the angle A H V, being equal to the exterior angle I H h, is also equal to the two interior angles H I A and H A I; and because the angles A V H and I V E are equal, and also the three angles of every triangle are equal to two right angles, therefore the two

angles V I E and S E H are together equal to the two angles A H V
and H A I, and therefore to the angle H I A and twice the angle
H A I (since A H V has been proved to be equal to H I A and
H A I). But V I E, being equal to the vertical angle S I i, is also

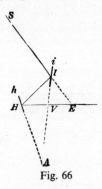

Fig. 66

equal to the angle H I A, therefore taking away these equals the
remainder of the angle S E H is equal to the remainder, twice the
angle H A I.

To use the sextant, it should be held up to the eye by the right
hand, so that the line of sight is in the direction of station Y (say
a tower), the operator standing exactly over the station X, and
the vertical axis of the instrument directly over its centre. With

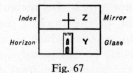

Fig. 67

the left hand the milled-headed screw is manipulated so that the
index mirror, being gradually turned in the direction of Z (the
2nd station), shall reflect the image (say a cross) at this point,
so that its centre is coincident with that of the tower Y, as in
Fig. 67. Thus the vernier will record the number of degrees and
sub-divisions contained in the angle Y X Z.

If the instrument, having been set at zero, does not show the
object to which it may be directed to be exactly in the same
vertical plane with the horizon and index glasses, it must be
adjusted by a key being applied to the key-hole at a (Fig. 65)

and turned right or left until the reflected images coincide exactly.

The necessary rules to be observed with the adjustment of the sextant are:

1st. That the two mirrors are parallel to each other when the zero of the vernier coincides with that of the graduated arc.

2nd. That the horizon glass is perpendicular to the plane of the instrument.

To correct this latter (*i.e.* the perpendicularity of the horizon glass to the plane of the instrument) it is necessary to observe whether the reflected and the direct images of the distant horizon appear as *one*. If two horizons appear we apply the key at *b* and turn it until they agree.

Clinometers – In addition to the operations of determining distance, and angular measurements between objects, it is frequently necessary to determine the slopes of the earth's

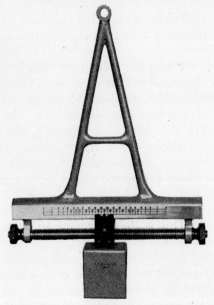

Fig. 68

surface, or between two points. The simplest form of clinometer consists of an angular protractor along which a sight is taken, the slope being shown by a string and plumb-bob where the string cuts the edge graduated in degrees and subdivisions of degrees. A further development in instruments such as the road tracer (Fig. 68) consists of a triangle pivoted at one angle with a weight sliding along the base, which is a hollow bar, graduated on the outside to show slopes in terms of tangents. The hollow bar is furnished with a pinhole at the eyepiece end and a cross bar at the other end, which is directed on a target. Another form, which depends on a weight to give a tilt to the instrument, is a reflecting clinometer, such as the DeLisle, but as this depends on the bisection of the reflection of the eye it comes obviously in the category of approximate instruments.

A further development, for instance in the Abney Level to be described, is the use of a spirit-level instead of a weight, the bubble of the level being reflected to the eye, and superimposed on the object which is viewed directly. There is a personal error introduced because the true angle of slope depends on the accurate bisection of the image of the bubble by a cross line of a target set on a staff to the level of the eye, or to the level of the axis of the instrument if fixed on a staff for facility of observation.

If clinometers are used as gradienters – that is, for the setting out of a grade on a road or railway, or for a sewer or drain – it must be remembered that the grade set on the instrument must take account of the fact that the traverse will certainly be somewhat longer than the final distance when curves are introduced at the angles of the traverse lines. Therefore, the instrument must be set to a slightly smaller angle or slope of inclination one which experience shows to be a good approximation.

The Abney level – This is the most popular form of reflecting clinometer, and is shown in Fig. 69.

It was invented by Captain Abney, and consists of a hollow arm containing a telescope. Attached to this arm is a vertical arc, each quadrant of which is divided right and left into 90 degrees and subdivisions. The arm is of sufficiently stout metal to enable at its centre a horizontal spindle to be fixed, carrying a spirit-level, the case of which has a slot underneath, so as to expose the bubble, so that in whichever position the arm is held

the bubble will be reflected on to the mirror. A vernier
(described later) fixed to the spindle and at right angles to the
arm of the bubble indicates the relative angles of acclivity or
declivity on the vertical arc. The instrument shown in the

Fig. 69

illustration is much more compact than the usual form, having
a telescopic tube which closes up into the body of the instrument and is drawn out when the level is to be used. Another
feature is the adjustment for moving the vernier arm and the
bubble tube attached to it by means of a worm-wheel fitted on
the vernier arbor. This arrangement also gives room for a
larger divided arc than usual.

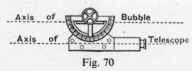

Fig. 70

Referring to Fig. 70, it will be observed that the instrument
in its entirety is in a truly horizontal position. Fig. 71 shows the
instrument being used for the angle of acclivity (which in this

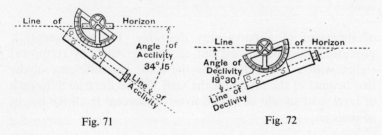

Fig. 71   Fig. 72

case is 34 deg. 15 min.), and Fig. 72 that of declivity, or 19 deg.
30 min., with the horizon. Thus the level tube is always horizon-

tal, and the arm of the vernier vertical, whilst the telescope assumes whatever angle it may be desired to observe, and the vertical arc consequently has its zero varying in position accordingly.

The Abney level may be made to fit on to a tripod with a ball-and-socket movement, whereby greater steadiness and consequently more accuracy may be attained. It will be necessary to use a target of equal height.

In order to adjust the spirit-level, select two stations, one on a mound, and take reciprocal sights from both stations. The mean of the two observations will be the true slope, which is set on the graduated arc, and the spirit-level adjusted until the bubble is bisected by the cross line on the target.

Hand level – Although the Abney level can perfectly well be set to zero and used as a hand level, it is irksome to do this continually in hilly country where reconnaissance demands a frequent determination of level. The small cost of a hand level, such as is shown in Fig. 73, makes the addition to the equipment

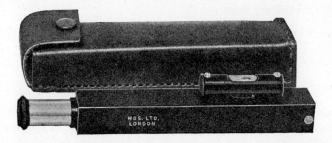

Fig. 73

of the chief of a party very desirable. The adjustment, if provided, must be carried out on level ground, by reciprocal sights, with a target sliding on the staff. The difference of the two heights of the target on the staff will be the true difference of level, and should be added to or subtracted from the height of the eye.

Indian clinometer – A very useful form of clinometer, designed for use with the plane table, which is very largely used for topographical work by the Survey of India, and in exploration work generally is shown in Fig. 74.

Fig. 74

The base is supported on three points, and is levelled by spirit-level by means of the screw at the eye-piece end. The fore and back sights fold down when not in use, but when they are erected the zero of the scales on the foresight is on a level with the pinhole in the backsight. A screw moves the target on the foresight into coincidence with the object observed, such as a cairn on a hill peak of a height approximating to that of the

E

plane table and clinometer. There are two scales on the foresight. On the one side it is graduated in angles of elevation and depression. On the other side it is graduated with a scale of natural tangents, so that a simple multiplication of the distance measured on the plan will give the difference in height. Adjustment is by means of reciprocal sights, preferably on the lefthand scale of angular graduation.

Experience has shown that the erection of cairns is very necessary, because, as the exploration proceeds, what may have appeared to be a well-marked object from one side of a ridge cannot be seen, or reliably identified, from the other side.

The "Bruton" pocket transit (Fig. 75) – A modification of the foregoing instrument will be found extremely valuable for ordinary work in the field. Being of a pocket size, it is, of course, only a hand instrument, but it does the work of a

Fig. 75

clinometer, prismatic compass and Abney level and by means of the folding sight on the lid it can also be used as a mining dial.

Mining dial – A more elaborate form of combined clinometer and compass is the mining dial, illustrated in Fig. 76. This has a circular compass, fitted with a vernier, giving readings as close as 3 minutes. There is a clamp and tangent screw, so that the object can be closely sighted through the hinged sights when raised. There is a ball and socket head with four levelling screws to level the instrument for inclined sights, the tilting of the base being effected by a gimbal mounting. The vertical arc reads to half a degree. While sufficiently accurate for some purposes, the degree of precision attainable is not great.

Fig. 76

Cross-sections by clinometer – The taking of cross-sections, at right angles to a line, is described on page 286. For rapid, but not such accurate work, the hand level can be used, but a Dumpy or other level on a stand will give much more accurate results. It is, however, necessary to take cross-sections at an angle to the leg of a traverse if the ground is to be contoured quickly in rough country. If there is no impediment to view, the tacheometer is the best instrument to use, as will be described later. If the ground is covered by scrub or forest, it is an arduous task to clear sufficiently for the comparatively long shots necessary. A small amount of clearing will enable cross-sections to be taken by clinometer, preferably by the Abney level, the observations being afterwards worked out and plotted. A number of "spot levels" will then provide material for drawing contours, as described in Chapter 9.

Cross-sections must be taken wherever the slope changes on the longitudinal section along the traverse, pegs being driven at such points by the leveller, who must record the ground levels at these pegs and furnish a list of them to the cross-section

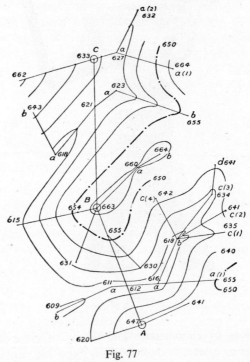

Fig. 77

taker. A prismatic compass is sufficiently accurate to record the direction of the cross-section and the changes in direction of the cross-section. Cross-sections on spurs, and where the slope changes between spurs and valleys, will often be on one bearing only, but in the valleys the bearing will often fork, if the contouring is to be done properly. Instead of taking bearings by compass, a plane table may be used to plot the direction of cross-section direct on the plan. The traverse, and the positions of the level pegs mentioned, will have been plotted before the plan is turned over to the cross-section taker.

The form of the field book must give all details necessary for the plotting, resulting in the plan shown in Fig. 77. Notice particularly the rather complicated work to the right of point 612 between stations A and B, extending to 300 feet from the traverse, with several changes in direction and forks. It was necessary to extend to this distance because the line of railway might be taken through the two spurs at one of the "cols." It would have been difficult to observe all this ground from any point on the traverse in forest. Notice also the chain dotted contour 650, making it easier to identify other contours. This sort of work has been done very satisfactorily by comparatively unskilled surveyors with good organisation and supervision.

Plane table – This consists of a drawing-board (Fig. 78), having a sheet of drawing paper strained on it, mounted on a portable three-legged stand. The table can be turned about a vertical axis and be adjusted by screws to a horizontal position by means of a spirit-level, either separate or attached to the frame. The vertical axis has a clamp. The usual sighting rule or alidade is a flat, straight-edged ruler, having upright sights at its end. These sights have slots similar to those in a prismatic compass or circumferentor. A small compass is also included in the outfit.

The use of the plane table resembles trigonometrical surveying on a small scale, except that the angles, instead of being read off on a horizontal circle and then plotted, are at once laid down on the paper in the field.

Fig. 79 is a simple illustration of the use of the plane table in the field. It is required to make a survey of the trapezium A C B D. Having set up rods at C, B, and D, the surveyor plants his table at A and brings the north point of his compass (360 deg.) directly under the needle when at rest. He makes a pencil point on some convenient part of his paper to represent his station in the field. It is often advised that this point shall be pricked with a needle, against which the fiducial or accurate

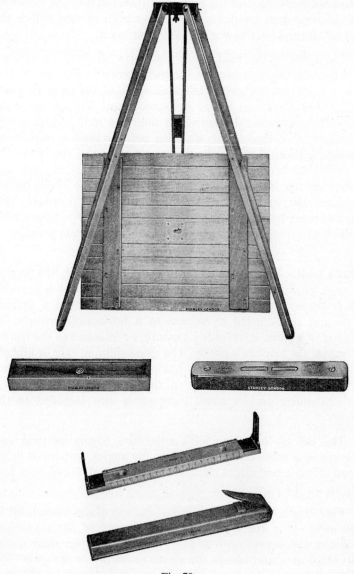

Fig. 78

edge of the alidade shall be set, but the experienced surveyor will not need this. He slides the alidade diagonally, in a parallel motion, to bring it to the required point. Directing the rule by means of the slots F F or G G (Fig. 80), he intersects a rod at B, and draws a faint pencil line. An H H pencil is perhaps the best, but in the tropics an H H H pencil may be used, because the lead becomes softer in hot climates. The rule is now directed towards

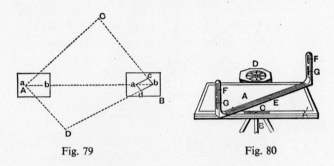

Fig. 79   Fig. 80

C and D and pencil lines drawn to cover the estimated distance away of those points. Alternatively, a line may be drawn near the edge of the paper and lightly marked with the letter assigned to the point.

He now proceeds to measure the distance A B, which is his base, and to plot the distance to scale along the line A B. He next proceeds to set up the table over B, directs his alidade along the line B A on the plan, and sets the table so that the sights on the rule intersect the rod at A. The table is now orientated, and C and D are again intersected without moving the table. The intersections of the rays taken from both A and B give the positions, to the scale of the plan, of C and D. If necessary, the accuracy of the work can be checked by chaining the distances B C and B D.

It may be well to mention that the plane table will be found to be very useful for ascertaining the area of the ground one is measuring. For example, suppose we have the irregular figure A B C D E (Fig. 81), and it is required to find its superficial contents. Plant the plane table at A and direct the index-rule to B, C, D, and E, measure on the ground and plot on the paper the length A B = 665, A C = 885, A D = 1030, and A E = 580, and make a correct plan of the ground. Now, if you erect perpendiculars B b = 424, C c = 595, and E e = 285, there will be by the

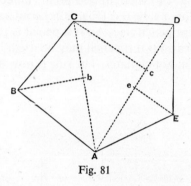

Fig. 81

well-known rule

$$\frac{\text{A C} \times b \text{ B}}{2} = \frac{885 \times 424}{2} = \qquad 187{,}620 \text{ sq. links}$$

and

$$\frac{\text{A D} \times (\text{C } c + e \text{ E})}{2} = \frac{1030 \times (595 + 285)}{2} = \frac{453200}{640820} \text{ sq. links}$$

= 6 acres, 1 rood, and 25·3 perches, the contents of the field.

It is recommended that the instrument shall be used as much as possible to intersect the positions of objects. It has been employed to a great extent to fill in topographical detail inside a triangulation, or lying adjacent to a traverse previously plotted to scale on the paper, chaining being reduced to a minimum. Of recent years, however, a tacheometrical alidade has been much employed, especially if the ground is to be contoured on the plan – for example, in surveys of oilfields. The advantage of the instrument lies in the saving of the booking of angular measurements, which have subsequently to be reduced and plotted.

Telescopic alidade – The ordinary rule and sights give only approximate accuracy, which can be considerably increased by the use of a telescope mounted on the alidade. In this telescope also can be fitted stadia for tacheometrical measurement, as described later. Such an alidade is shown in Fig. 82. The telescope stand is attached to a metal rule, provided with a spirit level. The rule is divided longitudinally, so as to make it a parallel ruler. It is not necessary to bring the edge of the rule exactly against the point representing the station from which observations are being taken. When the alidade has been

Fig. 82

aligned exactly the parallel ruler is slid until the edge comes against the station point and the ray is drawn. This saves a great deal of time.

It will be observed that this particular telescopic alidade is provided with a tangent scale. The distance from the station to the point is scaled, after fixing the point by intersection or measurement, and the distance is multiplied by the natural tangent to obtain the difference in height. Allowance must be made for the estimated height of the surface of the plane table if the survey requires such a degree of accuracy. This will only be needed for near points, as a rule. For more accurate work the alidade approaches the refinements of a theodolite. A vertical circle and vernier, a level on the telescope, clamp and tangent adjustments are necessary, besides stadia in the telescope.

Microptic alidade – Still greater accuracy and refinements are obtained in micrometer alidades such as the instruments made by Messrs Hilger and Watts and illustrated in Figure 83.

The accuracy of this type of alidade is such as to compare favourably with the small modern tacheometer. In the particular

Fig. 83

1	Telescope focusing knob	7	Telescope clamp
2	Scale illuminating window	8	Pivot adjustment screw
3	Circle reading eyepiece	9	Pillar levelling screwed
4	Telescope eyepiece	10	Wear adjustment screw
5	Telescope end cover	11	Telescope tangent screw
6	Bubble adjusting nut	12	Altitude bubble tangent screw

instrument illustrated the vertical scale is divided at intervals of 10 minutes and figured at every degree through 45 degrees of elevation and depression for both forward and backward sights. Two stadia scales are included graduated so that the stadia reading can be rapidly reduced to calculate the difference in elevation between instrument and staff and the true horizontal difference of the staff, thus considerably speeding up the work in the field.

Plane table stand – For rapid work, such as for military purposes, the stand may be quite simple. The requirements are a fair degree of rigidity when set up to an approximately level position of the top, with quick clamping and unclamping for the purpose of orientating the table and setting it in position. If the plane table is to be used for more accurate work, especially if contouring is to be done, and heights are to be obtained as well as distances, more elaborate means are necessary for setting the top level. Usually a ball-and-socket arrangement, as shown in Fig. 84, is adopted.

The table top is attached to the screw on *b*, and is set approximately level by fixing the tripod legs in the ground. The clamping nut *d* is released, and the sockets *b c* will then be free to allow orientation and levelling of the top. The nut *d* will then

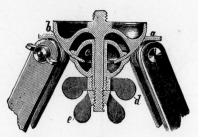

Fig. 84

be clamped again. Final orientation can be obtained by releasing the nut *e*, which leaves the hemispherical surface *b* free to move around the concave ring *a* of the tripod head.

Resection – It is frequently necessary, if the work is to be carried out rapidly, to find the position of the plane table on setting up in a position favourable for plotting the topography presented without necessarily setting it over a station already plotted on the plan. In order to achieve this it is necessary to be able to observe at least two, and preferably three, points plotted on the plan.

If two points can be observed, it is possible to orientate the table by the compass. The alidade can then be aligned on each point in turn and rays drawn, the intersection of which will give the position of the table. The accuracy of the result will depend largely on getting a good intersection, one which produces an angle at the plane table position of not less than 30 deg. The sluggishness and liability of the compass to be affected by metal objects do not make this method recommendable, but it is a rapid method.

In one of the survey pamphlets of the School of Military Engineering at Chatham a better method of resection from two points is given (see Figs. 85 to 88). The table is first set up at a

Fig. 85   Fig. 87

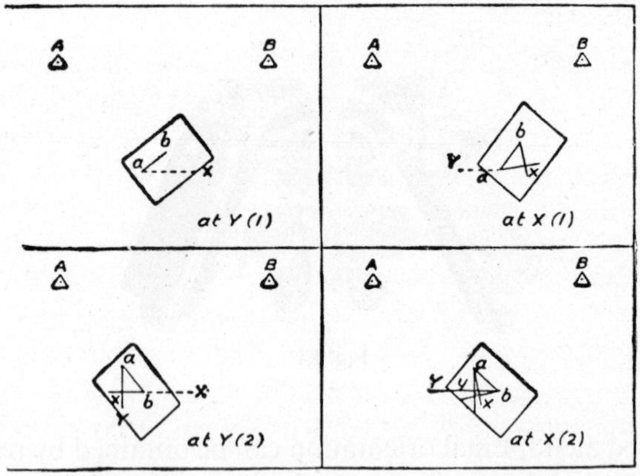

Fig. 86   Fig. 88

point Y some distance from the point X, of which the position is to be resected. The line between the two points X and Y should be more or less parallel to the line joining the two points A and B, from which position is to be resected. The distance X Y must be measured, but need not be longer than about half an inch on the scale if good intersections can be obtained at each end of the base. Any point can be assumed for the position of Y on the plan, or another piece of paper can be fixed over the plan. The object is to orientate the plane table, and then, by back rays from A and B, to find the point X on the plan.

There are four operations, two at each of the points Y and X. At Y, without any attempt to orientate, place the alidade along the line A B. Turn the table until A B is aligned on B, and draw a ray A X towards X. Then turn the table so that B A is aligned on A, and, sighting on X, find the intersection x.

Moving then to X, and again aligning the alidade along A B, repeat the procedure. Sight A B on B and draw a ray A Y, then sight B A on A and draw a ray B Y. There will now be two intersections, X and Y. The alidade being aligned along X Y and directed on Y, the table is set or orientated. Rays drawn through A and B intersecting in a new point X give the true position, and the topographical work can proceed. It is obvious that the labour is justified only if X be a very important point.

If three fixed points are in view, there are two methods of procedure. The first is an adaptation of the Three-point Problem. A piece of tracing paper, or cloth, is fixed on the table, and a station point marked on it. From this point rays are drawn to the three fixed points. Then, by manipulation of the tracing paper taken off the table so that the rays pass through the fixed points on the plan, the position of the table can be obtained. The table is then orientated by lining the alidade along the line joining the position thus found with any fixed point, and turning the table until the sights cut the fixed point. This is never a very satisfactory method, and fails entirely if the three fixed points and the position of the table lie on the circumference of a circle.

The more satisfactory method requires a certain amount of trial and error, and is called the "triangle of error." The plane table is orientated as nearly as possible, solely to reduce the size of the triangle. Rays are then drawn from the three points, and the result is nearly always a triangle. Then certain rules must be observed, see Fig. 89.

1. Observe the triangle formed by the three points. According as the "triangle of error" lies inside or outside the triangle of points, so the true position of the table will lie inside or outside the "triangle of error." In Fig. 89 it must lie outside, but less work will be involved if the table position is inside the triangle of points.

2. If outside the "triangle of error," the true position must lie, either to the right or to the left of all the rays forming the "triangle of error." The rays will form six sectors, as shown in

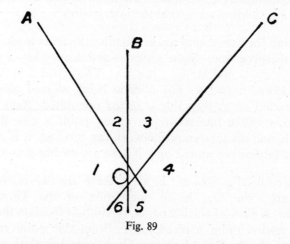

Fig. 89

Fig. 89. In the example, sector 4 is to the right and sector 1 to the left of all the rays. In one or other the true position lies, and in no other.

3. Perpendiculars dropped from the true position to the three rays must be proportional to the lengths of the three rays. This fixes the position in sector 1, and the trial position is as shown. To verify this, sight along the line, joining the trial position to the most distant point, C, in order to orientate the table by that point, and then sight on the other two points. If the result is not satisfactory a second "triangle of error" may have to be constructed, but usually the estimated position can be slightly corrected.

Sun compass – A rapid means of orientating the table, most useful in the tropics during long periods of fine weather, is to construct a sort of sundial. It is necessary to have some knowledge of astronomy, at least up to the stage of being able to calculate azimuths from the sun's position. The latitude and longitude must be known approximately, and fresh dials must be constructed as the work moves along, being pinned on the board as required. They must be fixed with reference to the true and not to the magnetic meridians. The compass is made out for every half hour or so, and a pin, set vertically in the circumference at the point corresponding to local sun time, by its shadow will show if the plane table is correctly set.

The formula for sun azimuth is

$$\tan A = \tan T \cos M \operatorname{cosec} [\pm M - (\pm L)]$$

where A = Azimuth
$\qquad$ T = Hour Angle
$\qquad$ L = Latitude
$\qquad$ and M is such an angle that
$\qquad\qquad$ tan M = tan D, sec T
$\qquad\qquad$ D = Declination.

Theodolite – For accurate angular measurement the theodolite is the most reliable instrument, especially since improvements in optical glass and in the graduation of horizontal and vertical circles have raised the accuracy to a high degree. Formerly, these circles had to be made of considerable diameters, but now a three or four inch circle can be divided with great accuracy. With modern micrometer devices it is possible to read to very small differences of angle, as will be mentioned. Fig. 90 shows a simple but thoroughly reliable form of theodolite, made by Stanley & Co., of London, and one which is still in general use in smaller offices. In any case the student will no doubt be required to obtain his initial field experience on one of these older types of theodolite for, owing to the high cost of modern instruments, it is hardly likely that he would be permitted to experiment on one. It is as well, therefore, that he should make himself thoroughly conversant with the type of instrument illustrated and it is principally for this reason that it has been included in this chapter. Although three levelling screws are shown in the illustration many of the older theodolites (and, indeed, levels) are of the 4-screw kind.

It should be emphasised that the accuracy of angular measurement depends on atmospheric conditions, and that the line of sight to an object is not necessarily straight, because the ray of light may be deflected from a straight path. Professor Einstein has demonstrated that this deflection takes place even in airless space. Much more is this tendency apparent in the disturbed condition of the atmosphere of the earth, and apart from any correction in vertical angular measurement as may be necessary for the curvature of the earth, this is a very important factor in rays of a primary triangulation, which may have sides

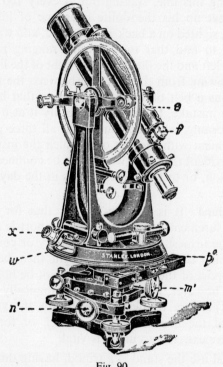

Fig. 90

as long as fifty miles. This factor, and that of vertical refraction, will be found on page 248. The general coefficient of refraction is 0·070, but is slightly higher in the United Kingdom, and lower in certain countries or in sights taken across the sea. It is held to be a minimum between the hours of 1.45 p.m. to 3.45 p.m.

F

In the tropics, where the ground is highly heated, peculiar phenomena may be observed. The writer once desired to check the straightness of a line, laid out by theodolite from one end for a railway, the straight being fourteen miles in length. He erected beacons about three miles apart on the alignment. Owing to the intense heat he judged it desirable to observe about 3.30 p.m. The beacons were seen in the telescope to be rising and falling, through a height of at least four feet.

On another occasion he had laid out a line to an intersection with a railway, so as to give a desired curve into a junction. He returned along this line, staking out at every 100 feet. About 11 a.m. he set up his theodolite over one of his previously aligned pegs, sighted on a back ranging rod, and transited.* He was amazed to find that two forward ranging rods lay, the nearer to the left and the farther to the right of the line. A strong wind was blowing from the left, and between the two forward rods there was a belt of scrub. Concluding that he had made some foolish mistake, he decided to rectify it at 6 a.m. on the following morning, when he found that all three pegs were in perfect alignment with the peg over which the instrument was set up. It is evident that such work must be confined to the cool or rainy season, or to the coolest hours in the day.

Theodolite stand – It is needless to say that for accuracy in angular measurement a firm and rigid support is necessary or desirable. The firmest support is a masonry or concrete pillar, and if this pillar has to be of some height then the scaffolding or other support of the observer should not be bonded into it. Such pillars, however, would only be economically justifiable in the case of primary triangulations, or for the very accurate laying out of the line for a long tunnel, or for some such purpose where extreme accuracy is vital.

For general use the stand is a tripod, having three legs, connected to a head. The instrument itself may screw on to the tripod head. When not in use this screw is protected by a cap. If the work is to be carried out on very rough ground, the tripod may have telescopic legs, so that, after the legs have been firmly

---

* i.e. rotating the telescope 180 degrees about its horizontal axis in a vertical plane.

pressed into the ground, away from a rock or stone, the head may be roughly levelled by manipulation of the telescopic legs. The legs can be provided with footholds, so that greater force can be applied in pressing them into the soil. To reduce vibration in a gale, or the chance of the whole being blown over, hooks can be provided on the inside of the legs to carry a net, which can be loaded with a heavy stone or two.

Centring plates – The instrument must be set up so that the vertical axis is vertically above the mark of the ranging rod on the station peg, and this is ensured by a plumb-bob hanging from the vertical axis, or from the head of the tripod if no means is available to centre the axis independently of the position of the legs. It requires care and experience to centre an instrument by pressing in the legs, and it is really only possible if the soil is soft and homogeneous. Means should be provided to lengthen or shorten the cord carrying the plumb-bob until the point is close to the mark or nail in the peg.

Much time and trouble will be saved if the instrument can be traversed on the head of the tripod. Such a device may be contained in the tripod head itself, one plate sliding over another fixed plate when a clamp is released, thus giving about half an inch in any direction. If the device is fitted in the base of the instrument, about one inch of play can be given by similar sliding plates with a clamp. A device made by Hilger and Watts Ltd. and other reputable makers of modern instruments, enables the rough centring to be done by hand, after which the motion can be clamped, and fine adjustment is carried out by two screws at right angles with a total motion of $2\frac{1}{4}$ in. The centring can be done after the instrument has been levelled finally, which is an advantage. Although primarily intended for mine surveying, which demands great accuracy, this device is now incorporated as standard practice in all modern instruments.

Levelling screws – Above or below the centring plates there are foot screws, three or four in number, usually three but in some countries there is still a preference for four. It is argued by those who favour three screws that they form the steadier and more certain support. Champions of four screws claim that steadiness is assured only by this form of construction. In either case good levelling of the base plate depends on the spirit-level being truly parallel to one pair of footscrews first, and to a line at right angles to that pair in the second part of the operation.

Parallel plates – These are fitted to the four-screw type, as shown in Figs. 91 and 92. They consist of two circular plates kept a certain distance apart by a ball-and-socket, and the four screws B^1, B^2, B^3, B^4 placed at right angles to each other, and called the parallel screws. The upper plate is pierced with four

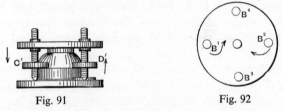

Fig. 91   Fig. 92

holes, which are tapped with a female screw, in which a screw having in its centre a milled head works but whose lower extremity rests and works upon the lower plate. In order to prevent the upper plate revolving there is a U-shaped guard round one of the screws.

Parallel plate screws – The action of the parallel plates is regulated by screwing and unscrewing each pair of opposite screws. Thus, if the right end of the plate, as D^1, Fig. 91, is required to be raised, then the left end C^1 must be depressed, which is effected simultaneously by turning the screws B^2 and B^1, Fig. 92, inwards, whereby B^2 is elongated and B^1 shortened. If, on the other hand, it is desired to elevate at C' and depress at D', then these screws must be turned outwards, whereby B^1 is elongated and B^2 shortened. Similarly, B^3 and B^4 have to be dealt with.

Three-screw theodolite – The purpose of both three or four screw action is to level up the theodolite once the instrument has been accurately set over the station. When levelling the instrument by the 4-screw action one spirit level should be moved parallel to screws B_1B_2 when the other will then be parallel to screws

B_3B_4. Each pair of screws should be turned exactly together – thumbs either towards each other or away from each other, *remembering that the bubble always travels in the same direction as the left thumb.* When the first bubble is in the centre of its run deal with the second pair of screws in the same way. Repeat the action if necessary.

The 3-screw type is similarly dealt with excepting that one bubble is placed parallel to two screws when the other will be at right angles to them. Screws A_1A_2 (Fig. 93) are adjusted as before

Fig. 93

and then screw B by itself. Never attempt to level up by adjusting A_1A_2 and afterwards A_1B (or A_2B). Screw B must be used on its own.

Most modern instrument makers provide only one plate bubble with a coincidence reading device (see later). In levelling the instrument in these circumstances it is necessary, after adjusting the bubble on the two screws, to turn through 90° before adjusting on the third footscrew.

Ball-and-socket arrangement – Referring to the ball-and-socket arrangement, it is necessary here to explain that it is the most important part of the four-screw type theodolite. The lower parallel plate has a dome-shaped socket accurately turned to receive the semi-spherical lower portion of the body-piece. The upper parallel plate has also a socket, upon which rests the shoulder of the body-piece; thus the four parallel screws serve to keep the upper and lower plates apart; and according to the elongation or shortening of each pair, so the ball-and-socket arrangement admits the elevation or depression of the upper plate as required. The object of this is to maintain the instrument in a truly horizontal position, as will be presently explained; but having by means of the four screws adjusted it level, it is necessary that they should all firmly bite the lower plate, *but not* *too much so*, otherwise the threads of the screws will be injured and indentations will appear on the plate.

Now the body-piece before referred to is hollow, but its interior is in the form of an inverted cone, within which works a solid spindle of similar shape, both being so accurately ground to fit that the axes of the two cones may be parallel.

Base or lower plate – This, by construction, is fixed at right angles to the vertical axis, with which it revolves, unless and until it is clamped to the part containing the footscrews, and thus to the stand. The base plate is bevelled and on the bevelled part is fixed a silver scale, graduated to 360 deg. and sub-divisions as a rule. In some countries, however, it is graduated into 400 grades and subdivisions, a system which is claimed to have advantages. This scale reads clockwise. The diameter of the circle distinguishes the particular size of the instrument. Formerly, difficulties in graduation demanded a considerable diameter for good accuracy, but now a three or four inch diameter is quite sufficient, and modern instruments are much lighter in consequence. The base plate and other features to be described later are shown in the modern micrometer theodolite (Fig. 94).

Upper or vernier plate – This is fixed at right angles to an inner cone, or vertical axis, and can be clamped to the base plate. It is of smaller diameter, and carries two verniers, or micrometers, fixed 180 deg. apart for the purpose of finer reading of the graduated scale by a system of differences. To this plate are fixed the spirit-levels, the box compass, when required, and the supports of the telescope.

The vernier – The vernier, in its ordinary sense, is a contrivance wherewith the intervals between the divisions on the primary scale may be accurately measured. It is a scale whose length is generally one less than a certain number on the primary scale, so that, supposing the lower plate is divided into degrees and half-degrees, if we take 29 of the subdivisions (or 14 deg. 30 min.*) and divide this length into one more or less parts than

* The degree is shown by a circle thus °, minutes by one dash thus ′, and seconds by two dashes thus ″.

those of the primary scale whose length regulates that of the vernier, we shall have a means of determining the actual number of minutes which intervene between the subdivisions.

Fig. 94

KEY

1. Telescope clamp
2. Circle reading eyepiece
3. Foresight
4. Circle selector knob
5. Horizontal circle micrometer knob
6. Plate bubble
7. Azimuth clamp
8. Case support lug
9. Cover to circle repetition knob
10. Azimuth slow motion screw
11. Optical plummet eyepiece
12. Cover screw for altitude bubble adjustment
13. Telescope eyepiece
14. Telescope focusing sleeve

It is customary to divide the vernier into thirty equal parts, so that it has thirty spaces to the twenty-nine subdivisions on the limb.

For greater minuteness of observation some modern theodolites are divided into thirds and fourths as well as into half-degrees, in which cases the verniers are divided into twenty and fifteen parts respectively, so as to accurately record the intervals between the subdivisions.

In consequence of the limb and vernier being circular in shape, it is found more easy to illustrate the relationship of the latter to the former by a straight line, and Figs. 95 to 97 will serve to do so.

Fig. 95 shows a portion of the primary scale drawn straight from 45 deg. to 72 deg., and from 50 deg. to 64 deg. 30 min. I have marked the 29 half-degrees as the length of the vernier. Now, taking this length and dividing it afresh into thirty equal parts, it will be seen by Fig. 96 that, whereas the vernier scale commences at 50 deg. and terminates exactly at 64 deg. 30 min., so that the commencement and termination are coincident with the division 50 deg. and 64 deg. 30 min. on the lower scale, yet not one of the divisions of the vernier intermediate between its commencement and termination will cut any one of the points in the lower scale between 50 deg. and 64 deg. 30 min. If the student can once grasp this fact, then the difficulty of the vernier is simplified.

Now if the foregoing argument be proven, it is easy to understand that once the vernier moves from 50 deg. it is possible for any *one* of its divisions to intersect any one of the divisions and subdivisions of the lower scale, but only *one* at a time.

As an illustration, the first division of the vernier may be in line with 50 deg. 30 min., and such being the case, the other twenty-nine divisions would not be coincident. This, then, would show the angle to be 50 deg. 1 min. Again, the tenth division may be coincident with 55 deg. This shows that ten minutes more than the 50 deg. or commencement have been recorded, in other words, 50 deg. 10 min. Further, if the twentieth division on the upper scale is coincident with any division or subdivision on the lower one, it must of necessity be at 60 deg.; consequently, the reading of the vernier is 50 deg. 20 min. And lastly, if the thirtieth division or end of the upper scale is coincident with one of the divisions or subdivisions of the lower one, it must be at 65 deg., and thus, thirty of the divisions in the upper scale having traversed from left to right, the arrow A (Fig. 96) will be coincident with the subdivisions between 50 deg. and 51 deg., or at 50 deg. 30 min. So we see

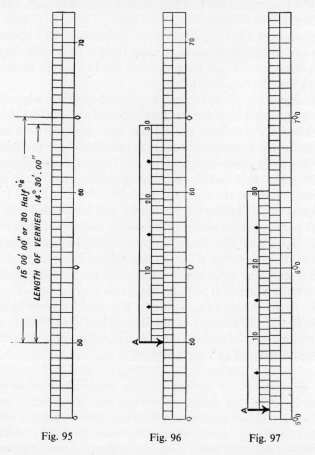

Fig. 95   Fig. 96   Fig. 97

that even if each of the thirty divisions of the upper scale be consecutively coincident with any division or subdivision of the lower one, at the end we have only moved one half-degree in a direction towards the right.

Now supposing it is discovered by aid of the microscope that the arrow A (Fig. 97) has passed 50 deg. 30 min., common sense will tell that the first half-degree in the lower plate has been passed, and it is desired to ascertain how many of the minutes in the second half-degree are recorded by the vernier.

In this case (Fig. 97) it will be seen that the seventh division of the upper scale is coincident with 54 deg., and seeing that the arrow A has passed the first half-degree beyond 50 deg., then the reading will be 50 deg. 30 min. +7 min. = 50 deg. 37 min., and supposing the thirtieth division of the vernier was coincident with any in the lower scale, it must be that at 65 deg. 30 min., when the arrow A will have reached the full length of the first degree past 50 deg. or 51 deg.

The foregoing remarks apply to those theodolites whose limbs are only divided into degrees and half-degrees; but in the larger instruments the degrees are divided into third parts of twenty minutes each. Suppose, for example, the limb is so divided, and that it is to be subdivided by a vernier to third parts of a minute or 20 secs., each subdivision being one-sixtieth part of the primary division, the length of the vernier will be $60 - 1 = 59$ divisions of the primary scale; and it will be divided into sixty equal parts, each equal to 59-60ths of a division of the primary scale. To make this more simple, it will be seen that each vernier division being $\frac{1}{60}$ or 20 secs. shorter than each division on the scale, the coincidence of any line on the vernier, with a line on the scale, will indicate the same number of $\frac{1}{60}$ths of a division, the index of the vernier is removed from a division on the scale, as the number of the line on the vernier.

In modern instruments the verniers are totally enclosed by glass plates, so as to keep out dust.

The micrometer – A vernier usually provides quite adequate subdivision of the larger divisions, and for some kinds of survey even closer subdivision than may be necessary. For some classes of survey, however, much closer reading is necessary, and theodolites are fitted with micrometer microscopes instead of verniers. These micrometers add to the weight, and also necessitate greater care in carrying and handling the instrument, since damage to them is a serious matter. At the same time, although such close reading may be unnecessary, a micrometer gives much more satisfaction and saves time in searching along the vernier for coincidence of the graduations, or in estimation of the difference if exact coincidence does not occur.

Micrometer microscopes, like verniers, are used in pairs, fitted at opposite ends of a diameter of the graduated circle, horizontal or vertical. They are adjustable, both for position or for degree of magnification. On looking into the eyepiece two thin wires can be observed (see Fig. 98). At the side of the microscope there is a drum, or micrometer head, and when the drum marks zero the two wires are in the centre of the field and should coincide with a notch as in A. The wires are moved across the field by rotating the drum, until the two wires straddle

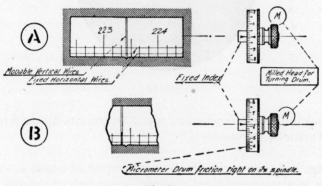

Fig. 98

one of the larger divisions on the graduated circle as in B. The displacement is measured by the drum, and the reading is thus obtained, probably to ten seconds with a five-inch circle, while closer reading can be obtained by estimation. The wires may be run to straddle the nearer divisions, or run invariably to straddle the division to the left or that to the right, as a matter of routine, and to save mistakes.

In certain modern instruments, by optical means, both ends of the diameter of the graduated circle are brought together into the field of a single microscope, as will be mentioned in the short description of the Wild theodolite. Messrs. Cooke, Troughton, and Simms are among the modern instrument makers who have introduced such a refinement in their Tavistock theodolite (so named because the original, first produced in 1928, was the outcome of a conference held at Tavistock between Survey Offices of the British Government and representatives of the instrument makers). Fig. 99 illustrates a

Fig. 99

reading of this micrometer and Fig. 100 shows an illustration of the Tavistock theodolite.

Clamps and slow motion screws – If a round of angles is to be taken in a trigonometrical survey it is necessary to clamp the base plate of the tripod head, and then by a slow motion screw to bring the central wire in the telescope to intersect the reference object or the beacon over some station. When running a traverse it is the best plan to set the vernier plate to read the back bearing and to bring the wire, by clamping and slow motion screw, to intersect the ranging rod held on the back peg. Similarly, when laying out curves, the base plate must be clamped and brought by slow motion into proper orientation. The vernier plate also must be capable of being clamped and brought by slow motion into its proper relation to the base plate. Clamping and slow motion must be used to bring the vertical wire in the telescope to intersection with a beacon or ranging rod, and also to bring the horizontal wire to intersect a target or a particular reading on a level staff in tacheometer work. It is important for the surveyor to familiarise himself with the various clamps and slow motion screws, because mistakes will arise if he handles the wrong screw, and the work may have to be done again.

Fig. 100 – Tavistock theodolite with detachable centring and levelling base

Spirit-levels – Theodolite work must be done in a plane at right angles to a radius of the earth, or the angles observed will not be correct. Horizontality is indicated by a spirit-level, of which two, a longer and a shorter, are fixed on the vernier plate, and therefore, by construction and by adjustment, are parallel to the base plate. One level at least is an essential, but the second and shorter one will save a little time in setting up. A level on the telescope, or fixed parallel to the zeros of the vernier arms, and adjustable to this position, is not absolutely essential, but again will save time in setting up. The longer the spirit-level, the more sensitive it should be, and therefore a spirit-level on the telescope is preferred by some. The writer prefers the other position, because the telescope is seldom horizontal and may be reversed, whereas the level in the other position is always open to inspection. A striding level, with which to test the horizontality of the telescope trunnions, may be provided, but is not fixed to the instrument. The adjustments of the spirit-levels will be described later.

A frames – The telescope is carried by trunnions at the top of two A frames, the trunnions supporting the axis on which the telescope is rotated. These trunnions are adjustable, so that the telescope axis may be horizontal, otherwise the central intersection of the wires will describe a circle which is not truly vertical. On the horizontal bar of both A frames there is a lug, over which fits the vertical arm of a T-piece on the horizontal arms of which there are verniers, or micrometers. This T-piece is attached to the lugs by antagonising screws which adjust the vertical arm in a correct position, and thus, by construction, the vernier arms will be horizontal, and correct angles of elevation or depression can be read after true adjustment, as will be described. In some instruments one antagonising screw is replaced by a spring.

The object of having a lug on both of the A frames is to be able to attach the T-piece to either frame. If the T-piece is attached to the right-hand frame the verniers can be read from the right, and if attached to the left-hand frame the reading is from the left of the instrument as set up. This statement is correct enough for work where rounds of angles are usually taken in a clockwise direction, but in traverse work, where the telescope may be transited, it is not correct unless it is understood to apply only in forward reading. Although practice does not always agree in the terms, the writer calls a reading with "face right" to mean a reading with the T-piece to the right, and "face left" a reading with the T-piece to the left, in clockwise or forward reading.

The object in having two points of attachment to the A frames is to eliminate errors in vertical angles, the telescope being turned over in changing the point of attachment. A little consideration will show that this can be attained by transiting the telescope during a certain number of rounds of angles, and in modern instruments this means of changing face is not provided. It is more important to be able to change face in this way for traverse work, but proper checks can be devised and are always advisable.

Vertical arc – The vertical arc is attached rigidly to the axis of the telescope, can be clamped to the T-piece, and actuated by a slow motion screw so that, as the horizontal wire in the telescope is brought to intersection, the vertical circle moves with it. The circle is graduated in 360 degrees and subdivisions of a degree, or into 400 grades and subdivisions of a grade. The zero or 360 deg. point of the graduation may be at the top or at the right-hand side, and generally a horizontal position is more convenient.

Telescope – Lastly, we come to the telescope with an object glass directed on the beacon, ranging rod, or level staff, and an eyepiece for reading. The telescope inverts the object. It could be made to show the object erect at the cost of inserting an additional lens, which would cause a loss of light. The object glass focuses the object on the diaphragm, and this is not at the axis of the telescope. To bring the object to the axis which is desirable, although not essential in tacheometer work, it would be necessary to insert an anallatic lens with a loss of light and a lengthening of the telescope which makes it impossible to transit without racking in the object glass, unless the A frames are made longer, and this detracts from the steadiness besides adding to the weight. To observe near objects the old form of telescope required racking out, and the sliding tube was apt to sag, thereby throwing out the balance and the line of collimation, or centre line of the tube. In modern instruments an internal focusing telescope is fixed, so that the length is constant. The internal focusing lens is racked by a screw rotating in the telescope axis, a very convenient position. Although this lens causes a certain diminution of light, and is not perfectly anallatic, leaving a small "constant" difference between telescope axis and diaphragm, its advantages outweigh these considerations.

Magnification – The modern telescope is much more efficient than the old type, and one of 10-inch focus is as good as an old one of double that length of focus. A high degree of magnification is not desirable, because the magnification of dust and haze in the atmosphere takes place. A power of twenty is sufficient.

Eyepiece – It is necessary to focus the rays coming in through the object glass on the diaphragm, and at the same time to focus the eyepiece on the diaphragm for good reading. In the old type telescopes the eyepiece fitted with a loose fit in a tube, and the focusing is done by sliding the eyepiece in or out with a screwing motion. In modern telescopes eyepieces of the type familiar in prismatic glasses are fitted. These show the diopters, plus or minus, so that once the particular diopter corresponding to the observer's eye has been ascertained, the eyepiece can always be set properly. For certain types of work with a high degree of elevation of the telescope, a prismatic eyepiece may be used for diagonal observation in a more comfortable position, and with this can be combined an erecting eyepiece for those who prefer it. This form is perhaps desirable for work in the tropics, where sun helmets must be worn, but a surveying umbrella is usually necessary.

Diaphragm – Various forms of diaphragm are shown in Fig. 101. D and E are for theodolites, and the others for tacheometers, although one of these is often fitted to a theodolite in any case. It is preferable to have a vertical line for adjustment. There is yet another type of diaphragm with vertical stadia, the short or long lines on either side of the horizontal line as shown in A, F and G. These vertical stadia are used in tunnel work, with a level staff held horizontally for measurement of distance, as will be described. The diaphragms are also used for levelling instruments.

Formerly the diaphragm wires were made of spider thread, and spiders are still kept for the purpose. Not every spider spins a sufficiently fine thread and the replacement of these threads is a delicate process which requires some practice. It is general practice now to use glass diaphragms with stadia ruled on glass, although the glass may get dusty and obstruct a little light.

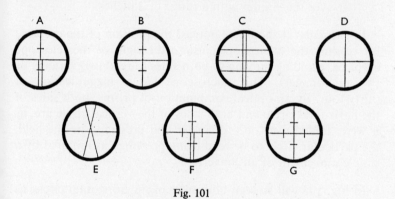

Fig. 101

It is necessary to be able to adjust the position of the diaphragm so that the line of collimation may pass through the intersection of the threads. It is also necessary, in some types of telescope, to be able to rotate the whole diaphragm so as to bring the horizontal and vertical wires into truth. It is more important to do this with the vertical wire, as will be explained. For this purpose screws will be found around the diaphragm position.

Wild universal theodolite – In Fig. 102 is shown one of the highest type of theodolite, made by Wild of Heerburg. A modification of this instrument is made by Hilger and Watts. It is not likely that the student will be allowed to handle such a costly instrument for instruction, although it is claimed to

G

possess great robustness, but he may well study how the features of the old type have been altered. The weight is only 24 lb. The telescope has a magnification of twenty-four up to forty or more and is efficient for shots up to 60 miles. The diameter of the horizontal circle is only $5\frac{1}{2}$ inches, and of the vertical circle 3·8 inches, yet it is claimed that the degree of precision is about quarter a second of arc of mean error. Features deserving notice are the bringing together or placing of the tangent screws and clamps, so that they are to hand without change of position from that of observation once the instrument has been set up. It is not mentioned in the Figure that the instrument can be centred over the station with a range of 2 inches.

In particular it should be noticed the position of the eyepiece for reading the microscope, just to the right of the telescope eyepiece, avoiding moving to both sides to read two verniers or two micrometers. This microscope has a magnification of thirty-four. By an optical combination of prisms, both sides of the horizontal circle and both sides of the vertical circle are, as it were, folded over on a diameter and presented in one field, the particular circle to be read being presented as required by a simple movement of an "inverter."

In Fig. 103 will be seen both sides of the horizontal circle, as presented before operation of the micrometer screw by turning a milled head to the right hand of the U-frame in Fig. 102. In Fig. 104 two divisions, on opposite sides of the circle, have been brought into coincidence, and the micrometer can be read to one second, or less by estimation.

Adjustment of this instrument is hardly possible in the field, but it is claimed that this is unnecessary, once the necessary adjustment has been made in the maker's workshop.

Adjustments of the theodolite – These are usually described as "permanent" adjustments, but should be corrected once a week or so. However carefully they may be made, it is wise in the system of work to carry out observations in such a manner that slight errors left after adjustment may be eliminated. Some cannot be eliminated, and any deviation from true adjustment

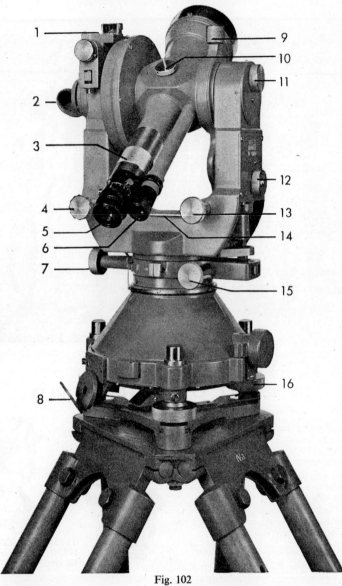

Fig. 102

1. Level prism	9. Vertical clamp
2. Mirror for vertical circle	10. Mirror knob
3. Focusing ring	11. Knob for optical micrometer
4. Screw for vertical circle level	12. Changing knob
5. Telescope eyepiece	13. Vertical tangent screw
6. Microscope eyepiece	14. Plate level
7. Horizontal clamp	15. Horizontal tangent screw
8. Mirror for horizontal circle	16. Levelling screw

noticed should be corrected at once. It is claimed by makers of the most modern instruments that workshop adjustments are permanent, but if readjustment cannot be carried out without

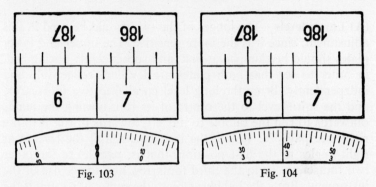

Fig. 103   Fig. 104

returning the instrument to a workshop, it is advisable to give this consideration full weight.

The adjustments are:

A.—To bring the spirit-level, or levels, at right angles to the vertical axis, so that when the bubbles are in the centre of their runs the axis shall be vertical. In fact, the spirit-level will be parallel to the lower and upper plates.

B.—To eliminate parallax from the eyepiece of the telescope, so that subsequent adjustments shall not be vitiated.

C.—To ensure that the axis on which the telescope revolves shall be at right angles to the vertical axis.

D.—To test the line of collimation through the centre of the telescope in azimuth. There may be two tests for this.

E.—To test the line of collimation in altitude.

F.—To adjust the vertical circle, so that when the line of collimation is horizontal the reading on the vertical circle shall be zero. Some instruments, graduated in grades, have 100 and 300 deg. at the horizontal position.

G.—To adjust the spirit-level on the vertical circle, so that when the line of collimation is horizontal the spirit-level shall be parallel to it, and, of course, to the lower plate levels.

It is presumed that the micrometers, if any, have been adjusted, as previously described, or that index errors have been noted when discovered.

(A) **Lower levels** – The longer of the two should be used in this adjustment, since it is the more sensitive. The upper and lower plates should be clamped at first, and subsequently unclamped, in order to see that both plates are levelled, collectively and independently. Bring the long level parallel to two footscrews, and the spirit-level to the centre of its run, turning the hands outwards to run the bubble to the left, inwards to run it to the right, see page 76. Rotate the instrument until the level is at right angles to the first position, that is, parallel to the other two footscrews or to the third footscrew and the centre of the instrument. Bring the bubble again to the centre of its run. If the bubble does not move on bringing the instrument back to the first position, or when it is rotated completely, the spirit-level is in adjustment. If the bubble leaves its central position, correct only half by the footscrews, and the other half by the screws at the ends of the spirit-level.

Students, and surveyors out of practice, find it a little difficult to see why this instruction is correct. Let us assume, in Fig. 105, that the spirit-level is inclined at 91 deg. to the vertical axis, that

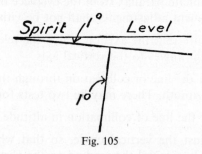

Fig. 105

is, one degree from a right angle. The bubble being in the centre of its run, the vertical axis is inclined at 1 deg. and by construction the base plate also. After rotation through 180 deg. (Fig. 106) the plate is still inclined at 1 deg. to the horizontal, but the spirit-level will be inclined at 2 deg. Consequently, we correct (automatically) 1 deg. by the footscrews and 1 deg. by the spirit-level screws. It may be necessary to correct again, since the base plate was not correctly levelled over the third footscrew, or other pair of footscrews.

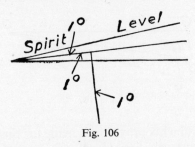

Fig. 106

Before touching the level (capstan) screws it is advisable to work out the effect of doing so. They will probably be right-handed screws, so that to bring the bubble to the right it is necessary to turn the lower screw on the right to the left. Before doing this the upper right-hand screw must be turned to the left slightly to enable the level tube to lift. On completing the adjustment all level tube screws should be tight, but not strained. Small tommy bars will be found in the box for turning capstan screws usually fitted.

(B) Parallax – This is a phenomenon to be noticed if the eyepiece is not accurately focused on the wires or scratches on the glass of the diaphragm. If the head is moved from side to side, the webs appear to move also. The older eyepieces are focused by moving them in or out in the tube at the near end of the telescope, and this is best done by a screwing movement. Modern instruments have a screw focusing eyepiece, familiar in prism field-glasses, with diopters marked plus or minus. This is very convenient for approximate setting. The rule for adjusting parallax is given on page 249.

(C) Telescope axis – If the trunnions of the triangular supports to the telescope are not of equal height above the base plate, owing to wear or other reasons, the horizontal angles to targets at widely different heights will not be correct, and the distance must be reduced by multiplying by the sine of the slope of the trunnions (see Fig. 107). If o be the reference object, and o G′ the horizontal plane, the angular measurement to a signal G above the plane will be o G′, whereas if G be below the horizontal plane the angular measurement will be o G″.

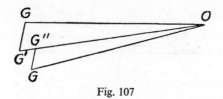

Fig. 107

In some instruments provision is made for this adjustment by a striding spirit-level, Fig. 90. If this be not available, the crosswires of the diaphragm should be brought to a well-defined mark, as high up as may be possible, and both horizontal plates well clamped. The telescope is then tilted carefully, and the object glass brought down until the crosswires nearly cut the ground. A peg is driven and a mark made on the peg, as directed by the observer, on the line of the crosswires. The telescope is then transited, the horizontal plates unclamped, and the instrument rotated until it can be brought by tangent screw to the high mark again. On depressing the object glass end the mark on the peg should coincide with the crosswires, otherwise the true vertical lies halfway between the two marks. One or other trunnion can then be adjusted until the crosswires follow a vertical path.

Many adjustments, and the elimination of many errors, are made by this sort of reciprocal observation, first "face right" and then "face left."

(D) Line of collimation in azimuth* – It is now necessary to ensure that the line of collimation, the line through the centre of the telescope, shall be at right angles to the transit axis. Here again the reciprocal method of adjustment is the one used in setting out long straight lines of railway. The base plates being clamped, a sight is taken on a mark, such as a ranging rod or a nail on a peg, and the telescope is transited. A peg is driven

---

* An azimuth bearing is the angle that any line makes with the meridian measured round in the same direction as the hands of a clock, from zero to 360°.

and a mark made on it where the crosswires cut. The instrument is now rotated through 180 deg. and brought to the backsight by slow motion screw on the vernier plate. After transiting again, a second peg is driven and marked. The true point on the line continued through the vertical axis of the instrument from the back sight lies halfway between the marks on the two pegs.

It is necessary, however, to divide the distance between the true point and one or other of the false marks by two. The adjustment this time is made by the screws at the sides of the eyepiece, loosening one and tightening the other until the crosswires fall on the "quarter-point," the remaining distance to the true point being made up by the slow motion screw on one or other horizontal plate. The reason for this must be given.

In Fig. 108 A is the back sight, I the instrument, B^1 is the first mark in foresight, and B^2 the second mark in foresight. Q is the

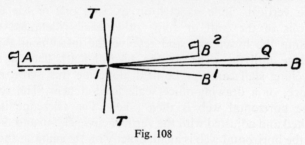

Fig. 108

quarter-point, B is on the straight line through A I. If we assume that the angles A I B^1 and A I B^2 are equal to 180–2 deg., then the line of collimation A I B is out by 1 deg. to the axis of the trunnions T T, and adjustment to the angle A I Q will adjust the collimation in azimuth.

Should the observer have to set out a straight line with a theodolite of the Everest type, which does not transit, he can proceed as follows. With both lower plates clamped, sight on A. Unclamp the upper plate, rotate, and set to 180 deg. Make the first foresight mark B^1. Then, with both plates clamped, direct the crosswires on A, being careful to use the slow motion of the bottom plate for final co-incidence. Again unclamp the upper plate and rotate until the vernier is set at 360 deg. Make the second foresight mark B², and B, the halfway point, not Q, is on the line A I produced.

To adjust an Everest theodolite for collimation in azimuth proceed as for the transit instrument, but very carefully change from "face right" to "face left" instead of transiting.

(E) Line of collimation in altitude – To test the collimation in altitude any convenient back station may again be taken, but it should be so situated that a mark can be made in front without disturbing the telescope in altitude. As an instance, assume the ground is fairly level. If no natural object is available have a ranging rod fixed for the back station. The instrument being properly levelled, the telescope is directed to the back mark and another mark fixed in front by transiting the telescope as before. Next turn the telescope on to the back station and adjust the horizontal web by means of the clamp and tangent to the vertical circle exactly on to, say, one of the colour divisions of the staff or some other easily identified mark. Unclamp the lower axis and revolve the instrument through 180 deg. until the webs cut the vertical mark fixed in front. A levelling staff can now be held alongside this mark, if at a distance, or a drawing-office scale fixed if near. The reading of the horizontal web is then taken. The telescope is now transited and adjusted with the vertical circle clamp and tangent until the horizontal web is again exactly on the mark at the back station. Unclamp the vertical axis and again turn the instrument through 180 deg., clamping it with the intersection of the webs on the vertical mark in front. The horizontal web should now give the same reading on the staff or scale as before. If it does not, take the difference of the two readings, and set the webs to read a quarter of this difference from the last reading taken, using the vertical pair of collimating screws for the purpose. As it may be necessary to slacken off one of the horizontal collimating screws to enable this to be done, the value of having the vertical reference mark will be seen, as it can be observed, after all the collimating screws have been tightened up, whether the adjustment in azimuth is still correct. Previous remarks as to repetition apply here also. When the webs are being adjusted care should be taken to see that the horizontal web is horizontal. This may be tested by slowly revolving the instrument so that the web traverses some mark right across the field of view in the telescope, and, if necessary, tapping the collimating screws with some light object, one up and the other down, as may be necessary, the holes being slightly slotted to enable this to be done. The foregoing adjustments having been skilfully made, the telescope should be in proper collimation, the methods given being applicable either to the ordinary or internal focusing telescope.

(F and G) Vertical circle – Select a convenient mark for sighting some distance away and at any elevation. Read the angle of elevation. Transit the telescope, revolve the instrument through 180 deg. and again sight the mark and read the angle of elevation. If this angle is the same as before, everything is correct; but if it differs, take the mean of the two readings and set the verniers of the vertical circle exactly at this. Bring the web on to the mark sighted by means of the antagonising screws, taking care not to touch the tangent screw to the vertical circle. If the bubble is on the vernier arm it will now have been moved out of the centre. Bring it back by adjusting the level only.

If the spirit-level is on the telescope, the vertical circle must first be brought to zero on the vernier, the spirit-level being on the top of the telescope. The level is then adjusted by the capstan screws only.

The foregoing operations all having been properly performed, we should know that, when our vertical axis has been set truly vertical, all our bubbles will assume the centre position of their run when the line of collimation is horizontal, and that the vertical circle will read zero, thus eliminating any so-called index error. If the verniers to the vertical circle have been carelessly set during the bubble adjustments, an index error may exist, but it would be entirely through our own fault.

Photo-theodolite – The subject of photographic surveying or photogrammetry is touched on briefly in Chapter 12, but its application is so specialised as to be beyond the scope of this chapter except in the simplest outline. It is particularly suitable when the season for surveying is short, and where the country is mountainous or very open, since forest obviously restricts the record of the camera. As in all methods of surveying, the selection of stations is of the highest importance, and the

Fig. 109

Watts Microptic Theodolites were used by the British
Commonwealth Trans-Antarctic Expedition

Watts Theodolites, Levels,

Field Accessories and

Instruments for geophysical

prospecting & photogrammetry

HILGER & WATTS LIMITED
98 ST. PANCRAS WAY · LONDON · N.W.I.
Telephone: GULliver 5636

HW/113

intersections must be good. As much information as possible must be recorded on the photographic plate for subsequent identification and ease of orientation when plotting.

Figure 109 illustrates a camera mounted on a Watts Microptic Theodolite No. 1.

The camera gives a perspective view at a constant distance, corresponding to the focal length of the lens, all negatives being taken without any extension of the camera, the lens being stopped down as much as is necessary to bring all points into sharp focus. Positives may be enlarged, all to the same degree, so as to maintain the constant focal length necessary. The vertical and horizontal collimation of the camera must be recorded on the negative and print, and all distances of points to be plotted from these two co-ordinates must be laid off on a line drawn on the plan at the focal, or enlarged focal, length from the station. Threads from the stations through these distances as plotted will give intersections. Contouring is more difficult, a tangential instead of a direct scale being used.

Subtense measurement – On page 308 and following pages are given means for finding height with a theodolite, by measurement of a base. It is, however, easy to measure distance across ground, over which chaining is difficult, by measuring the angle subtended by a distant base, or subtense rod, such as a ten-foot level staff, supported on a tripod. Means should be provided for sighting, so that the rod shall be at right angles to the line of sight from the theodolite. The advantage of this method is that the calculation of distance is independent of the height of the rod above or below the axis of the instrument, but since it will probably be required to obtain difference of height also, it will be necessary to provide a means of measuring, from the ground or peg, the height to a definite horizontal mark on the rod.

The distance is calculated from the rule that one degree subtends one foot at a distance of 57·293 feet, or in proportion. One degree is not a large angle, and if a ten-foot subtense rod is used it will subtend one degree at a distance of 573 feet only. An error of one minute in reading will mean an error of nine feet at that distance. It is usual to use the method of repetition, but the instrument must be free from "backlash," which develops through wear in the slow motion screws.

Figure 110 illustrates the Zeiss Subtense Staff.

Fig. 110

A number of instrument makers produce a subtense staff which, in conjunction with tables supplied with the instrument, enables horizontal distances to be measured with extreme accuracy. Provided the staff is used in conjunction with a precision seconds theodolite an accuracy of 1:200,000 is claimed by the firm of Carl Zeiss whose subtense staff is illustrated in Fig. 110.

The staff is of Invar and is 2 metres in length. It can be provided with illumination of the target for use in the dark. Since the theodolite measures the angle subtended in a horizontal plane the distance calculated is the *horizontal distance* and the elevation angle is not required in the computation. The horizontal distance is given by the relation

$$D = \frac{L}{2} \operatorname{Cot} \frac{A}{2}$$

where L is the length of the subtense staff and A the subtended angle but, as previously mentioned, the provision of tables obviates any calculation.

Provision is made for the staff to be quickly and accurately levelled by means of spirit levels. There are a number of ways in which the subtense staff may be used to obtain horizontal distances between two stations but probably the most usual manner is to erect the staff at one station and the theodolite at the other. Alternatively, the staff may be set approximately midway between the two stations and the theodolite set up at each station in turn.

Repetition of angles – Supposing that the subtended angle is about 39 minutes, the procedure is as follows. The vernier plate is clamped to the base plate and brought to zero on the vernier, or micrometer zero, by the slow motion screw. The telescope is then sighted on one end of the subtense rod and brought into coincidence by base plate slow motion. The vernier plate is then unclamped, and the telescope traversed to the other end of the rod, the vernier plate clamped, and coincidence obtained by vernier plate slow motion. Then the base plate is unclamped and the wire brought back to the first end of the subtense rod, and the process repeated until on the graduations there is a sum of say six repetitions. The sum, let us say 3° 52′ 30″, being divided by six, gives a true angle of 0° 38′ 45″. It is as well to read and record the angle at each repetition, to be sure that no mistake has occurred by a wrong sequence of operation.

In certain traverse operations, such as may be carried out in mines, this method may be modified to obtain a much closer result than can be obtained by one observation only. It cannot, however, compete with the very accurate measurement possible with really high-class modern instruments.

Rangefinder – Messrs Barr and Stroud of Glasgow are the

Fig. 111

makers of a number of rangefinders which, although not accurate to the degree usually required by the surveyor in precise work, nevertheless have a number of uses in approximations of distances in land, river and coastal surveys.

The instrument illustrated in Fig. 111 has a range of 10 – 1,000 yards and the approximate accuracy of observation obtainable by a reasonably good observer, under average practical conditions, is claimed to be 0·05 yards at the range of 10 yards to 75 yards at a range of 1,000 yards. It will be obvious that such errors would be unacceptable in general work but where only approximate estimates are needed the simplicity and rapidity of this small hand instrument will be found to be invaluable. The larger instruments are, of course, very much more accurate and both this firm and other well known makers produce a variety of rangefinders and subtense staves.

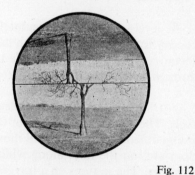 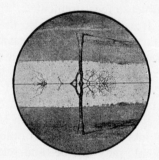

Fig. 112

1 – Images out of coincidence   2 – Images in coincidence

The system works on the principle of coincidence, the observer only requiring to turn the head until the two images appear in alignment as shown in Fig. 112. He then reads the range through high magnification lens on top of the rangefinder. The eyepiece is provided with a calibrated focussing adjustment for straight line of vision.

Stadia measurements – When surveying over very rough ground the process of chain surveying becomes slow and has a tendency to be unreliable, owing partly to difficulty in sighting and partly to the necessity to follow the method described on page 163. A method has therefore been devised of telemetric measurement by reading the intercept on a level staff by two stadia at the eyepiece of the telescope. These stadia may consist of platino-iridium pointers, which in some climates are

H

not entirely free from a tendency to rust. Or, preferably, they may be lines ruled on glass. The pointers, or glass diaphragms, are fixed at such a point in the telescope that the intercept on the level staff, the telescope being horizontal, is one foot for every hundred feet of distance from the object glass to the level staff in normal conditions. Such conditions are not always to be found, and at comparatively long distances the line of light from the bottom of the staff is subject to a different refraction index from that appertaining to the line of light to the upper end of the staff. This difference may be noticeable when the ground is much heated by the sun, and it may be desirable to calibrate for work in such conditions, or to use the method of subtense measurement.

It will be obvious also that the level staff must be accurately graduated, and it may be necessary to use a staff into which has been let a strip of Invar, a metal composition not so liable to expansion and contraction through differences of temperature.

Stadia – Forms of stadia are illustrated in Fig. 101. Nowadays they will also be found in levels. The level should be set up at points most suitable for obtaining differences of level, and those points may not be, and seldom are, on the lines along which distance measurements are necessary. The stations on a traverse are often occupied by other instrument observers. There is a tendency in a poor light to mistake the upper or lower stadia for the central line on the diaphragm.

The fitting of stadia to the theodolite is not to be criticised in the same way, and in fact is much to be recommended, because it is frequently necessary to prepare a contoured plan, for instance, in railway surveying and in surveying for hydro-electric schemes, where the area and capacity of reservoirs are to be determined. It is a tedious process to run many lines of levels over the area, whereas by stadia measurement the field work is much reduced, although the labour of reduction of the observations may be considerable, as will be seen.

Telescope constant – Stadia measurement is not quite so simple as the recording of the readings of the upper and lower stadia on the level staff, the calculation of the difference of readings, and the moving of a decimal point two places to the left. The result is the distance from the *object glass* of the instrument to the staff, and not the distance of the station, over which the instrument is set up, from the staff. Therefore, if an ordinary telescope be fitted on the instrument, there should be added a constant, which may amount to 1 foot. The telescope may be fitted with what is called an anallatic lens, an additional lens which eliminates this constant. This lens, however, reduces the amount of light available for reading the intercept, and this may be important in dull weather. The internal focusing telescope does not entirely eliminate the constant, but reduces it to about five inches, an amount which may in many cases be disregarded.

It may be repugnant to the surveyor, who takes pride in his accuracy, to disregard even this small constant, a true constant, not varying whether the shot is taken over 100 or 700 feet. It should not be disregarded, perhaps, for the distances measured by stadia along a traverse. For the side observations necessary in the preparation of a contoured plan, the disregarding of the constant is of less importance. There are two reasons for this. It is not practically possible to plot to one foot, even on a scale of $\frac{1}{100}$, a larger scale than would be adopted, except in the most broken country. Even if it were desired to plot the level staff position with the greatest accuracy, it is very unlikely that a contour will pass exactly through that station, and the estimation of the contour lines cannot be more than approximate. A very long experience convinces the writer that nothing is to be gained by close attention to correction of results by adding the constant. Predicted longitudinal sections on the centre lines of railways in the roughest country have not differed appreciably from levelled sections made after actual location, not even by one foot of level.

Fieldwork – The selection of level staff stations, with a view to contouring the ground with a minimum of observations from the tacheometer, requires a great deal of experience and practice. Contouring is dealt with in Chapter 9.

If the stadia cut the level staff at 6·27 and 2·35 respectively, the difference, or intercept, or generating number, is 3·92 feet, so that the distance of the staff from the instrument, if the telescope is level, is 392 feet, subject to addition of the constant. It is important that the staff shall be held in a truly vertical position, for which purpose it is desirable that a circular level shall be fitted at the back of the staff for the guidance of the staff-holder (Fig. 113).

Fig. 113

Reduction – Almost never will the line of sight of the instrument be level. The very fact that the ground is to be contoured on the plan presupposes inclined lines of sight. This introduces complications and the necessity for reduction of stadia measurements to the horizontal, while not only have differences of level to be calculated, but they have to be correlated to the level of the instrument station.

In Fig. 114 let A B represent the inclined sight to the staff C D. The centre web cuts the staff at B and one stadia web at C, the space between the two as read on the staff being s. Let B C′ = s′, the space that would be included between the webs if the staff were held square to the line of sight. The angle C C′ B will then not be exactly a right angle, but so near it that we can call it one without introducing any sensible error in the longest sights, especially since in practice we read the distance between the stadia webs, not that between one of them and the centre web. Then, since the angle C′ B C is equal to the angle of inclination a, $s' = s \cos a$. If we call the instrument ratio K, then the inclined distance from the instrument to the staff

$$= \text{K } s' + \text{constant to be added}$$
$$= \text{K } s \cos a + \text{constant.}$$

The horizontal distance is equal to $\cos a \times$ inclined distance. The vertical height is equal to $\sin a \times$ inclined distance.

∴ Horizontal distance $= \text{K } s \cos^2 a + (\cos a \times \text{constant}).$

Vertical height $\quad = \text{K } s \cos a \sin a + (\sin a \times \text{constant}).$

On page 407 it is shown that sin 2A = 2 sin A cos A—

$$\text{Whence } \frac{\sin 2A}{2} = \sin A \cos A.$$

Our formula for vertical height then becomes—

$$= K s \frac{\sin 2a}{2} + (\sin a \times \text{constant}).$$

Tacheometer reduction tables of $\cos^2 a$ and $\dfrac{\sin 2a}{2}$ are published, but we will show how the height and distance are obtained by ordinary tables, which will also incidentally show how the special tables are calculated.

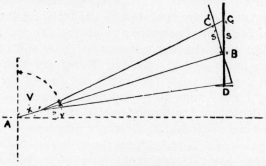

Fig. 114

Assume that with a stadia instrument, the ratio of which is 1 to 100, the constant to be added 1 foot, the angle of inclination is 15° and the space between the webs read from the staff is 4·14 ft.

Then log cos 15° = $\bar{1}$·9849438. Multiply by 2

log cos² 15° = $\bar{1}$·9698876.

Whence cos² 15° = 0·93301.

Again $\dfrac{\sin 2a}{2} = \dfrac{\sin 30}{2} = \dfrac{0·50000}{2} = 0·25000$

These values would be exactly the same if looked out direct from tacheometer tables.

In our example then—

Horizontal distance = 414 × 0·93301 + 0·9659 = 387·23 ft.

Vertical height = 414 × 0·25000 + 0·2588 = 103·76 ft.

An increase in the inclination of the line of sight decreases the natural cosine and increases the natural sine. Inclinations of 30 deg. are seldom necessary, so that the addition of a difference on account of the constant will seldom be more than 0·5 of the constant in height, while we have seen that the difference in distance will be negligible. Slight inequalities in the rough ground cannot be shown if the vertical intervals are as small as five feet, so that the reduction of the constant can be neglected also. Otherwise, it is advisable to construct a diagram, giving the reductions for the constant at varying inclinations of the line of sight, so that inspection and not calculation will be required.

Reduction of the generating number, in the manner shown, by logarithmic functions is an arduous task. Tables for facilitating reduction are published by the Technical Press Ltd. of London. The limit of generating number is 250, which is too small for foot units, although sufficient for metre units, but this limit applies up to 10 deg. only. For 20 deg. the limit is 175, and for 30 deg. 100 only. The Tables are framed for angles differing by 2 and 3 minutes, so that interpolation is necessary by rough calculation. The turning over of the pages is a labour in itself, and the writer prefers the use of diagrams.

Tacheographs – Some tacheographs have been published by Thacker and Co., London. One tacheograph gives by inspection the reduction of length for sight inclinations up to 24 deg. for generating numbers up to 200 feet. For smaller angles, larger generating numbers are shown, as great as 600 feet for 14 deg., and 800 feet for 11 deg. The graduation is to five minutes, but in most cases interpolation is easy to two minutes. It requires at least ten minutes of angle to give an error of one foot in reduction of length, within the diagram limits. There are other diagrams published, but this method gives much closer results.

For differences of height there are two graphs. The first is for angles of inclination up to 12 deg., and the second for angles from 10 to 27 deg., the first being capable of interpolation to 2 minutes, and the second to 5 minutes. The limit of generating number is 400, but for greater numbers it is only necessary to divide by two and multiply the height difference by two. Most satisfactory and rapid reduction has been proved possible by the use of these graphs, which can be adapted to metric measure-

ments also. By suitable mounting on cloth these graphs can
be used in the field for plane table work with the tacheometric
alidade.

The labour of reduction has called for various designs of
automatic reducing instruments, which will be mentioned later.
In some cases there is no check on the observations if doubt
arises subsequently, as, in the writer's experience, is liable to
arise. The most highly trained surveyors can recall inexplicable
mistakes in observing. Care and attention to detail is essential
to obviate such errors.

Correlation of height level – In stadia surveying it is absolutely
necessary to record the reading of the central wire. It is, in the
first place, a most valuable check on the correctness of the
stadia readings. Thus, in our example of readings of 6·27 and
2·35, the sum is 8·62. The central wire should have read half of
this sum, giving 4·31, or 1·96 above the lower and below the
upper reading of the stadia. It should be a matter of routine to
make this rapid check in the field before moving the staff
holder to another point. If the height of the axis of the instrument is measured and recorded, and if the central wire is set
on that same height on the staff as is possible in a very large
proportion of sights, the check can be made at any time in case
of doubt. The sum of the stadia readings should be double the
height of axis above the peg. This will, of course, limit the
length of sight to about 900 feet, but this distance is usually
ample.

The height of the axis of the instrument h above the peg has
invariably to be measured and added to the reduced level of the
top of the peg, to give the reduced level of the origin of the

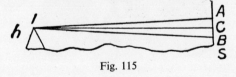

Fig. 115

line of collimation I C in Fig. 115. To this has to be added or
subtracted the height difference.

$$A B \frac{(\sin 2a)}{2} + (\sin a \times \text{constant}).$$

From the sum will be deducted the reading of the central wire on the staff C, to derive the reduced level of the ground at the staff station S. These calculations require five columns in the field-book.

The practice of setting the central wire to the height of the axis of the instrument above the station peg reduces the number of columns to two, with less labour and few chances of mistake. It is obvious that the country, however rough, must be open for the full advantage to be reaped. Stadia measurement in forest is hardly practicable without much clearing.

Fig. 116

Tacheometer – The tacheometer, in its simplest form, is a theodolite of the transit type, but invariably fitted with a vertical arc, and furnished with a stadia diaphragm. If the accuracy of results demands it, the telescope should be anallatic, but for practical purposes the constant should be kept as small as possible by the use of an internal focusing telescope. It is not necessary to have a base plate of more than five inches in diameter, and the vernier may read to one minute for use along the traverse, since it will hardly be practical to attempt to plot the side observations to such accuracy. For certain work, such as the survey above ground, and construction below ground of tube railways, the highest class of instrument with micrometer attachments will be required, such as the Carl Zeiss Tacheometer Theo 030 illustrated in Fig. 116. Since contouring will be required on rough ground, the stand must be capable of being set up in all sorts of awkward situations, and special centering baseplate arrangements must be provided. It should be realised, however, that one great advantage of the instrument is that a hillside may be surveyed from the opposite hillside at any favourable station, provided it be not too far away.

It should be mentioned that an anallatic telescope is so long that transiting will not be possible unless the trunnion supports are made relatively high, thereby adding to the weight and detracting from the compactness of the instrument. The internal focusing telescope has not this disadvantage.

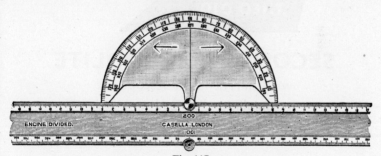

Fig. 117

When surveying with a tacheometer the method of plotting the bearings from the instrument station to the numerous staff stations must be borne in mind. The best method is to refer all bearings to one meridian, whether that be true North or magnetic North. Not only does this facilitate the plotting of the instrument stations by latitudes and departures, but it facilitates the plotting of the staff stations. In Fig. 117 is shown a very

convenient combination of protractor and plotting scale. If a plane table and tacheometric alidade are in use, the directions of the staff stations are obtained by sighting the alidade and plotting the reduced distances, obtained by stadia measurement. Office contouring should always be revised on a plane table in the field.

Tacheometry with staff tilted – When a staff station is considerably above, or below, the tacheometer station it becomes of greater importance that the staff shall be held vertically, a matter which depends on the reliability of the staff-holder. If the staff be tilted forward or backward so that it is at right angles to the line of sight from the tacheometer, or swayed slightly as is the custom in levelling, the observer can take the lowest reading in all three cases from the horizontal wire and the two stadia, and be certain that the staff is in the right position. Unfortunately, this method introduces reductions, which in the writer's opinion destroy the advantages.

It will be seen from Fig. 118 that to the distance X C, to which may be added the telescope "constant," must be added

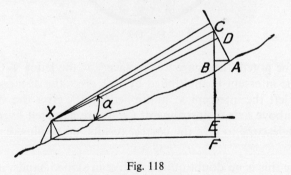

Fig. 118

the distance B A. The angle A C B equals the angle of elevation, and therefore $BA = AC \sin a$. Also the reading on the staff at C must be reduced to give the true height B C above the staff station, A. $BC = AC \cos a$. Since the reading A C will vary in every case, unless the slow motion screw is used to bring the horizontal wire to an even foot reading, the calculation requires a set of tables and more columns in the field-book. The height

C E above the axis of the instrument is X C sin *a*, from which must be deducted B C to find the level of the staff station above the axis of instrument, and E F must be added to find the level of staff station above ground at X.

Direct reading devices – The labour of reduction has perhaps been exaggerated, especially if tacheographs are used, and devices have been invented to avoid this labour. A direct reading tacheometer was invented by Dr. Jeffcott, late Secretary of the Institution of Civil Engineers. The stadia pointers are movable, see Fig. 119, which shows the field of view on a staff, on which,

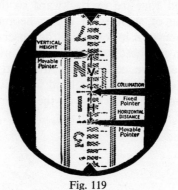

Fig. 119

it may be noted, the figure 9 is replaced by the letter N. On the right the intercept H, multiplied by 100, gives the distance, and on the left the intercept V, multiplied by 10, gives the vertical height above axis of instrument. Cams are actuated by the tilt of the telescope to give the correct results, up to plus or minus 30 deg.

While this is no doubt quite effective in skilled hands, it must be remembered that skilled observers are highly paid in tropical countries. There is no check on the observations, and the valuable relation, that the sum of the stadia readings equal twice the reading of the horizontal wire, is lost.

When a tacheometric alidade is used on a plane table considerations of time make quicker reduction a desirability, especially if the observer has no booker, who can consult a tacheograph. In such a case a stadia arc may be used, such as the Beaman arc, although Stanley introduced such a device over fifty years ago. This arc is illustrated in Fig. 120.

The telescope is sighted on the staff anywhere, and the bubble on the T-piece of the alidade is brought to the centre. The telescope is then slightly elevated or depressed, until the index v coincides with a whole number on the tangential scale x. The index is actually shown at zero on the scale. The intercept is read by difference of stadia readings, and the difference of height is given by the whole number multiplied by the intercept.

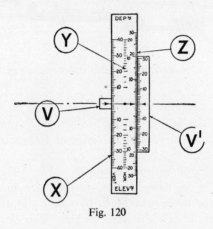

Fig. 120

There ensues the correlation of levels, due to the difference between the reading of the axial wire and the height of the axis of the alidade, and this is so much simplified by setting the axial wire at height of instrument, as recommended earlier.

Reduction of horizontal distance is obtained from the continuation of the index line across the scale Y, which gives the *percentage* correction to be deducted from the intercept, multiplied by 100. This introduces a possibility of mistake, which is avoided by using the tacheographs, in which the actual deduction is worked out.

Zeiss "Redta" 002 tacheometer – The telescope of the most recent form of tacheometer is shown diagrammatically in Fig. 121. The rays passing along the upper and lower lines shown are brought together in the eyepiece, with a displacement of the image. By means of lenses, which are actuated by cams, this displacement is varied according to the degree of tilt of the telescope. The instrument is made by Carl Zeiss, and has been described by the inventor in a book entitled "Optical Distance

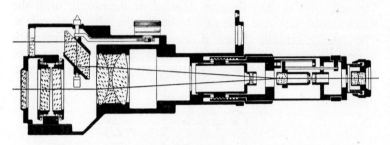

Fig. 121 – Cross section of "Redta" telescope and optical path

Measurement and Polar Co-ordinate Methods." The instrument includes the labour-saving devices mentioned in the Wild theodolite. The mean error at a range of 100 metres is given as ±2 cms.

A horizontal staff is used, as shown in Fig. 122, with a tripod support, and a sighting device, just at the junction of the vertical with the horizontal staff, by which the observer at the instrument can check the staff holder. The verniers on the horizontal staff are serrated and marked in the latest pattern, so that the observer is in no doubt when reading the displaced image. The staff is shown in Fig. 122, and the displaced image in Fig. 123. With a 5 ft. 6 in. staff the range is 490 feet, but with a 7 ft. 3 in. staff the range is increased to 650 feet, and if required a special instrument and staff can be supplied, reading up to 1600 feet, with a mean error of 4 inches.

It will be seen in Fig. 122 that the vertical support also is graduated, and in the image presented in the micrometer reader there are shown graduations in natural tangents. When using the instrument in this manner, the lower system can be cut out, so that there is no longer any displacement.

Levelling – Although for many purposes the calculation of heights by vertical angular measurements and the measurement of distances may be adequate, and even the only way if summits

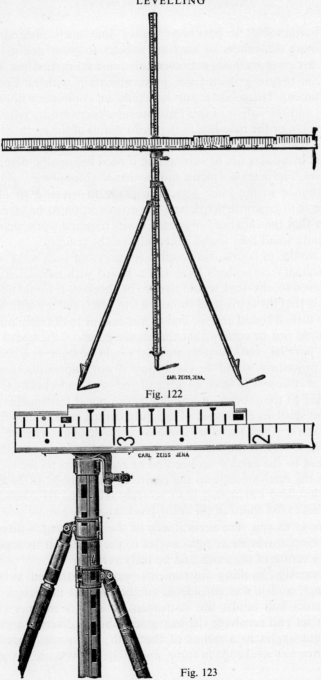

Fig. 122

Fig. 123

are inaccessible, it has been shown that such methods of obtaining differences of level are subject to some doubt. The only accurate method, and even this must be carried out with care, is to use a spirit-level, in combination with an optical instrument. No geodetic survey would be complete without a base, and the length of this base must be corrected by reducing the height or the base-line to the mean radius of the earth, or the mean sea-level. This cannot be done unless the height is determined by adding up, or subtracting if need be, small differences of level. The heights which a railway has to surmount have to be determined in the same way. The grade to which a canal or sewer is to be constructed, and the cross-section to be given in order that the canal or sewer may do its required work, depend on quite small falls in the general lie of the country.

It would, of course, be possible to carry out such work with an ordinary carpenter's level and a board with parallel edges, but, even so, the work would have to be checked. It would not be certain that the spirit-level showed a true level, and it would have to be turned round end for end as a check, or to obtain a mean. It would not be certain that the planed edges of the board are truly parallel, and the same turning would be done as a check. The procedure would be cumbrous, if not impossible, and is only mentioned to give an idea of the care and checks to be applied to the process of levelling with optical instruments.

The spirit-level consists of a lightly curved tube, partly filled with spirit, which therefore contains a bubble of air. This bubble comes to rest in the tube when the chord to the curved arc is tangent to the earth's surface and at right angles to the radius from the earth's centre to the centre of the bubble. If the base of a levelling instrument is to be truly level, the base must be parallel to the chord of the spirit-level, when the bubble is in the centre of its run. The vertical axis of the instrument, assuming it to be constructed at right angles to the base, will then point to the centre of the earth and be truly vertical.

Formerly, levelling instruments were constructed in this manner, and it was considered of the greatest importance to construct and adjust the instrument in such a manner that, when set and revolved, the instrument should describe a plane at right angles to a radius of the earth. For some years this doctrine has weakened in force, and modern levels are designed

I

to show the observer if his instrument is level at the moment of observation, rather than to be level throughout the period between one setting up and the next.

The Dumpy level is of the first type. It has been modified in order to reduce the labour of adjustment by such levels as the Y, the Cooke, and such instruments as provided for the removal of the telescope and for turning it end for end; but these modified instruments are seldom bought. The Dumpy level, see Fig. 124, requires that the line of collimation – that is, the line

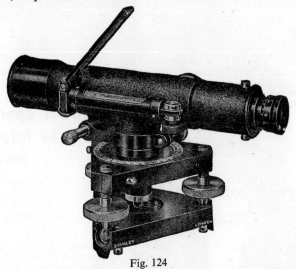

Fig. 124

through the centre of the telescope – shall be adjusted at right angles to the vertical axis, and also that the spirit-level shall be adjusted to the same position. Then, the axis being truly vertical, as shown by the spirit-level, the line of collimation will describe a plane at right angles to the vertical axis if the telescope be revolved. It will not be correct to re-level the instrument for each sight, because the axis will not be necessarily vertical.

A horizontal circle is shown, and to some instruments a prismatic compass is fitted.* This practice the writer deprecates, because the instrument can seldom be set up in such

* The particular level illustrated (Fig. 124) is one of the extensive range of instruments manufactured by the old established and reliable firm of W. F. Stanley & Co., of London.

a position that differences of levels and horizontal angles are best observed from one instrument station, or even by the same observer. Speed and accuracy are best obtained by keeping a separate observer for the level. It is of advantage to have a hinged reflector, in which the position of the bubble can be seen from the eyepiece end of the telescope, and which will protect the spirit-level when shut down (see Fig. 125).

Fig. 125

In the second and modern type of level the verticality of the axis is unimportant, because the telescope is made to tilt about it. It is still necessary to ensure that the line of collimation shall be horizontal, when the bubble of the spirit-level is in the centre of its run, a condition which in some types is reflected into the eyepiece, both ends being shown. It is an advantage to use a coincidence level reader (Fig. 126), by Messrs. Cooke, Troughton & Simms, Ltd. This type of levelling instrument, with modifications, is standard practice by many of the reputable makers today. Fig. 127 shows an engineers "Precise" level.

NOT LEVEL   LEVEL

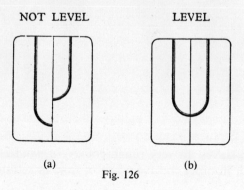

(a)   (b)

Fig. 126

Setting up – It is easier to set up a level than a theodolite, because there is no necessity to centre the instrument over a station. Any position will do, provided that the line of collimation of the levelled instrument will cut graduations on both

Fig. 127

of the level staves. In very rough country a hand level should be supplied, in order to save waste of time in setting up in an unsuitable position. The process of setting up will follow the instructions given for the theodolite. It should be noted again that, in levelling up, if the bubble is to be run to the right, the hands on the levelling screws must be turned inwards. If the bubble is to be run to the left, the motion is outwards. The spirit-level must be parallel to the line through the centre of the two screws, and this want of parallelism is a frequent cause of bad setting up. This is not so important in setting up a modern tilting level.

No record is made of the exact position of a level, but in precise work it is always desirable to set up half-way between the two staves. If a Dumpy level is in use, this practice will eliminate errors of adjustment, or reduce them to a minimum.

Adjustment of a Dumpy level – The adjustments are:

A.—To bring the spirit-level at right angles to the vertical axis, so that when the bubble is in the centre of its run the axis shall be vertical.

B.—To eliminate parallax from the eyepiece.

C.—To make the line of collimation of the telescope at right angles to the vertical axis, and parallel to the spirit-level in consequence.

The first two of these have been dealt with among the adjustments of a theodolite, with an explanation of the necessity of the first, but this is not so important if the levelling can be so arranged as invariably to maintain a central position between the two staves X and Y, Fig. 128, in which case any obliquity of

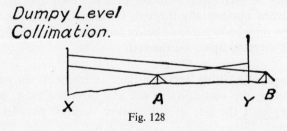

Fig. 128

the vertical axis or of the line of collimation will cancel out. This operation, of setting up midway and observing two staves, is the preliminary part of the third adjustment, so as to ascertain the exact difference of level. If now the instrument is taken to B, a little distance outside, and to one side of the line joining the two staves, and the bubble brought to the centre of its run, the difference of level ought to be the same. If it is not the same, (see Fig. 128), a sum in proportion, based on B Y/B X, will show whether the line of collimation is rising or dipping, and will show how much the reading on the far staff should be altered to make the proportion correspond with the distances to the two staves. The adjustment will be made solely by the two capstan screws, above and below the eyepiece diaphragm, assuming that the first two adjustments have assured a true level and no apparent motion of the diaphragm wires.

Adjustment of a reversible level – The last adjustment described is a little tedious, and can hardly be carried out in the field at any moment when doubt arises about the accuracy of adjustment. Levels of the Y, Cooke, Cushing, and other reversible types were designed to allow of quicker adjustment. The telescope may be rotated through 180 deg. in its bearings, any difference in readings A B on a single staff, see Fig. 129, showing

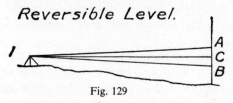

Fig. 129

that the line of collimation I C is not truly central. The object glass may be exchanged with the eyepiece end, and the instrument turned horizontally through 180 deg. Or again, the whole telescope may be capable of being removed and turned end for end and directed again on the staff.

Adjustment of a tilting level – In these instruments the necessity for ensuring the verticality of the axis does not exist, but it is necessary that the line of collimation shall be parallel to the spirit-level. Either method described may be used, with two staves or with one staff. In the Zeiss level object glass and eyepiece end are interchangeable, so that the true reading on the staff can be ascertained (Fig. 129), as described in the last paragraph. With a "self-adjusting" or "self-checking" level, the

true reading is ascertained (see Fig. 130) by reading first with
the spirit-level on the right and secondly on the left, taking the
mean, adjusting the horizontal wire to that mean by the micrometer screw, and finally adjusting the spirit-level so that the

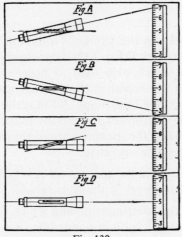

Fig. 130

bubble shall come to the centre of its run. In the precise tilting
level provision is made for a slight movement of the reading
prism to effect this delicate adjustment.

Precision levelling – In precision levelling it is not sufficient to

Fig. 131

make an estimate of the staff reading, in such cases where the
wire does not coincide with the edge of a graduation, but cuts it.

It is possible to use the gradienter, see Fig. 131, in combination with stadia wires to give the distance, and thus to calculate the value of the displacement of the wire over the graduation. In the gradienter shown one division on the drum tilts the line of sight by 1 in 50,000.

Self-aligning level – In the Cooke, Troughton & Simms Series S.700 Self-aligning Level (Fig. 132) the main spirit-level vial and the tilting screw which were used to bring the bubble to the centre of its run are replaced by a compensating unit which keeps the sighting line horizontal. All that the surveyor has to do is to level the instrument roughly by means of the circular level provided, when the moving part of the compensator will swing free and become operative.

The level, apart from the compensator, is generally similar to any other surveyor's level, without its tubular spirit vial.

The design of the compensating unit which has been adopted for this self-aligning level is the outcome of a prolonged joint effort by Hilger & Watts Ltd. and Cooke, Troughton & Simms Ltd.; the optical principle of which is based on a patent lodged by the former.

Except for the compensator and optical system, the level otherwise follows the Companies' traditional design, the telescope features are:

Internal focusing.

Aperture	$1\frac{9}{16}$ in.
Magnification	32 ×
Field of view	1° 20′
Shortest focusing distance	6 ft.
Distance at which ·01 ft. can be resolved	1,000 ft.
Stadia lines ratio	1 : 100
Stadia correction	Nil

An additional lens has been incorporated in the telescope to enable the compensator to be accommodated between the focusing lens and the reticule.

The focusing control provides a two-speed movement to the internal focusing lens, the fine movement being brought into action by reversing the direction of rotation of the control knob.

Interior glass surfaces in the telescope are coated with the object of reducing glare and improving the transmission of light.

The telescope body is supported on its vertical axis on a hardened cylindrical bearing.

Fig. 132

Compensator – Within its working range the compensator projects the horizontal ray coming from the object on the same point of the reticule. Since the centre of the reticule has been adjusted to this point, the compensator always sets the sighting line horizontal, even if the telescope is only roughly levelled.

The moving part of the compensator carries two reflecting prisms and is suspended from the frame by four metallic strips, crossed in pairs to form a flexure-pivot, or, more specifically, an asymmetrical crossed spring pivot, whose axis is the line joining the intersections of the four strips. This pivot is constructed so that it behaves as a frictionless bearing. Within the range of movement allowed by the damper, the swinging prisms always hang in a vertical plane. The sighting line is adjusted by the compensator to an accuracy of less than ± 1 sec.

The frame of the compensator carries a third reflecting prism so that a horizontal line of sight through the whole unit moves through twice the angle that the frame may be turned through but in opposite direction. Thus, if the reading point is connected to the frame, a three-fold relative magnification is obtained. It follows that, if the compensator unit is placed in the telescope body at a distance from the reticule equal to $\frac{1}{4}$ of the focal length of the telescope, the appearance of the field of view will not alter if the telescope line of sight is turned out of the horizontal plane. The complete telescope with the compensator gives an erect image since the third prism has a roof.

Movement of the swinging section of the compensator is restricted to 20 minutes each way by a double-acting air damper which also serves to take the main weight of the swinging prism mount when the level is in transit.

The use of a compensator in place of the conventional spirit level vial eliminates the hazard of exposure to direct sun.

Very extensive tests have been undertaken to confirm that the instrument continues to give accurate results throughout a wide temperature range. The ability of the compensator to withstand continuous vibration and violent bumping tests has also been investigated at length.

The weight of the instrument itself is only 5 lbs. 5 oz.

Level staff – The form of staff in ordinary use is the Sopwith telescopic, shown in Fig. 133. It is in three parts, the lowest reading from zero to five feet, the next section from five to nine and a half feet, and the top section from nine and a half to fourteen feet. It is necessary to be careful when drawing out the sections to see that the catches engage, and the observer should satisfy himself that this has been done properly. A longer staff, sixteen or eighteen feet long, may be useful when surveying in mountainous country, but the extra weight is a disadvantage. The graduations may be to hundredths or fiftieths of a foot, or to centimetres or half-centimetres. They will, of course, be seen upside down in the instrument, and sometimes the figuring is painted upside down, so as to become erect when observed. This inversion leads to a possibility of mistake between 6 and 9, so that it is good practice to replace the number 9 throughout by N. The small figures on the left of

Fig. 133

the graduations in Fig. 133 are useful when the staff is read at a short distance and when the large foot figures may not come into the field. The surveyor should be very careful to observe where the top and bottom of the figures representing tenths lie in comparison with the hundredth or fiftieth graduations. When reading, he should invariably read in a routine order, feet, tenths, hundredths, book in that order, and observe again for check.

The graduations may be on varnished paper, to be pasted on the face of the staff, or may be painted on. For precise levelling staves, the graduations are cut on Invar alloy, which is fixed at one end only to the steel shoe of the staff, and thus is not affected by the wood. These staves are not telescopic, and are therefore only ten feet long. They are fitted with a spirit-level, plummet, handles, and steadying poles.

For tacheometer work a ten-foot folding staff will be sufficient if the central wire is always directed to its own height, as recommended, but as this may not be always possible it is better to have a margin and to use a staff of the type shown in Fig. 133. A spirit-level or plummet, for the purpose of holding the staff vertical, is a necessary attachment.

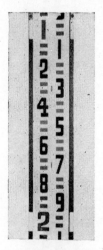

Fig. 134

In Fig. 134 is shown a form of graduation, devised by A. E. Gayer, for levelling and tacheometer work. This staff is made in

12, 14, or 16 foot lengths, and the graduation figures are inverted on the staff, so that they are erected in the instrument. It requires a little practice to become acquainted with the relative readings, and the writer in his practice has always insisted on such practice being given to surveyors for a day or two, before starting serious work for the season.

Cowley automatic level – Although the Cowley level (Fig. 135(a) and (b)) produced by Messrs Hilger and Watts of London, will be found in more general use on Civil Engineering and building sites than in the surveyors office, a brief description of the unique features of this useful instrument will not be out of place in this chapter.

Fig. 135(a)

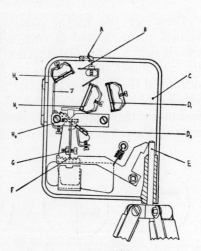

Fig. 135(b)

A. Eyepiece
B. Mask
C. Optical centre
D1. 1st Mirror L.H. system
D2. 2nd Mirror L.H. system
E. Tripod peg

F. Pendulum clamp
G. Pendulum balance adjusting screw
H1. 1st Mirror R.H. system
H2. 2nd Mirror R.H. system
H3. 3rd Mirror R.H. system
J. Image division bar

By means of a system of mirrors contained within the instrument (which is no larger than a small camera) the level is made completely automatic; there are no adjustments whatsoever and even the tripod need only be approximately positioned.

The instrument contains five mirrors in all, one being attached to a weighted pendulum which performs the automatic levelling device (Fig. 135(b)). The action of placing the instrument on the tripod releases a clamp locking this pendulum and the instrument is thus immediately brought into adjustment for taking readings. A special 5 feet staff is provided on which a horizontal "target" can slide vertically (see Fig. 136). The staff may be extended by an additional 3 or 4 feet length if required.

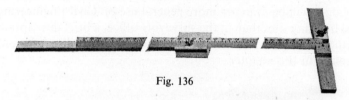

Fig. 136

There are two mirror systems, one each side of a central vertical plane, placed in such a position that a ray of light travelling in a horizontal direction towards the optical centre of the instrument always leaves the left and right hand system of mirrors at the same angle of 100° to the horizontal. Thus, when viewing objects in the horizontal datum plane defined by the instrument they appear in the same position in either the left or right systems. The effect of coincidence is observed when using

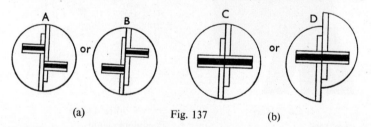

(a)   Fig. 137   (b)

the staff in conjunction with the target. When "off level" the target and staff might appear as in Fig. 137(a). "On level" is obtained by the staff holder moving the target up or down as shown until coincidence is obtained as in Fig. 137(b). The reading indicated by the target position is then read off the staff.

The makers claim an accuracy of $\frac{1}{4}$ inch in 100 feet (the effective range) but when the instrument is set midway between two distant stations an overall distance of 200 feet can be read.

Aneroid barometer – This instrument cannot be relied on to give precise differences of level, but in the hands of an experienced observer, acquainted with the factors determining its use, and constantly watching atmospheric conditions, it gives approximate, and may give surprisingly close, results. In certain conditions it is essential, for instance in aircraft navigation as an altimeter, since no other instrument has yet proved a superiority. In explanatory survey, or whenever considerable differences of level have to be obtained quickly, and heights cannot be readily calculated by distance and angular measurement, it is invaluable.

Its invention is attributed to M. Vidi of Paris, but the instrument has been improved by Col. Watkin, and recently by a Swede, in the Paulin altimeter. It is actually a pressure gauge, depending on atmospheric pressure on a metallic box (*a* in Fig. 138 and D D in Fig. 139), hermetically sealed and partially exhausted of air. The box is corrugated, and by its distortion, through a complicated system of levers or chains and springs, it actuates an index hand, which moves over a graduated dial.

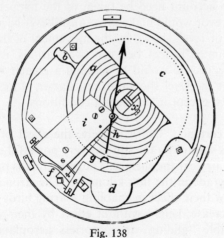

Fig. 138

This dial may be graduated in inches, and, if of sufficient size, to hundredths of an inch like a mercury barometer. It has the advantage over a mercury barometer in that no correction is necessary for the effects of gravity, or temperature, or capillary action, on the column of mercury. The instrument is made of metal, and must therefore be susceptible to differences of temperature, but the effects of temperature are prevented from communicating themselves to the index hand by a bar (or better a helix), compounded of two metals, mutually eliminating the temperature effects. If this bar forms a part of the system, the

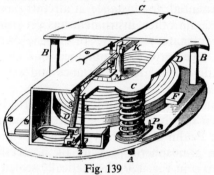

Fig. 139

instrument is marked "compensated," but it must not be assumed, as is a common mistake, that in converting pressure into level no account need be taken of the temperature of the air. The surveyor would make great mistakes if he assumed that a difference of level, shown by the movement of the index over a scale graduated in feet between two stations, represents the actual difference. He would be making a greater mistake if he assumed that the level shown at any station is the actual level above the sea, except in accidental conditions.

Ascensional currents – Unfortunately, the effect of the heating of the earth's surface by the sun has very powerful effects on the strata of the air near the surface. The lapse rate is probably only 4 deg. Centigrade in the first kilometre. The strong ascensional currents show their effect in enabling soaring birds to maintain, and even increase, height without effort by their wings. These currents enable "gliding" in motorless aeroplanes, and one observer has noticed twigs borne up in the air to 3,000 feet. A series of observations between two bench marks, taken by the writer's staff, showed very considerable variations of calculated height in very hot weather. This factor may seriously limit the time available for work, both on the ground and for aerial surveying, but in this case some three hours about exhausts the pilot's endurance.

Selection of instrument – In considering the instrument to be provided, the range of graduation must be considerably more than the estimated heights to be reached, on account of the factors mentioned. It is preferable to calculate height differences from pressures in inches, instead of applying coefficients to a graduated scale in feet. Temperatures must be observed at every station, both on arrival and before departure, at the same time as the aneroid is read, it being essential that as short a time as possible should elapse between readings of the aneroid to calculate height difference. In camp the aneroid should be read hourly and the results plotted so as to forecast the probable trend of pressure variation, or to estimate the variation during working hours. The recital of the factors, which make work with the aneroid suspect, should not discourage the surveyor, because the writer has obtained quite remarkable results by applying intelligent corrections.

Fig. 140

The scale, whether in inches or in feet, should be as open as possible, and it can be arranged that the pointer can make three revolutions over the dial. This makes it easy to read to one-hundredth of an inch between pressure of 31 to 21 inches (with a little care in reading) where the circles on the dial change.

In Fig. 140 is shown a form of surveying aneroid which has the advantage of an attached reading glass.

K

Geodetic and specialist surveying – The student is referred to Chapter 12 for a brief outline of the instruments used in this highest form of surveying.

Examination Questions

1. A theodolite was set up at P, the end of a survey line on uniformly sloping ground and the readings taken at approx. 100 ft. intervals along the line as follows:

At	Point	Elevation angle	Stadia readings		
P	A	4° 16′	3·66	4·16	4·66
	B	,,	2·45	3·46	4·47
	C	5° 6′	1·30	2·82	4·34
	D	,,	5·87	7·88	9·89
	E	,,	6·15	8·65	11·15

An error of booking was apparent when reducing the observations. Find this error, the levels of the points ABCDE and the gradient PE, if the ground level below the instrument was 104·20 O.D. and height of instrument 4·75. Instrument constants 100 and 0.

(University of London B.Sc. (Eng.) 1957)

2. Write brief notes on four of the following:
   station pointers; parallel-plate micrometer; parallax bar; subtense bar; metre base range finder; telescopic alidade.

   (Institution of Civil Engineers, April 1958)

3. In measuring horizontal and vertical angles with a theodolite explain clearly what would be the effect of the following: Error in levelling the base plates; lack of verticality between the vertical and transit axes; index error on the vertical circle; error in centring over the ground mark; failure to eliminate parallax in the telescope.

   (Institution of Civil Engineers, April 1956)

4. (a) Describe concisely the essential parts of a plane table.

   (b) Explain the meaning of resection as applied to plane-table work and describe how you would carry out this process in the field.

   (University of London B.Sc. Estate Management 1956)

5. Describe how you would test a dumpy level for possible instrumental errors, and explain in detail how you would use such an instrument for fixing accurately the datum level of a building, assuming that the instrument used is found to be out of adjustment. Draw sketches to illustrate your description.
          (*Royal Institution of Chartered Surveyors*, 1958)

6. Describe briefly what is meant by the following:
   (i) Parallax.
  (ii) A trigonometrical point.
 (iii) A change plate.
 (iv) A boning rod.
  (v) An optical square.
 (vi) A beam compass.
          (*Royal Institution of Chartered Surveyors*, 1956)

7. Make a clear diagram in good proportion showing the interior arrangement of a box sextant, and give a geometric proof of the principle involved. Indicate the practical limitations of the instrument.
          (*Institution of Municipal Engineers* 1949)

8. (a) Assuming a converging lens of focal length f, and conjugate focal distances f_1 and f_2,
$$\text{show that } \frac{1}{f} = \frac{1}{f_1} + \frac{1}{f_2}$$

  (b) Using the rule proved in (a) show that the stadia constant and constant of instrument are $\dfrac{f}{i}$ and $f+d$ respectively for a tacheometer where—
      f = focal length of object glass;
      i = interval between stadia webs of the diaphragm; and
      d = distance between the optical centre of the object glass and the vertical axis of the instrument.

  (c) Describe briefly the experimental determination of the tacheometric constants in the field.
          (*Institution of Municipal Engineers* 1949)

Chapter 3

LAND SURVEYING EQUIPMENT

Standards of measure—Chains—Engineers' chain—Gunter's chain—
Divisions of the chain—Arrows—Testing the chain—Test gauge—
Offset staff—Tapes—Ranging rods and poles—Whites.

Standards of measure – In this country we are accustomed to
the duodecimal system of measurement, the yard being the
standard unit of length subdivided into feet and inches.
Elsewhere the metric system is almost universally adopted.

Chains – For surveying purposes in England there are two
forms of chains in general use, the Engineers' or 100 feet chain,
and the Gunter's 100 link chain. Both chains are made of stout
steel or iron links and both are divided into 100 divisions – the
Engineers' into 1 foot lengths and the Gunter into 1 link
lengths (1 link = 7·92 inches).

Engineers' chain – As its name implies this chain is used by
engineers mainly because their work is more concerned with
the design of structures and the calculation of volumes and
weights than in the determination of areas. The foot unit is
normally used by engineers. The Engineers' chain is 100 feet
long and is divided into 100 divisions, each of 1 foot in length.

Gunter's chain – Sometimes referred to as the Surveyors' chain,
it is also divided into 100 links but the chain is 66 feet long, each
link is 7·92 inches or 1/100 part of 66 feet. It was invented in the
early part of the seventeenth century by the Reverend Edmund
Gunter, an eminent professor of astronomy at Greshen College.
At every 10 links is fastened a brass "tally" of different shapes
to denote its value in tens, whilst at each end is a conveniently
constructed brass handle.

140

Divisions of the chain – The first 10 links is distinguished by a tally like this $\overset{10}{\wedge}$; the 20 thus, $\overset{20}{\wedge}$; the 30 thus, $\overset{30}{\wedge}$; the 40 thus, $\overset{40}{\wedge}$; and 50 links or the centre of the chain (33 ft. or 50 ft. in the case of the Engineers' chain) by a circular tablet thus, $\overset{50}{\wedge}$; so that from each end of the chain are tallys of similar shape and position, and the number of links is counted therefrom. But it is necessary to explain that, having reached the centre of the chain (or 50 links from one end) in proceeding to the other extremity, what represents 40 links from that end is really 60 from the commencement, and similarly 30 is 70, 20 is 80, and 10 is 90, whilst the handle represents 100 links. The following sketch may serve to illustrate this.

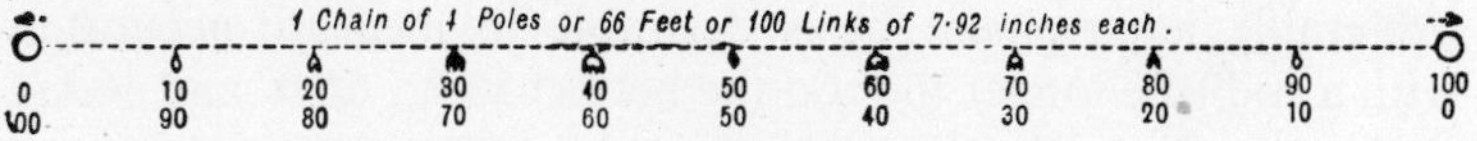

					1 Chain of 4 Poles or 66 Feet or 100 Links of 7·92 inches each.					
0	10	20	30	40	50	60	70	80	90	100
100	90	80	70	60	50	40	30	20	10	0

Fig. 141

So that the 1st, 2nd, 3rd, 4th, and 5th tabs represent 10, 20, 30, 40, and 50 links respectively from either end. Very little practice is necessary for the student to acquire proficiency in reading the chain.

Arrows – Accompanying each chain are 10 arrows, or skewers, about 9 in. long, pointed at one end and having a ring* at the other for greater facility in carrying. These arrows are made of stout wire, and are used to mark upon the ground the end of each chain. The reason why ten is the number adopted is that ten chains (66 ft.) equal one furlong, and eight furlongs or eighty chains equal one mile. Again, an acre of land is ten square chains.

Testing the chain – Before commencing chaining, the surveyor should satisfy himself as to the accuracy of his chain. If it has been used before, either from constant pulling through

---

* It is usual to tie a piece of red cloth or tape round the handle of the arrows, so that they may be the more easily distinguishable when stuck in the midst of grass or plants, etc.

fences or other causes, it may become elongated, or in going over rough ground, by treading upon some of the links they may become bent (Fig. 143) and consequently shortened, as in the accompanying sketch.

CHAIN STRAIGHT

Fig. 142

BENT LINK

Fig. 143

Test gauge – To form a test gauge upon an even surface, preferably a pavement, it is desirable to measure accurately with a rod (the longer the rod the better) 33 ft., 66 ft. and 100 ft. in the same line. These lengths should be tested by measurement from the other end, and having been determined, marks should be cut in the pavement with a hammer and chisel at each end and in the centre. In the absence of pavement, upon level ground drive in stout pegs, 66 ft., 33 ft. and 100 ft. apart, and

1 CHAIN or 66 FEET

Fig. 144

1 CHAIN or 66 FEET

Fig. 145

having accurately gauged the two lengths, drive nails into the pegs to mark the exact points (see Fig. 144). A test gauge should be established in close proximity to every surveyor's office for constant comparison; but in a large survey it is desirable to make one close to the scene of operations, so that each day before commencing work the chain may be applied, and if longer may be adjusted by removing one or more of the connecting links, or, if short, by straightening the wire links.

A Government standard of all kinds of English measures has been established in Trafalgar Square, by means of permanent bronze marks let into the granite plinth of the terrace wall in front of the National Gallery. There is also a standard in the Guildhall, belonging to the Corporation of London; and in nearly every city and town in the kingdom, the Borough Surveyor has arranged certain marks wherewith to test his chains, and these, on request, will doubtless be put at the service of any surveyor who may be working in the neighbourhood.

There is an art in doing up and throwing out the chain. In the former case, the chain should be taken at its centre (with the circular tablet) and gradually each pair of links towards the end should be cylindrically folded diagonally over the last until the handles are reached, so that when tied up the chain represents almost a wheatsheaf. The accompanying sketch (Fig. 146) shows the chain folded up and the arrows.

Fig. 146 – Chain and arrows

In throwing out, the handles should be held in the left hand with a few links loose, whilst the rest of the folded chain is held with the right, and by this means thrown smartly away, retaining hold of the two handles.

Offset staff – Besides the chain, the surveyor should be provided with a small staff or rod (called an offset staff), 6 ft. 7·20 in. long, divided into 10 parts or links. This staff should be made of well-seasoned wood, painted in link lengths black and white alternately; it should have an iron spike at one end and at the other a stout open ring (as sketch, Fig. 147) for forcing or drawing the chain through a hedge.

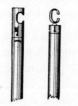

Fig. 147 – Offset staff

Tapes – Offsets and ties (page 153) may be measured with a steel or linen tape but for very accurate work when plans are to be prepared to a large scale linen tapes are not too reliable as they are apt to stretch. Both should be checked regularly against a standard length, and should never be wound back into the case if wet or dirty.

Both steel and linen tapes are contained in circular leather or plastic boxes into which they are wound. They can be obtained in 33, 66, or 100 feet lengths. One side of the tape is figured in feet and inches and the reverse side in links.

Ranging rods and poles – These wooden rods with steel shoes are about $1\frac{1}{2}$ inches in diameter and are painted in red, white and black bands of 1 foot or 1 link lengths. They can be obtained in 5 feet to 12 feet lengths, the 6 feet length being the most convenient to use. It is often necessary to fly a small coloured flag on the top of the pole to help distinguish the rod when positioned at considerable range, or in difficult country. These rods are usually in sets of six but many more than this number would be required in a survey of any size. Long poles are necessary in certain circumstances, particularly in long surveys or in heavily wooded or undulating country. Such poles are from 10-20 feet in length about $2\frac{1}{2}$ to 3 inches in diameter at the bottom, tapering to about 1 inch at the top. They should be perfectly straight and may be painted red and white or black and white. Sometimes they are iron shod and it is convenient to surmount these with a coloured flag for use of identification from long distances.

Whites – Varying from 15 in. to 3 ft. in length, they are simply wood laths, as straight as possible, pointed at one end and having a cleft cut in the other for the purpose of inserting pieces of white paper. These are very useful in ranging out lines or for establishing stations.

Chapter 4

CHAIN SURVEYING

Reconnaissance – The first essential for the surveyor is to make himself thoroughly acquainted with the land he has to survey. He should walk the estate, making a careful note of the boundaries, obstructions and special features that he will encounter and deciding upon the principle chain lines. The time spent in such a reconnoitre is more than amply repaid by subsequent time spent in obviating difficulties that are otherwise bound to occur if chain lines are selected arbitrarily without due consideration of the many unexpected problems that will arise.

Sketch map – It is always advisable for the surveyor to prepare a rough sketch map of the survey, before commencing the work, on which the main chain lines can be drawn and numbered and any features, obstacles, boundaries and the like clearly marked. If an Ordnance map of the site is available, a rough tracing can be prepared in the office beforehand and examined, and corrected in the field in relation to the conditions found

146

during the preliminary reconnaissance. It is never advisable to assume that the Ordnance map is correct in every detail, thus making it unnecessary to walk over the ground; features, boundaries and physical demarkations might have been altered since the Ordnance Survey was completed and it could happen that the land now bears little relation to the deliniation on the map.

Stations – To make a survey of even a simple field, equally with an extensive estate, it is necessary to establish stations at those points to which it may be desirable to run lines. Thus A B C and D (Fig. 148) represent stations which comprehend a

Fig. 148 – Stations

complete investigation of this figure, whereby lines from A to B, B to C, C to D, and D to A will be necessary to enable the boundaries of the field to be taken.

Main stations – Stations are of a twofold character, main and subsidiary. Main stations represent those chief points which, whether the figure to be surveyed be regular or irregular, embrace such lines as will command the boundaries of the survey. These stations are shown in various ways, according to circumstances. If the survey is of only a temporary character (such as can be executed in a single day) then poles or ranging-rods may be fixed for the purpose, but if required for an extensive survey, then stout pegs should be driven into the ground, while in some cases special posts, built up and well strutted into the ground may be necessary. If pegs are used they should be 5 in. to 8 in. long and $1\frac{1}{4}$ in. square, driven with about $1\frac{1}{2}$ in. standing out of the ground, and in pasture land the turf should be cut round them in the form of a triangle (see sketch, Fig. 149). In order to easily identify these pegs I usually cut off a corner of the top (see Fig. 150) and mark the top with a letter corresponding with the sketch plan. Upon an extensive survey a large quantity of pegs will be found necessary. Temporary stations (required the same day) may be established by whites or marks on the ground. In pasture land, it is

Fig. 149 – Station mark

Fig. 150 – Station peg

customary to cut the turf in some conventional form, but under all circumstances I confess a preference for pegs. If pegs are placed in the ground to denote stations to which a line is to be run, the peg should in due course be drawn and a ranging-rod or pole put in its place.

Subsidiary stations – Subsidiary stations have reference to those points upon the base or other main survey-lines, where it is necessary to run auxiliary lines, to pick up the boundaries of internal fences, etc., and are determined according to circumstances, as the process of chaining the main lines is carried on. If in the case of an ordinary field (Fig. 151), when after chaining

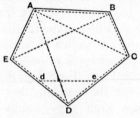

Fig. 151

A B and B C, we proceed to take up C D, it will be necessary at *e* to have a station, and similarly on line D E to do the same at *d*, for the purpose of measuring the "tie" or "check" line *d e*. Anticipating my remarks upon the field-book, each station should be marked round with a circle or oval.

Chain-men – In all chaining operations, there is one person to drag the chain, called the leader, and another to follow, called the follower. Of these two (supposing two men are employed to assist the surveyor) the follower should be the more intelligent and trustworthy.

In all organised surveys there should always be ample assistance. Two men at least are required, so that the surveyor may be free to make observations, sketch, and enter measurements in his field-book, and generally superintend operations.

Leader's duties – Reverting to the leader and follower, it is necessary to instruct each in their respective duties. To the leader should be explained that, at the commencement of work, he is to receive (and count for his own satisfaction) the arrows, for which he will be held responsible. His duty is to precede the follower in a direction indicated and to draw the chain gently after, and upon reaching the limit of its length he is to turn half round to face the follower, holding the handle of the chain in his hand with one of the arrows between the inside of the handle and the inside of his fingers thus (Fig. 152), and to watch for a

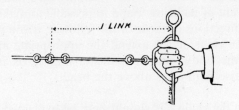

Fig. 152 – How to hold chain

signal from the follower as to how he should move laterally right or left, taking care (on his part) to keep the chain straight, by gentle shaking up.

Some surveyors insist that the leader should completely face the follower at the end of each chain, but my experience has been that, by so doing, his body often obscures a forward point, and by very little practice he can be made to do the work as well sideways. It is necessary that he should hold the arrow perfectly upright, and only move it gradually right or left, so as to mark the exact spot indicated by the follower.

It is useful to range out several points in a line by means of laths or whites, which will be helpful in guiding the leader to keep in the direction it is necessary to go.

Duty of follower – The duty of the follower, having previously had the destination of the line explained, is to retain the other end of the chain in hand, and to direct the leader as to the direction he should take; to call out when the chain is at its full length; to hold the extremity of the handle against the centre of the station whence the line starts, or against the arrow which had been previously placed in the ground (taking care to hold the outside of the handle against the point); to see that the chain is stretched perfectly straight and lies evenly in a true line with the forward station; to direct the leader to move his body altogether right or left, and when approximately in line, to instruct him by slight lateral movement of his hand, right or left, until the exact point is obtained. If within hearing range he should call "To you" or "From you," or if beyond earshot, by moving the hand right or left; and to convey to the leader that he is right, and it is necessary to fix an arrow in the ground to mark the spot, either call out "Mark," or convey that meaning by a nod.

In the event of its being found impossible to make the leader hear your directions or those of the follower, if you want him to move to the right or left extend the appropriate arm at right angles to the body; and to indicate that he is in the right position, raise both arms above the head.

How to use the chain – It should here be explained that as the chain measures 66 ft., or 100 links, between the ends of the handles, it would not be right to hold one extremity against the arrows or pegs at each end, for by so doing, the length of the line is diminished by the number of half-thicknesses of the arrows or pegs, corresponding with as many chain-lengths as have been measured. When pegs are used, if the end of each handle is held in the centre (or with arrows, if the leader holds the inside of his handle against the arrow, whilst the follower holds his handle outside (Fig. 152) against the arrow at his end) the proper length may be adjusted.

After placing an arrow in the ground at the end of the first chain, the leader proceeds in direction of the goal, until he has reached the limit of the chain. The follower, having walked to the first arrow, and held his end of the chain thereto, now directs the leader so as to mark the second chain, which having been duly accomplished, the men go forward (the follower having previously picked up the first arrow), and so they continue, until the leader has expended all his arrows, when, having placed his last in the ground, he calls out "Ten," which should be acknowledged by the surveyor and booked accordingly. The surveyor now proceeds to the tenth arrow, and putting his offset staff in the place of the tenth arrow, the follower, having reached this point, picks up the tenth arrow, and counts the ten arrows before handing them over to the leader, who on his part again counts them to see that he receives the right number.

This point is known as a "Tally" point (i.e. 10 chains = 1,000 links) and should always be booked in the field book.

The foregoing is a description of the method of chaining a simple line between the points, supposing it to be necessary only to ascertain the length of a line, but it seldom happens even in a checkline that such an operation can be performed without crossing through hedges or fences of some description.

Crossing hedges, etc. (Fig. 153) – In these cases the leader and follower must wait before moving forward, to allow the surveyor to note the chainage of such intersection. For instance, if after three chains have been measured a hedge intervene between the third and fourth chain, then the follower, noting at

Fig. 153 – Chaining through hedges

what point the leader's end of the chain should pass through the hedge, gives the necessary directions, which having been done, the chain is now pulled tight, and a fourth arrow having been adjusted in place, the chain is allowed to rest until the number of links is ascertained where the fence crosses the chain. In the case supposed (Fig. 153) the number of links is 47, so that the crossing of the hedge on our chain-line should be booked 347 – that is, 3 chains 47 links.

Hedge and ditch – Confusion often exists as to the owner of a hedge with a ditch on one side. In the absence of local custom which might define the ownership it is usual to assume both hedge and ditch as belonging to the property (B) more remote from the ditch – that is, the boundary is the side of the ditch which is further from the hedge (see Fig. 154).

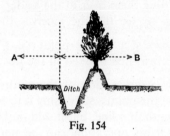

Fig. 154

How to measure fence – Since in the course of time the edges of the ditch break down and consequently widen the distance it is often more convenient to take all measurements to the centre, or root, of the hedge, and make the necessary allowance for the edge of the ditch therefrom. The usual allowance is six links, unless custom varies the length, and it will be prudent of the surveyor to make inquiries in the locality as to that custom.

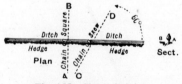

Fig. 155 – Skew chaining

This allowance of six links is, of course, upon the square – as A B (Fig. 155) – for, if the chain crosses in an oblique direction (as C D), then the distance will be greater. For instance, suppose the edge of the ditch on the square is six links, as A B, but the chain crosses instead at an angle of 60°, then the length from the hedge to the edge of the ditch will be nearly seven links instead of six.

Foot-set hedges – It may happen that a hedge has a ditch on either side, or none at all, and yet divides two properties, and in such a case the centre or root of the hedge should be taken.

Offsets – The process of surveying, after the necessary lines have been laid out, consists of determining the various boundaries, buildings, etc., by means of lateral measurements, to such points right or left of the chain-line, as may distinguish any alteration in shape of the fence, or the angles of the buildings

These lateral measurements are called offsets, and are always taken at right angles to the chain-line. As it is possible upon the ground, no matter how uneven, to lay out a straight line, which on paper is drawn with a pencil and straight-edge, so it is possible also upon the ground to set out a right angle. Under the head of "Instruments" (Chap. 2) I have described the cross-staff (p. 42) and optical square. I have described these appliances for setting out a right angle; and for taking offsets the latter will be found to be the most useful and accurate. But for general work, the surveyor soon gets accustomed, with the eye alone, to find the exact position on the chain at right angles to any clearly defined point. A greater help is to lay down the

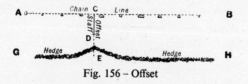

Fig. 156 – Offset

offset staff as nearly square with the chain as it is possible to judge, and then, looking along the rod, to mark with the eye any point in line therewith in the fence, as shown by the dotted line D E (Fig. 156) when A B is the chain, G H the fence, and E a point to which it is necessary to take an offset; C D is the staff, and C E the offset. In using a cross-staff, great care has to be observed that the rod on which it is fixed is in a vertical position, and

L

exactly upon the chain-line. The box is directed so that two of the slots are in line with the chain-line, as *a b* (Fig. 157), when, by looking through *c d* in direction C D, we have a right angle with A B.

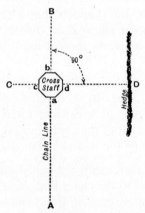

Fig. 157 – Offset with staff

Using the optical square – In the case of the optical square, the operator holds the instrument in his left hand, and having placed a flag at D, or a piece of paper in the hedge, walks along the chain-line keeping his eye upon the advanced flag B until the flag or mark at D becomes coincident with the flag B (as in Fig. 158), when C D is at right angles with A B.

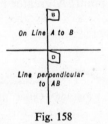

Fig. 158

Offsets should be taken at all points of divergence in the line of fences, or at angles formed by two fences. It is not necessary to take offsets at every chain if the hedge is fairly straight, but may be done every second or third, but when there is any appreciable bend or kink, as in Fig. 159, it will be necessary to take offsets at 1*a*, 2*b*, 3*c*, 4*d*, and 9*f* on the right-hand side of

the chain, and 6e on the left. It will be seen, that the fence from
d to e crosses the chain diagonally, as does that from e to f, and
in addition to the offsets 4d, 6e, and 9f, the distances along the
fence 5d, e5, e7, should also be measured, and to fix the corner

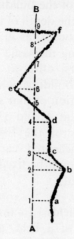

Fig. 159

f a temporary station in the chain-line, as at 8, should be noted,
and the distance 8f measured as a check. If the ditch is on the
other side of the hedge to the chain-line, then it is customary to
take the offset to the centre, or root, of the hedge and add six
links for the edge of the ditch, and if the ditch is on the same
side, either to take the offset to the edge, or to measure to the
root of hedge, and deduct six links.

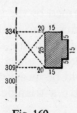

Fig. 160

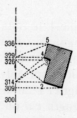

Fig. 161

As to buildings – Buildings require to be very carefully taken at
each angle, and the right angle must be very accurately set out;
in the case of Fig. 160, when a building is square with the

chain-line, it is only necessary to take offsets to the face of the building. It will be seen that after the third chain, at 309 and 334 are points whence the two corners of the building run, and the difference between 309 and 334 should be the same as measuring along the face of the building, viz. 25 links. All that is necessary is to measure the depth of the building together with any projections that may occur, as in Fig. 160. In the example shown by Fig. 161, keeping the same points on our chain-line, it will be seen that the first offset at 309 is to 1, which is the angle of the back of the building, whilst 314 to 2 is the front corner, 326 is the termination of that same plane, 329 the angle formed by the projection at 4, and 336 the other angle of the same plane. The lengths of the frontage, sides, back, and projection, should be measured carefully, and the various angles of the buildings should be fixed by diagonal tie-lines, as shown in Figs. 160 and 161.

As to taking corners of fields – In the case of commencing a chain-line in the corner of a field, as in Fig. 162, it is not sufficient to take one offset from A to *d* on line 1, and one from

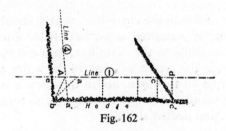

Fig. 162

A to *e* on line 4, to obtain the angle *b* formed by the two fences, but the diagonals A *b* and *a b* are necessary to accurately fix the point of intersection. Equally, when the chain-line crosses the fence at *c* it is not only necessary to take one offset at *d* to *c'*, but the length *c c'* along the hedge should be measured, so that with the length *c d* on the chain we have a triangle to fix the exact position of *c'*.

To fix position of an intersection – It may happen that the intersection of a fence on the other side of the hedge requires to be accurately determined, for which purpose a simple offset would hardly be sufficient. Set out a triangle, with one side on the chain, as in Fig. 163, as *a* at 320 and *b* at 337, and then measure the length *a c* and *b c*. And again, to fix the angles of a

Fig. 163

building when a right angle is deemed insufficient, as in Fig. 164, leave stations A B and C at 304, 315, 347, from which measure the lengths A *d*, B *d*, B *b*, and C *b* to the corners of the building.

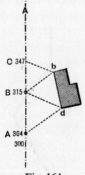

Fig. 164

Well and ill-condition angles – In taking ties every care should be taken to see that the angles are as near equilateral as possible. If any of the three angles of the triangle so found is less than 30 degrees the triangles are said to be "ill-conditioned." Triangles whose angles are more than the 30 degrees are said to be "well-conditioned." The reason that angles should be more than the 30 degrees is apparant when the work of plotting the survey comes to be done, when it will be found that in drawing arcs to bisect very acute angles the exact point of bisection is very difficult to obtain. Similarly, in the field, slight errors in measuring acute angles can have serious results.

Limit of offsets – No hard and fast rule can be laid down as to what should constitute the maximum length of an offset. Much will depend upon circumstances, common sense and the judgement of the surveyor in the field, but it is always advisable to keep the offsets as short as possible, particularly where the work has to be plotted to a large scale. It is often claimed that 50 links shall be the limit of any offset, and this is fairly safe for general surveys when land is of no great importance and when the scale of the plan is small. Where land is valuable, however, and where a large scale is to be used in plotting, the maximum offset should be much reduced. A good practical rule to adopt in all work is to keep the offsets to no more than would be represented by $\frac{1}{2}$ inch long on the plan. Thus, if the plan is drawn to a scale of 1 chain to 1 inch, 50 links would then be the maximum offset, but if the plan is to be drawn to a scale of, say, 20 feet to 1 inch, 10 feet would be the maximum offset.

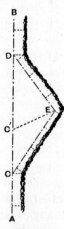

Fig. 165

Long offsets are generally the result of laziness; for rather than set out a small triangle from a chain-line, when a considerable bend in a fence occurs, and from the sides C E and E D of this triangle take short offsets, as shown in Fig. 165, many surveyors who advocate long offsets would take to the bend direct from the chain-line A B. And here let me say that a triangle such as C D E cannot be considered correct unless a tie-line such as c′ E is measured.

Offset staff – The method of taking offsets when using an offset staff is to stand over the chain line as nearly opposite the point that is to be measured as possible and with the staff pointing towards the object with one end touching the chain, look at the angles found by staff and chain. If they are not right angles adjust until they are equal. To use the offset staff for measuring turn it over carefully, so that it does not slip back; to prevent this, place your toe against the end, and so on until you have reached the point. A little practice will soon render the task simple.

Ranging out lines – Once the positions of the main and subsidiary stations have been determined the next operation is to range out the lines that will form the basis of the chain survey. Ranging rods or poles are placed at the intersection of the lines and the lines themselves must be "boned-in". The method of boning-in a line is quite simple but it takes practice and requires a good "eye" on the part of the surveyor who places himself a yard or so behind the first station point so that he can observe the forward station point. One assistant now moves forward along the line with a bundle of whites and ranging rods. He places a ranging rod in position between the first and last stations and the surveyor ranges him in accurately. When the correct position has been fixed a white or lath is exchanged for the ranging rod. It is advisable to range out a number of intermediate points, especially in undulating ground, as, not only may it not be possible to command the forward station if in a valley, but they are extremely useful in guiding both the leader and follower in the chaining operations that follow.

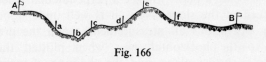

Fig. 166

This is illustrated in Fig. 166. If A and B represent the stations of a line which has to pass across a valley, it is obvious that unless such points as *a b c d e* and *f* have been previously established, it would be impossible to chain the line A B. It sometimes happens, owing to inequality of the ground, that, in running a line, the forward mark is lost to sight while at the same time enough cannot be seen of the poles already planted to allow the setting out of the line to be continued by ranging from them.

Such a case is illustrated in Fig. 166 when station B cannot be observed from station A because of the hillock which intervenes between points *d*, *e* and *f*. The procedure in such cases is as follows: the surveyor goes to the top of the hillock with a ranging rod *e* and as nearly as he can judge he lines one assistant holding a rod at *d* in line with himself at station A and another assistant with a rod at *f* in line with himself and station B. Assistant at *d* now indicates which way the surveyor must move his rod to get into line between *d* and *f*. Assistant at *f* now indicates in which direction he must move his rod to line up between *f* and *d* and the process is repeated until A *d e*, *d e f* and *e f* B all fall in a straight line. The intermediates *a*, *b*, *c* can then be boned in.

What is level ground ? – Any ground of a fairly level character may be treated as being quite level – that is, any ground whose slope does not form a greater angle with the horizon than five degrees. But beyond this it is necessary to adopt some means of regulating our measurements. If we take a pair of compasses, as in Fig. 167, and with A as a centre and B (the foot of the slope) as a radius, and strike the arc B C until it cuts the horizontal line A C, it will be seen that the line A C is greater

Fig. 167

than A *b*, *b* being a point whence a perpendicular is let drop to cut the foot of the slope. Now, it is well understood that in surveying operations all measurements upon the ground are reduced to the horizontal, as, "when plotted the survey represents a perfect plane, and the chaining of inclined lines should be so conducted, that every length is exactly equal to the base of a right-angled triangle."

In the case of Fig. 167, if we plotted the line A B exactly as measured along the slope, which in this case is 715 links, we should make our line 24·31 links longer than is should appear, and consequently our plan would be inaccurate. It is therefore necessary to reduce *all* measurements to the horizontal.

There are several ways of doing this; chiefly by reducing the hypotenusal measure by calculation, having obtained the angle of slopes, and by "stepping." Of the former, much may be argued for and against, and I propose to say a few words on both sides. With an Abney level or clinometer it is very simple to observe the angle of slope and to make the necessary reduction in the chainage as the work proceeds. But the greatest care is necessary in determining these angles. It very seldom happens that the slope of a hill-side is regular; on the contrary, it is often made up of constantly varying inclinations, some flat, some steep, and to accurately determine the hypotenusal correction separate angles will have to be observed at each point of variation. Fig. 168 will better illustrate my meaning, for

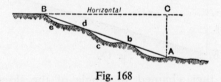

Fig. 168

between A and B it would not be sufficient to observe the angle formed with the horizon by A B, because, to be correct, the hypotenuse should be measured along the line A B, whereas (that being impossible) we follow the undulations of the ground between these points, such as A *b c d e* B, and use the length so measured as the multiple of cos angle of slope. Thus, whereas the line A *b c d e* B measured along the surface of the ground is 720, the angle A B C (the angle of slope with the horizon) being 25°, the hypotenusal deduction would be 72·38 links, whereas strictly speaking it should only be 70·50 links, by reason of having taken the angle from A to B. So that, to be accurate, it is necessary to observe the angles of slope at A *b c a* and *e*, and for each separate angle to take the length along the slope between the points.

Observing angle of slope – To obtain the angle of slope by means of a clinometer or theodolite (both instruments are described in Chapter 2) it is advisable for the surveyor to sight onto a staff or vane adjusted to the height of his eyes (Fig. 169) so that at

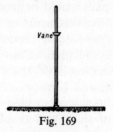

Fig. 169

any point the true line parallel with the slope of the ground will be obtained.

Thus, in Fig. 170, B is the position of the clinometer at eye level and A the vane held by the assistant. The distance of the

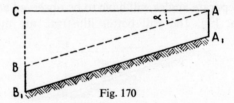

Fig. 170

slope A_1B_1 is then chained, the angle of the slope $= \alpha$. The required horizontal distance is A C.

Then, since $\dfrac{A C}{A_1B_1} = \text{Cos. } \alpha$. A C $= A_1B_1 \cos \alpha$.

The following is a table of allowance to be made for the difference between hypotenusal and horizontal measurement:*

Degrees	Links	Degrees	Links	Degrees	Links	Degrees	Links
5	00·4	14	03·0	23	07·9	32	15·2
6	00·6	15	03·4	24	08·6	33	16·1
7	00·7	16	03·9	25	09·4	34	17·1
8	01·0	17	04·4	26	10·1	35	18·1
9	01·2	18	04·9	27	10·9	36	19·1
10	01·5	19	05·4	28	11·7	37	20·1
11	01·8	20	06·0	29	12·5	38	21·2
12	02·2	21	06·6	30	13·4	39	22·3
13	02·6	22	07·3	31	14·3	40	23·4

* To accurately determine this allowance, multiply the versine of the angle of inclination by the length measured. The above table can also be used for 100 feet chain, the numbers given under "links" are then read as "feet".

Adjusting the allowance for slope – It should be explained that many surveyors, having calculated or obtained the necessary allowance, either move the arrows in accordance with the reduction from the length of slope, or make the alteration in the field-book; the former method, however, is best, as any offsets that may be required will be more favourably affected than by the latter. To use the clinometer a very steady hand is required, and possibly the best instrument for the purpose is the Abney level (described in Chap. 2); but a primitive and very useful little clinometer may be made by cutting a stout piece of cardboard into the shape of a semicircle and dividing it right and left of the centre into 45 degrees, each of which may be marked with the figures given in the table. It is held in one hand and held up to the eye, and looking along the diameter of the card you note when this line cuts the vane of the staff, when a small plummet hanging from the centre marks the angle, which should be read by one of your men.

Stepping – It is seldom that a perfectly even slope will be found and in order to obtain accuracy by calculation as described above a number of observations are often necessary. This wastes time and increases errors so that the more generally accepted method of obtaining the horizontal measurement is by the system known as stepping. This is illustrated in Fig. 171.

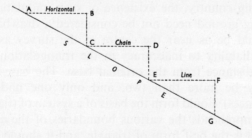

Fig. 171

It will be more convenient to use half the chain length in order to avoid excessive sag and to work downhill, rather than uphill, since it is quite simple to hold a chain at A while it is being pulled tight at B, but extremely difficult to hold the chain at B, directly over point C, while it is being pulled tight to obtain A.

In chaining the horizontal measurement the follower would hold the end of the chain firmly against a special arrow at A while the leader, taking the 50th link, stretches the chain horizontal and drops a plumb-bob from this link and puts an arrow at the point where the plumb-bob touches the ground. The follower leaves the chain end at A and moves down to take the 50th link which he places against the arrow at C. The leader then plumbs down from D to E at the 100th link and the process is repeated until the slope has been measured.

If offsets are to be taken while chaining downhill it is better to take them with the chain lying on the ground, but since the chain will no longer reach both arrows a slight adjustment should be made at both ends and when taking offsets.

Base-lines – In all surveys, large or small, there should be base-lines intersecting the figure to be surveyed. The letter X is the best form for the base-lines to take, care being observed that their direction is upon as level ground as possible, for upon the correctness of the length of these lines the accuracy of the whole of the details depends. No greater undulation than say 4 deg. should be allowed in general survey working without horizontal adjustment. Gentle slopes have comparatively slight effect upon linear measurements, and if the ends of the base-lines are otherwise well situated, so as to command an uninterrupted view of surrounding country, the existence of such undulations in the intervening ground need not be considered a drawback. Base-lines should be as near the centre of the survey as possible, since the liability to inaccuracy in the triangulation increases with the distance from the original base. The base-lines (and there may be more than two, and only one under certain circumstances) should form the basis of a system of triangulation which comprehends the various boundaries of the estate. The equilateral is the best form of triangle, and it should be sought to lay out this figure as much as possible, but of course this is not always practicable. The sides of the triangles formed upon these base-lines are called chain- or survey-lines, which are so arranged as to take the boundaries of the property, and from these again are subsidiary chain-lines, to pick up any of the fences or other objects that intersect the estate.

A very simple illustration of the base- and survey-lines will be seen in Fig. 172, in which A B is the main base-line and C D the other; the survey-lines are A C, C B, B D, D A. Now three sides of a triangle, however carefully measured, are no guarantee of its accuracy; there must be a proof or tie line. It has been recommended to test the accuracy of a triangle by letting drop a perpendicular from the apex to the base; this is all very well on

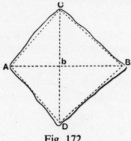

Fig. 172

paper, but upon the ground it is not always either practicable or expedient. In Fig. 172, quite by accident the line C D crosses the line A B from the apex of each triangle A C B and A D B at as near 90 deg. as possible, consequently the length C *b* will test the triangle A B C, and *b* D will prove A B D.

I have borrowed an excellent example (Fig. 173) from a well-known work (on surveying) which illustrates my argument exactly, where it will be seen that the property consists of two fields adjoining a road, which are together in the form of an

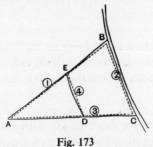

Fig. 173

irregular triangle. The three sides A B, B C, and C A embrace the exterior boundaries, whilst the direction of the internal fence is of a character that a line E D may serve the double purpose of taking up this hedge and acting as a check to the triangle. For if the lengths A E on line A B and A D on the line A C be carefully measured, then the length E D will be proved to fall exactly within these points after the triangle has been plotted.

Fig. 174 shows how the irregular figure A B C D E F may be divided into triangles, and by C F all four triangles may be tied, although I should recommend a further check, such as D *d*.

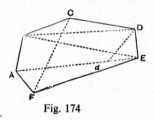

Fig. 174

It does not always follow that a survey must consist only of triangles, although it is always advisable to adopt this figure when possible, for, as in the case of Fig. 175, A B C D is in the

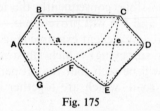

Fig. 175

form of a trapesium, and so long as the line B C is checked by such ties as B *a* C *e* the work will be all right. The line C *e* produced to E, checks the triangle *a* D E, as does a part of B G the figure A *a* F G.

Chain-angles – We have dealt so far with simple figures, whose outlines can be ascertained by running lines in various directions to take up the boundaries and intersecting fences, which lines are checked by such means as I have briefly described; but there are cases, such as woods or ponds, which it is impossible to get through or across, where it is necessary to chain round, taking the exterior boundary, and fix the relative directions of the lines circumscribing the figure by means of what are called chain-angles.

I have already explained that three sides of a triangle measured is no proof of accuracy, to ensure which a fourth or tie-line is required. This is all the more necessary in the case under consideration, where we have, as in Fig. 176, to run our lines all round outside, and have to prove our work. Here we have to tie our lines in such a manner as to comprehend the outline of the wood, through which it is quite impossible to survey. Briefly, to prolong lines 1 and 4 and to tie their extremities by the line A *a* would not be sufficient to ensure the angle, therefore a second tie *a a'* is necessary, and, similarly,

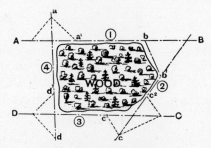

Fig. 176 – Chain-angles

lines 3 and 4 by means of the ties D *d'* and D *d*. The acute angle formed by lines 1 and 2, although tied by *b b'* (which serves the double purpose of a survey-line), could hardly be trusted unless checked at the other extremity of 2 by the ties *c c'*, *c* C, C *c²*.

I might give numbers of instances of how such figures may be circumscribed by means of lines and chain-angles, but in these days when instrumental observations have superseded such methods it is unnecessary to dwell upon the subject.

Inaccessible distances – It rarely happens that a survey of any extent can be carried out without some difficulties being encountered, such as base- or important chain-lines being interrupted by obstacles, in the form of rivers, arms of lakes, ponds, buildings, etc., when it is necessary to resort to some means of working round in the one case, or by geometric construction or angular observation to ascertain the intervening distance. This strengthens my argument in favour of reconnoitre previous to commencing a survey, as in undulating ground a building or other obstacle which had been unobserved might come directly in the line, which by careful arrangement beforehand might have been avoided. In the absence of any instrument, such as a box sextant or optical square, a right angle may be approximately set out on level ground by the following simple method. Measure forty links on the chain-line, and put arrows, as at A and B (Fig. 177), then with the end of the chain held carefully at A take eighty links and instruct another chainman to hold the eightieth link at B; take the fiftieth link in your

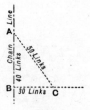

Fig. 177

hand and pull from A and B until they are fairly tight, when an arrow at C will be perpendicular with the line A B, in other words A B will equal 40, B C 30, and C A 50 links.

I have said this may be done approximately on level ground, but I do not recommend any reliance being placed upon a right angle set out in the manner above described if intended to overcome a difficulty such as is represented in Fig. 178, where the line A B is interrupted by a house. In this case it is assumed that if at *a*, on the line A B, a right angle be set out (as explained) and a sufficient distance *a* C, say 60 links, measured, and C D (made perpendicular to *a* C) 80 links, and D *b* at right angles to C D measuring also 60 links, and *b* B made perpendicular to *b* D, then *a b* will be between the points A and B, in other words in the same line, supposing the building did not obstruct. Thus four right angles have to be set out and measured to carry the line A B past the building. I recommend the student to practise this problem on perfectly level ground, and I think he will agree with me that, unless the line *b* B has been ranged from A upon sufficiently high ground to see over the building, very little reliance must be placed in the prolongation of the line A *a* by such means as I have described. I can only say that I should observe the greatest care in checking with a theodolite such work before I should trust to such a prolongation.

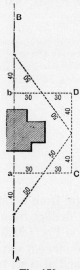

Fig. 178

I have selected one or two such examples of measuring over inaccessible distances, across rivers or ponds, by the chain only, as appear to me to be capable of satisfactory results if great care and accuracy be observed, for, unlike the case of the building, you can command all points. Suppose, as in Fig. 179, the line A B is intercepted by a river, the width of which is too great to ascertain by measurement across. We must therefore proceed to set out such a figure on one side of the stream as will enable us to range across it a line which shall so intersect the line A B, that this point of intersection shall be equidistant from a given point to another point, to which we are able to measure on the ground.

Range the line A B across the stream, sending a man with rods to establish on the other side, where directed, in the first instance the point B. From any convenient point *b* measure towards A

M

such a distance as judgment tells to be greater than that across the river, say 400 links. At A the extremity of 400, and *b*, set out right angles, and from *b* measure 300 links to *b'*, and from A 600 links to *a'*. Place rods at *a'* and *b'* (having previously checked the lines A *b'* and *a' b'*, which should respectively be 500 links); now range through *a'* and *b'* the point *c* on the line A B, then *c b'* will equal *a' b'*, viz. 500 links, and *b c* will equal

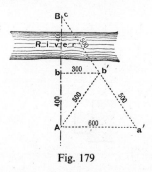

Fig. 179

A *b*, viz. 400 links. Measure from each edge of the stream to *b* and *c*, the sum of which deduct from 400, and you have the width of the river. Again, in Fig. 180 at C on the line A B set out the perpendicular C D, and make it some equal number of links, say 400; bisect C D in *b*, and at D set out the right angle C D *c*, make D *c* = 300 links, place rods at *c* and *b* and range the line

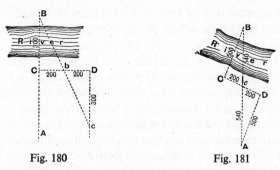

Fig. 180   Fig. 181

through until it intersects A B in B, then C B will equal D *c* = 300 links. Similarly, if the line passes obliquely (Fig. 181), set out any line parallel (approximately) with the bank of the river, as C D, measure 200 links either way, at each end set off the perpendiculars D A, C B, then will c B = c A = 540 links. Again, as in Fig. 182, measure off the perpendiculars B C, D E, ranging the point C in line with A E; then

$$\text{A B} : \text{B C} :: \text{C}\,d : d\,\text{E}$$

$$\therefore \text{A B} = \frac{\text{B C} \times \text{C}\,d}{d\,\text{E}} = \frac{\text{B C} \times \text{B D}}{\text{D E} - \text{B C}}$$

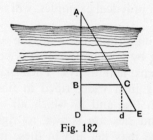

Fig. 182

All the foregoing are fairly good methods of determining inaccessible distances, in the absence of instruments for taking angles, but I need hardly say that the right angles should be set out with an optical square or other reliable appliance, and even then the very greatest care must be observed.

The simplest, quickest, and most reliable method of determining an inaccessible distance is as follows: (Fig. 183) at C, with a box sextant or theodolite set out the line C D at right angles with A B, measure any distance C D, and at D observe the angle E D C. Then

C E = nat. tan. E D C × C D.

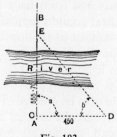

Fig. 183

For example, the angle E D C is 51°, and the length C D = 450 links. Now nat. tan. of 51° = 1·2349.

∴ 1·2349 × 450 = 555·7050 links, which is the length C E.

Should there be any doubt as to the accuracy of the observation or calculation, place the instrument at E and observe the angle C E D, which should equal $90° - 51° = 39$.

Surveying with the chain – Having dealt with the basic principles of chain surveying and the methods used in setting out and overcoming difficulties and obstacles, the more detailed field work, together with practical examples, will now be considered.

Field book – This important book to the surveyor measures some 7 inches long by 5 inches wide. It is bound in leather or stiff card and opens lengthways. Each page has a central column of about $\frac{3}{4}$ inch wide, ruled in fine red or blue, to represent the chain line and in which all chain readings are entered. Offsets and ties are shown to right or left of this column, as the case may be, and in these margins all objects surveyed must also be sketched. Great care should be taken in keeping the book and the student should bear in mind that the chainage, ties, offsets, sketches and the like must be entered in such a way that the work can be easily plotted by another who may perhaps have never seen the site of the survey. It will be advisable, therefore, to include as much detail as reasonably possible; to leave plenty of room and never attempt to crowd the work; to make certain that it is clear to what point each offset or tie refers and from which point on the chainage line it was taken.

The surveyor should always begin at the bottom of the last page and work upwards and from back to front of the book. This is because the central column represents the chain line and by working from the bottom to the top he enters the readings in the book in the same direction as he is walking.

Besides the chainage lengths against the points of offsets and ties, the tally points (i.e. each length of 10 chains – 1,000, 2,000, 3,000 links, etc.) should also be entered. The beginning and end of each chain-line must also be entered and the fact that it is the beginning or the end, as the case may be, stated. Include also the position of ties from the chainage to the point of measurement by means of thin lines to which arrows may be added if desired. Where features occur reference should be made on the sketches, such as "pond," "corner of house," "fence," "hedge," "wall," etc. It is not necessary to attempt to draw the sketches to scale or in proportion; indeed, it is better to exaggerate irregularities and to allow plenty of room in the margins between the central column and the sketch when dealing with short offsets.

The base and survey lines should be numbered from 1 upwards and principle stations may be lettered A, B, C etc., for one cannot have too much detail in the field book, particularly when it is remembered that another might have to plot the work.

Fig. 184 illustrates the field book entered up in connection with a very simple survey and showing the chainage, offsets and sketch features. If the student plots this survey from the details he will find that the plotted work bears little resemblance to the sketches which emphasises the point made that the sketches do not have to be at all accurate.

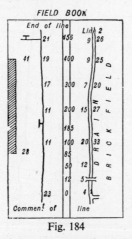

Fig. 184

In dealing with obstructions and features along the line of survey, these should be picked up and clearly indicated during the chainage. For instance, supposing we have a fence crossing our chain-line obliquely, it would have to be entered in the book as in Fig. 185; or if a fence crosses our chain-line at right angles, but at the point of intersection another fence joins in an oblique direction, it would have to appear as in Fig. 186, the word "at" written against the sketch distinguishing that at 316 the oblique fence C joins A B at the point where it is intersected by the chain. Again, if our chain-line runs at a point on the

edge of the ditch, so that in plotting at such a point the fence
will impinge on the survey-line, it will have to be shown in the

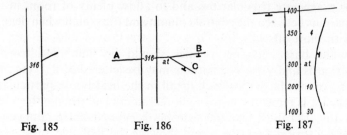

Fig. 185   Fig. 186   Fig. 187

field-book as in Fig. 187, the word "at" at 300 signifying that
this is the point of impingement.

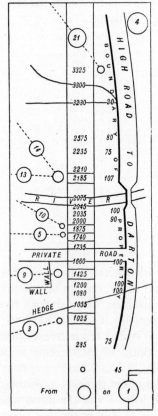

Fig. 188

Fig. 188 gives a page from a field book showing how to deal with the convergence of stations on the survey lines. It will be seen that stations occur at 1025 for line No. 3 to the left; at 1425 for No. 9; 1740 and 1875 for lines Nos. 5 and 10: while at 2185 we have a station for the intersection of lines 13 and 14, and 3325 a station for No. 21; all being on the left side of the chain-line; the point of the station being delineated by a small circle outside the column against the chainage, with a dotted line to represent the direction of the line diverging from this station, whilst a circle enclosing a number indicates the line to which it refers.

Some surveys prefer to place a ring around the chainage point at the intersection of station points instead of drawing a horizontal line above and below the station in the central column (Fig. 189).

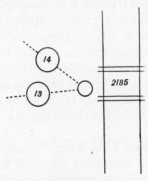

Fig. 189

Single line instead of double line – A field book containing a single line instead of the double line column is preferred by some surveyors who claim that it is more simple to use and less likely to lead to errors, but it is really a matter of personal taste as to which system is adopted and, although the double column is more generally used, the student would no doubt adopt the method he finds in use in his office.

Chain survey of Wimbledon Park – Plate 1 is an example of a complete chain survey and the field book is reproduced in the pages following it. This is a survey of somewhat undulating ground, the rise from B to G being about 90 feet. Commencing at A at the north-eastern end of the property for line 1, it was found impossible to restrict the offsets to fifty links, as the point B was an important station; consequently we had offsets of ninety-nine links, which, as a rule, is too much; but as this survey was for a special purpose, connected with the higher ground, the absolute accuracy of this particular fence, to the left of the line 1, was not a matter of great moment, especially as in the subsequent operations of traversing the road this fence was carefully adjusted. On reaching B (at the end of line 1), we ran the line No. 2 to C; thence a third line to D, and from A to D by line 4. This trapesium was tied by the base-line B D and a check-line from g to A; an additional check-line E′ G completely secures the accuracy of this figure. The south-western corner of the property had to be taken by a triangle B E E′, tied by E e; whilst a further small triangle was necessary, b^1 b^2 E, tied by b^2, b^3. Line No. 6 from E to F, passing through B C at E′ and C D at G, was a survey-line to take up the post-and-rail of the fencing of the road to Wimbledon Park. A small triangle is formed by line 7 from C to F, as much to keep up the curve of the fence on the western side as to accurately fix the position of the line E F. The north-western indent was taken up by means of a triangle H J D on the line C D, with a check-line H h.

Few lines as possible – Thus it will be seen that the whole of this figure has been accurately surveyed by means of as few lines as possible, and the accompanying field book, which is given in detail, will enable the student to plot this work for himself. Referring to line 1, it will be seen that the first point of importance at 550 is the gate, the position of which should be fixed by a small triangle upon the chain-line formed by 63 and 61 links at 600; the width of the gate in links between the posts to be noted in the field book next. At 700 is a point on the chain-line which it is necessary to measure from to the corner where the small stack fence cuts the main fence. Similarly, each of the other corners should be fixed upon the chain-line by means of triangles as shown; and finally the small pond near the end of line 1 should be so treated. It should be noted that any defined point, such as an indentation in a fence, the position of a gate-post, the intersection of one fence with another, should be

PLATE 1

PART OF WIMBLEDON PARK

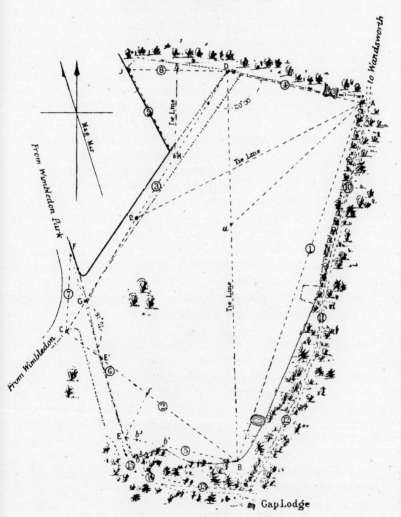

Scale: 4 Chains to an Inch

(to face page 176)

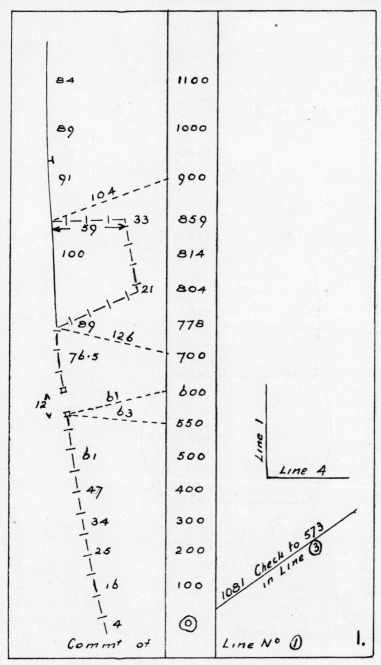

84   1100

89   1000

91   900

104

59   33   859

100   814

21   804

89   778

126

76.5   700

    600

12

61   600

63   550

61   500

47   400

34   300

25   200

16   100

4   ⓪

Comm^t of

Line 1

Line 4

1081 Check to 573 in Line ③

Line N° ①   1.

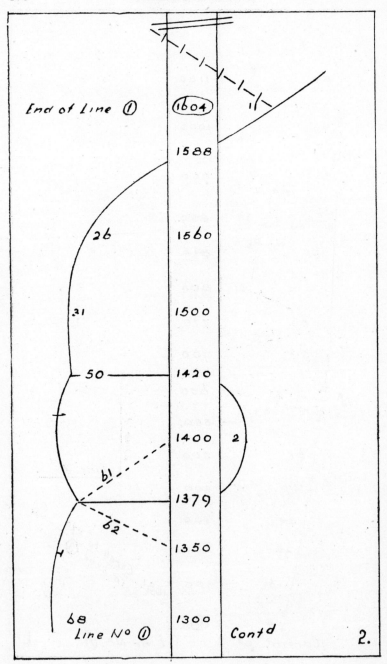

2.

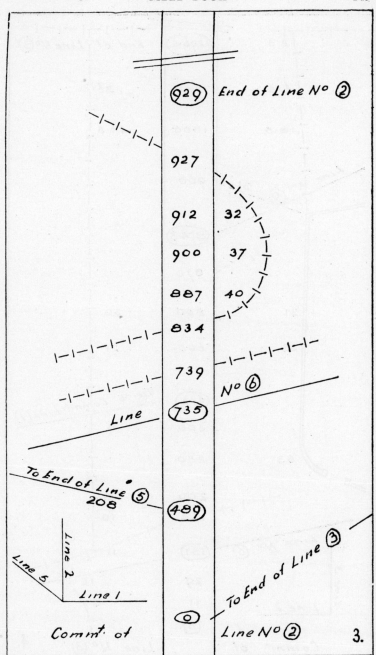

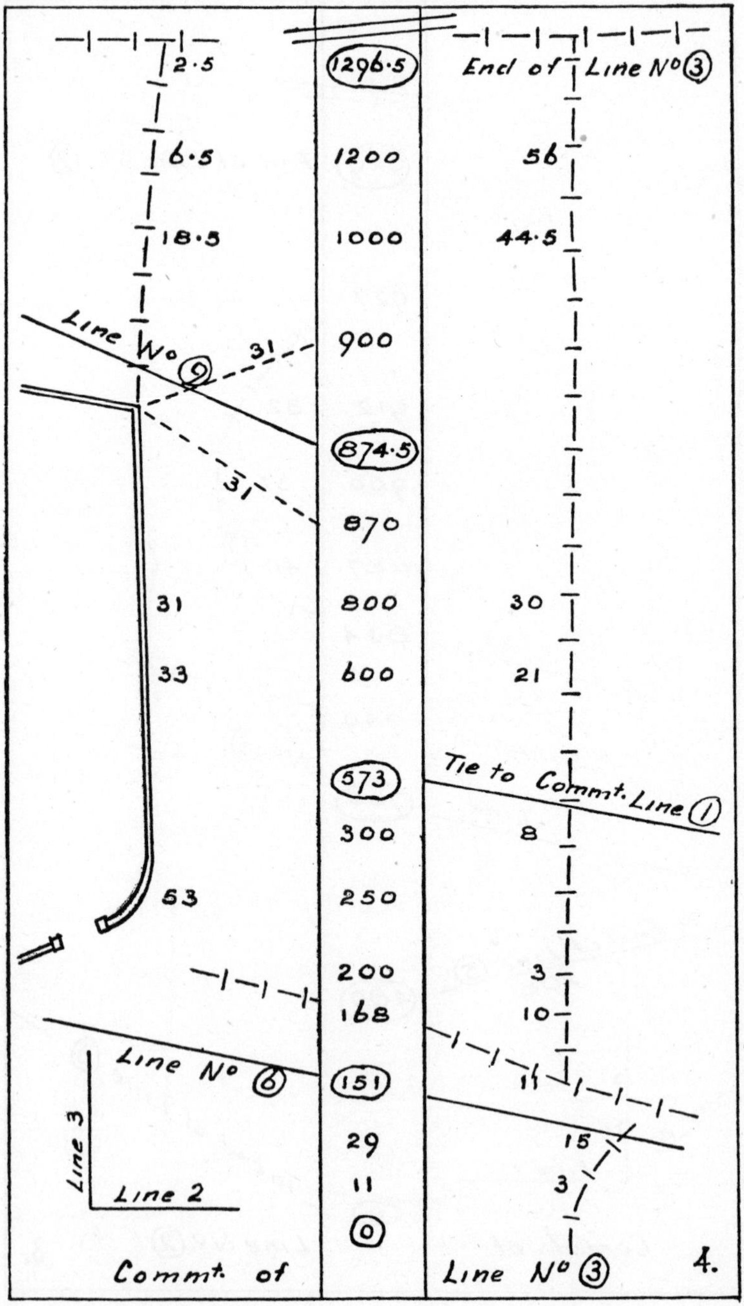
1296·5
End of Line No 3
2·5
6·5
1200
56
18·5
1000
44·5
Line No 9
31
900
874·5
31
870
31
800
30
33
600
21
573
Tie to Commt. Line 1
300
8
53
250
200
3
168
10
Line No 6
151
11
29
15
11
3
0
Line 3
Line 2
Commt. of
Line No 3
4.

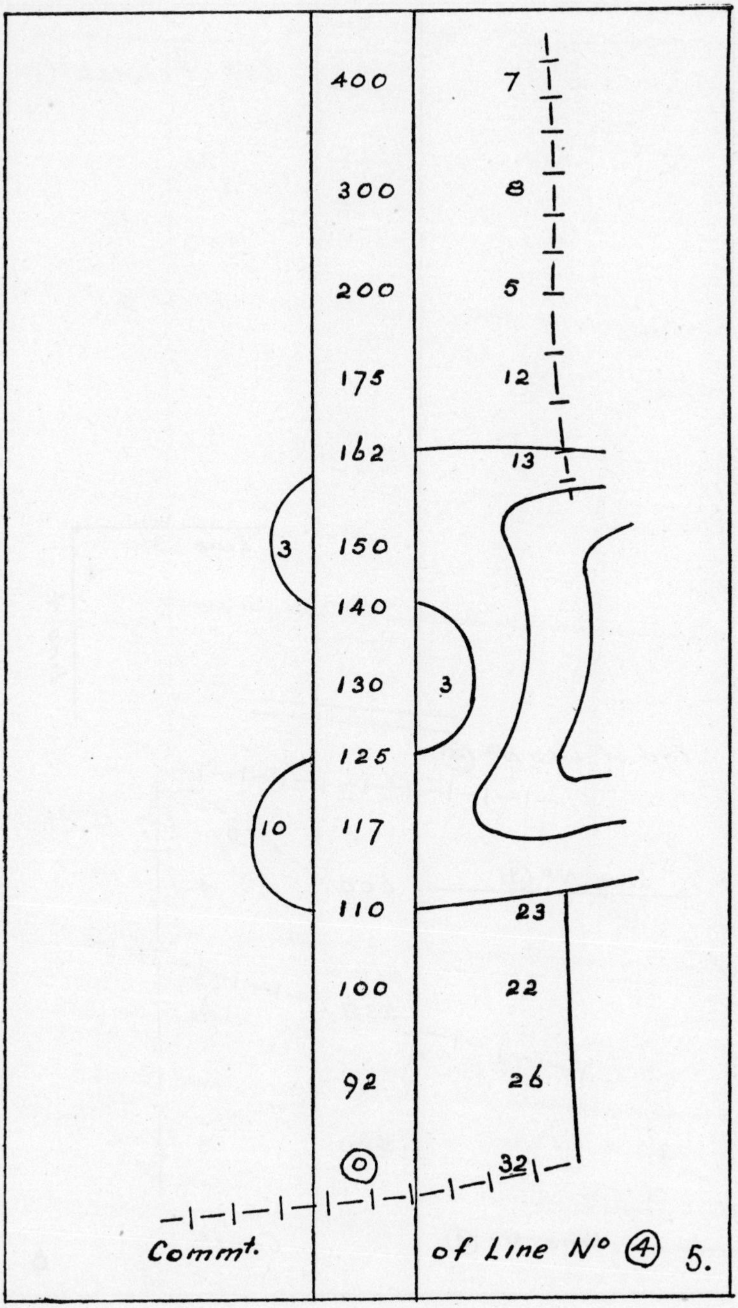

400   7

300   8

200   5

175   12

162   13

3   150

140

130   3

125

10   117

110   23

100   22

92   26

⊚   32

—|—|—|—|—|—|—|—|32|—

Commt.   of Line Nº ④ 5.

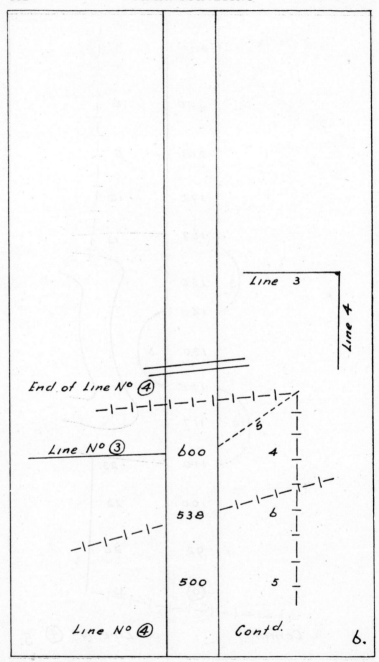

Line 3

Line 4

End of Line Nº ④

Line Nº ③   600

5

4

538   6

500   5

Line Nº ④   Contd.

b.

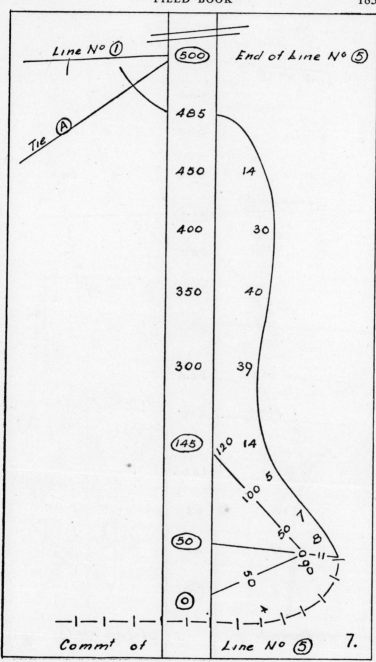

Line Nº ①

Tie Ⓐ

⑤₀₀ End of Line Nº ⑤

485

450   14

400   30

350   40

300   39

⑭₅ 120 14

100 5

      7

50   8

⑤₀ ⊙ −11
     9
     0

50

⓪

Commᵗ of   Line Nº ⑤   7.

N

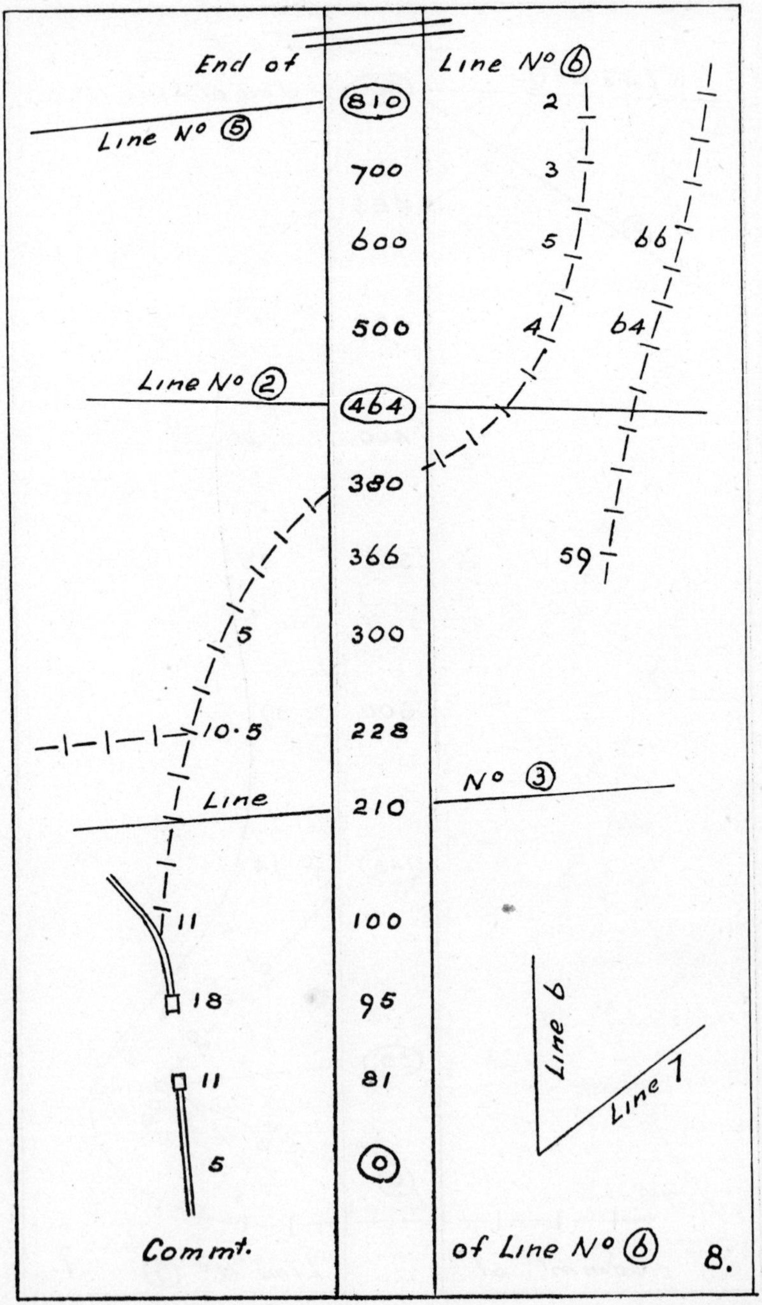
End of
Line No ⑥
810
2
Line No ⑤
700
3
600
5
66
500
4
64
Line No ②
464
380
366
59
5
300
10·5
228
No ③
Line
210
11
100
18
95
11
81
5
0
Line 6
Line 7
Commt.
of Line No ⑥
8.

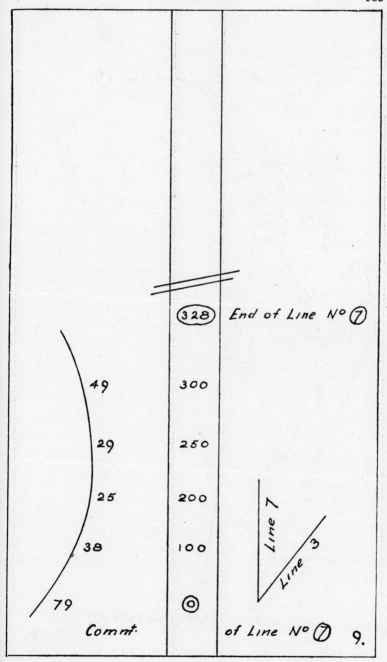

328 End of Line Nº 7

49	300
29	250
25	200
38	100
79	◉

Line 7

Line 3

Comnt̄ of Line Nº 7 9.

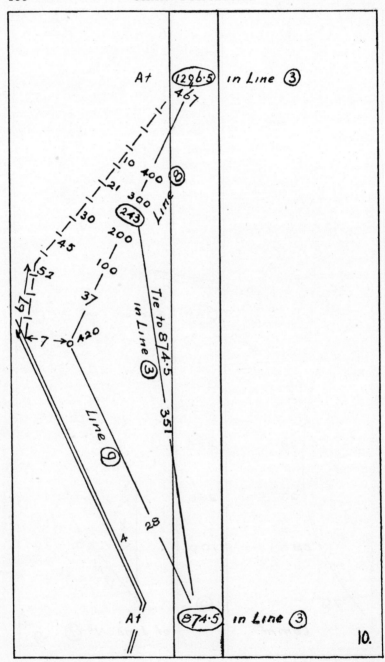

At ⬭1296·5⬮ in Line ③
467
|
|
|
|10   400
|21   300   Line ⑧
|30   ⬭243⬮
|45   200
|52   100   Tie to 874·5
|19   37   in Line ③
| 7 →o A20
                   351

              Line ⑨

              28
              A

At   ⬭874·5⬮ in Line ③

10.

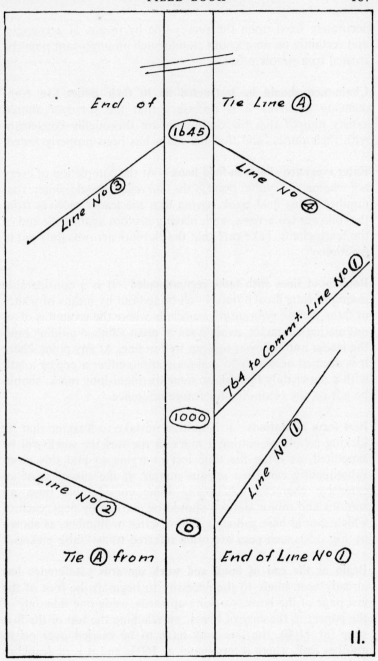

End of — Tie Line Ⓐ

1645

Line No③

Line No④

764 to Commt. Line No①

1000

Line No②

Line No①

0

Tie Ⓐ from — End of Line No①

II.

accurately fixed upon the survey-line by means of a triangle, and certainly on no account should such an important point be trusted to a simple offset.

Chain-men should be instructed as to their duties – In commencing a survey it is necessary that the surveyor should satisfy himself that his chain-men are thoroughly conversant with their duties, and that his chain has been properly tested.

Enter every ten chains in field book – At the completion of every ten chains (i.e. tally point), the surveyor should enter that number in his field book, seeing that the leader receives from the follower ten arrows, and, placing his foot against the end of the tenth chain. Take care that the eleventh arrow is duly put in position.

Boning-out lines with laths recommended – It is a considerable saving of time if each line is well boned-out by means of whites or laths, before referred to, especially where the ground is of an undulating character, as they are of great value in guiding both the leader and follower to keep well in line. At any point where it is deemed necessary to make a station, either a peg or a lath with a paper duly figured, or some distinguishing mark, should be left on the chain-line for future reference.

Best form of stations – It is quite a mistake to imagine that by kicking a hole or cutting a mark in the turf the work will be expedited, as often the time lost in trying to find this point subsequently can be a serious matter. If the survey is of an extensive character, occupying some considerable time, all stations and minor stations should be marked by pegs, each of which should have a distinguishing letter or number, as shown by Fig. 150, such pegs are often referred to as "false pickets."

Begin at the end of book and work upwards – Reference has already been made to the necessity to begin at the foot of the last page of the book, working upwards, using one side only of the paper; in the case of line 1, on reaching the top of the first page (at 1100), the line may have to be carried over on to another leaf, where it terminates at 1604; and it is desirable to draw two dashes across the book to represent that you have finished that line, taking care to write at the beginning, "Commencement of line 1," and at the finish, "End of line 1."

Let each line have a separate page – On no account attempt to commence another line on the same page, as paper is cheap enough to obviate such a necessity. In line 1 it will be seen that all the offsets are on the left-hand side. Line 2 on the third page should be designated "Commencement of line 2," At 489 is a station for a check-line to the end of line 5, and again at 735 there is another in connection with line 6. 739, 834, and 927, in line 2, intersect the post-and-rail fence which forms the boundary of the road, and between 834 and 927 there are points where it will be found necessary to take offsets to the right of the line to pick up the curvature of the aforesaid fence, while the final station of line 2 is at its termination 929. Here again it is necessary to draw two dashes across the book to show the completion of this line, and I find it most convenient to indicate all stations by an oval enclosing the figures, thus $\textcircled{\tiny 929}$, and, by means of one or more lines as the case may require, indicating the direction and nature of other lines connected with that station. Line 3, which commences at the end of line 2, crosses the road to Wimbledon Park and intersects line 6 at 151; a small line from the commencement of line 3 to the end of line 6 forms a triangle as much to check the position of these lines as to take up the curved fence on the left-hand side. Line 3 crosses the post-and-rail fence running alongside line 6, and thence, at the various points indicated, there are offsets on the right to the post-and-rail fence, and on the left to the boundary wall; at 573 there is a station for a tie-line to the commencement of line 1. At 870 and 900 are points whence a small triangle is formed to take up the corner of the boundary wall, whilst at 874·5 is a station for line 9 for the triangle necessary to take up the indentation at the north-west portion of the survey, the end of line 3 being the other point of the triangle on this line at 1296·5, for line 8. From this point also the base-line to the end of line 1 is commenced. Upon page marked (10), is a detailed sketch of lines 8 and 9 before referred to, which needs no explanation. Line 4, beginning at the commencement of line 1, runs to the end of line 3, and crosses the edge of a pond on the right-hand side, the boundaries of which have been fixed by the points where it crossed, and also by offsets; and, further on the right-hand side, the post-and-rail fence was taken up by offsets, and on reaching the end of this line the junction of the two fences was determined by a diagonal offset from the station. From this point the tie-line to the end of line 1 was carefully measured over very undulating ground. The reason for taking this step will now be seen, as from the end of line 1 we were able to survey the two triangles on the left-hand side of line 2 on lines 5, 6, and 7.

In order that the student may the better follow and understand the system of procedure illustrated in the foregoing example, he is recommended to plot this survey from the field book, to a scale of 2 chains to an inch, which will afford him excellent practice both in plotting and in the *modus operandi* with the chain only.

Mark intersection of lines by small circles – In plotting a survey, at all points of intersection of lines with stations it is desirable to draw a very small circle round a point of intersection, and, after the principal lines have been carefully plotted (the exact length being determined by a puncture with a very fine needle before any detail is plotted) it is absolutely necessary that these lines be finally drawn in with lake or carmine. On no account should a survey be plotted from pencil lines.

Best form of base-lines – Previously in this Chapter I expressed an opinion that a survey is best accomplished by treating its two main base-lines as intersecting the estate surveyed in the form of the letter X, and I cannot inpress too strongly upon the student the desirability of doing this wherever practicable. As these lines should form the basis of a complete network of triangulation, it need hardly be said that where possible it is always desirable that the figures formed upon them should be triangles.

Plate 2 is an illustration of a part chain and a part theodolite survey, and, having been first surveyed with the chain only, it is applicable to the present consideration.

Line 1 commences at an acute angle of a fence A and runs to B. A station is left at *b*, for the purpose of tying-in other lines.

PLATE 2

SURVEY OF FIELD PEN-Y-LAN, CARDIFF

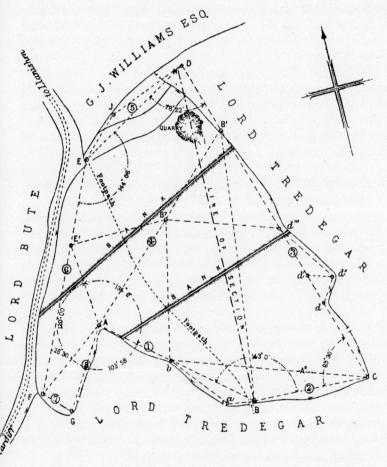

Scale, 6 Chains to an Inch

(to face page 190

Line 2 from B to C is tied to line 1 by the line marked A". Line 3 from C to D is the longest line of the survey, and has upon it stations at d, d', and d''', and B'. From the stations d and d''', a triangle d, d'', d''' is set out for the purpose of taking up an indented fence on the eastern side of line 3, which triangle is tied by the line d' d''. Line 4 from B' is really a tie-line to complete the construction of the chain survey proper, and the lines 3 and 1 are tied in by lines $B^2 d'''$ on line 4 and $B^2 b$ on line 1, while the diagonal line from the end of line 1 at B to B' in line 3 completely secures the figure.

From the end of line 3, line 5 from D to E, and line 6 from E to F, line 7 from F to G, and line 8 from G to A, complete the exterior boundaries of the survey. Lines 6, 7, and 8 are fixed to the other portions of the survey by the tie-lines F A, E' A, and $E' B^2$.

It will be seen that running nearly parallel east and west are two banks or mounds and a footpath shown by a dotted line from E to B. This should be shown in the field book by a sketch in the margin.

Foot-paths and cart-tracks – Foot-paths should always be shown by a single dotted line, cart-tracks by a double dotted line; but in taking the latter it is customary to ascertain the average width, the offsets of which are always taken and booked to the centre thereof unless for very exceptional reasons to the contrary.

Gates – In picking up a gate in a fence it is necessary to fix the position of one of the posts accurately by means of a triangle and then to ascertain the width of the gate; it is not absolutely necessary to take both posts.

How to mark hedge and ditch – It will be seen in the course of this survey that the fences are shown by a strong line, which indicates that it is a hedge; the little T's indicate the ownership of the hedge. In the case of Plate 1 it will be seen that the northern and a greater part of the eastern fence are shown by dotted lines, with crossed dashes; this indicates that it is a post-and-rail fence, and where the line is firm it is evident that it is an ordinary hedge. The north-western fence F H J is a double line, from which it is to be understood that it is a wall.

Avoid crossing fences – On a large survey it often happens that many of the lines cut through a number of fences. It is always advisable to keep hedge crossing to a minimum and if the surveyor can find a high point on or close to the estate to be surveyed where he can command an uninterrupted view of the surrounding country he can often save himself a great deal of time and trouble in deciding the best routes for the survey and base lines. If it is not physically possible to view the site in this way, greater care should be taken in preliminary reconnaissance and in the selection of survey lines.

Be careful not to cut fences unnecessarily – There are many parts of England where the hedges are not only very thick but exceedingly high and it is often necessary to take special precautions in ranging out the survey lines to avoid causing damage to hedges and trees; hacking a way through a fully grown hedge or felling young trees merely to provide adequate lines of sight, if by a slight adjustment of the stations this would be avoided, is inexcusable and can be the cause of a great deal of trouble from irate owners. Care should be exercised, particularly in the country, to see that gates are closed and that the owners and tenants are aware of the operations that are to be carried out.

Clear up the ground after you – After having completed the survey, before leaving the ground insist upon the chain-men removing all pegs and laths, which are often considered not worth carrying away, and pieces of paper that may have been used in the operations. In fact, leave the ground as nearly as possible in the state in which you found it.

Cautions – In putting pegs in the ground, especially in meadow land, care should be observed that they project very slightly above the surface, as otherwise serious injury is often done to cattle and horses grazing thereon.

The chain should be tested every morning before commencing operations.

If a station has been made by driving a peg into the ground, it is necessary to remove the peg if a rod is to remain there for the purpose of chaining to, as it should be exactly in the same position as the peg.

Hints on plotting the survey – General hints in draughtsmanship have already been given in Chapter 1 and the following additional points should be studied when plotting surveys.

Roughly plot the survey-lines – 1st. Roughly plot the chief lines of your survey to see what form it will take, so that you may arrange it symmetrically upon the paper upon which you intend to plot it.

Draw a scale on paper before commencing – 2nd. Before commencing to plot your survey draw the scale upon the paper, so that you may apply your boxwood scales from time to time to ascertain whether the paper has been affected by temperature.

Plot survey north and south – 3rd. Always plot your survey looking north, so that the top, bottom, left, and right respectively represent north, south, west, and east.

Paper perfectly flat – 4th. Keep your paper perfectly flat, and endeavour not to move it from the drawing-table during the process of plotting.

Laying down the survey-lines on paper – 5th. Having made a rough plan of your principal lines, proceed to lay them down carefully upon the permanent paper, commencing with your principal base-lines.

Check measurement – 6th. Measure each line from left to right (using a pricker) upon a faint pencil-line, and check back from right to left and test its accuracy.

Marking stations – 7th. Mark round the puncture representing a station with a pencil-ring thus ⊙, and opposite each station in faint pencil enter the distance, thus 213⊙418.

Straight-edge – 8th. Having plotted your principal base and survey-lines with a steel straight-edge (the longer the better), proceed to draw in these with a fine red line* (carmine or crimson lake), being specially careful that the lines are drawn accurately between the points only.

Never plot from pencil lines – 9th. Under no circumstances plot your offsets or any detail lines from pencil chain-lines.

As to plotting long lines – 10th. If the base or any other lines are longer than your straight-edge, a silk thread stretched tightly between the extreme ends is useful. With a pricker (held perfectly vertical) make punctures at frequent points, then afterwards the straight-edge is applied.

Plot all survey-lines first – 11th. It is much better to plot all the survey-lines previous to commencing details, as any error, if detected, may be adjusted by re-measurement upon the ground, which might seriously affect the position of certain points of offset.

Plot each day's work as soon as possible – 12th. Generally speaking, it is better to plot each day's work as soon as possible after leaving the field.

Examination Questions

1. A triangle L M N of a chain survey has a check line measured from the corner M to a peg P in the line L N. The lengths of the sides L M, M N, N L, are respectively 27·67, 17·24 and 37·50 chains; L P is 22·50 chains, and M P is 12·135 chains. Test by calculation whether the triangle L M N checks correctly.

NOTE: One of the following or any other formulae may be used:

Area of triangle A B C $= \sqrt{[s(s-a)(s-b)(s-c)]} = \frac{1}{2}ab\sin C$ $= \frac{1}{2}bc\sin A = \frac{1}{2}ca\sin B$: where letters in the formulae have their usual meanings.

As a check on a quadrilateral of a chain survey, both diagonals and the distances of their point of intersection from

---

* A good surveyor need never be afraid of leaving the survey-lines upon his plan.

the four corners of the quadrilateral are measured. Indicate how a check, by calculation, upon the quadrilateral may be made.

(*Institution of Municipal Engineers* 1944)

2. Describe concisely how the following obstacles to chain surveying may be overcome without the use of surveying instruments other than the chain, tape, and ranging rods:

   (a) A hill, impeding sighting between stations on a line to be pegged out and chained;

   (b) A building, passable on one side only, which impedes chaining and sighting;

   (c) A wide river, impeding chaining but not sighting;

   (d) A wall of considerable height, impeding both chaining and sighting.

Brief descriptions of detailed operations and of special methods to ensure accuracy of chaining and alignment should be given and illustrated by neat sketches.

(*Institution of Municipal Engineers* 1944)

3. A chain line A E crosses a pond but there is no obstacle to ranging the line across it. To continue with the measurement of distance, however, points B and D to the right and to the left respectively of the chain-line are selected so that the triangle A B D surrounds the pond. The point of intersection C of the main line A E and the line B D is then located. The following distances (in ft.) are as measured: A B 632; B C 227; C D 245; D A 598.

Calculate the distance A C.

(*University of London B.Sc. Estate Management* 1957)

4. Explain and give the sign of the correction which should be applied in the case of:

   (a) The use of a tape that is longer than its stated length.

   (b) A reduced level if the line of sight of the level telescope is inclined upward from the horizontal.

   (c) Chaining down a fairly steep slope.

   (d) The measurement of an angle included between two pointings taken by theodolite on the left face only, if there is a horizontal collimation error of $+10''$ on face left readings.

   (e) An angle taken by sextant between two points at different levels when the horizontal angle is required.

(*Royal Institution of Chartered Surveyors*, 1954)

5. A chain survey is to be made of the area shown in the Plan "W" attached. Illustrate on the plan how you would set out the main chain-lines. Also explain how you would obtain the O.D. level at the manhole marked A.

(*Royal Institution of Chartered Surveyors*, 1958)

PLAN W

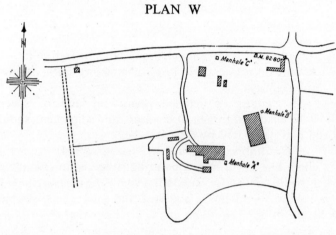

Not to Scale

Chapter 5

AREAS

Table of superficial measures—Averages of fences—Computing by triangles—To ascertain areas upon the ground—The computation scale—How to use computation scale—Various kinds of computation scales—Areas by different scales to plan—Planimeter—Averaging uneven fence lines—Examination questions.

THE surveyor has not performed all his duties when he has plotted and finished his plan, for a matter of the greatest importance next to an accurate survey is to have a true record of the areas of the various properties shown upon the plan, and in this Chapter it is proposed to deal with some of the methods used in obtaining these areas.

The following are the items of superficial measure of chief importance to the surveyor:

Sq. links	*Sq. ft.*	*Sq. yards*	*Sq. perches*	*Sq. chains*	*Roods*	*Acres*
2·296	1					
20·661	9	1				
625	272¼	30¼	1			
10,000	4,356	484	16	1		
25,000	10,890	1,210	40	2½	1	
100,000	43,560	4,840	160	10	4	1

1 Mile a chain wide = 8 Acres.

1 Square Mile { = 640 Acres.
= 3,097,600 Square Yards.
= 27,878,400 ,, Feet. }

To convert Acres into Square Miles multiply by 0·0015625.
To convert Square Yards into Square Miles multiply by 0·000000323.

A strip of land 10 chains long and 1 chain wide is 1 acre; 10

chains = 1 furlong; there are 8 furlongs to a mile; and consequently if 10 sq. chains = 1 acre, then 8 furlongs, 1 chain wide, will give the result of 8 acres per lineal mile.

Suppose we have a piece of ground which measures $23\frac{1}{4}$ chains long and $6\frac{1}{2}$ chains wide, then

$$23 \cdot 25 \times 6 \cdot 5 = 151 \cdot 125 \text{ square chains.}$$

Now if we divide 151·125 by 10 we get 15·1125 acres, the decimal part of which should be multiplied by 4 to reduce it to roods, and the decimal part of the remainder by 40 to reduce it to perches, thus—

	A.	A.	R.	P.
	$15 \cdot 1125 =$	15	0	18.

Averages in fence lines – In practice it is seldom that the boundaries of a parcel of land form a regular figure; the fences or boundaries are usually irregular and it is necessary to adjust them so that the inequalities may be accounted for. Fig. 190 is a simple illustration of this. The boundary fence A B curves in and out, so that it is necessary to establish a mean line that will

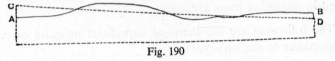

Fig. 190

represent fairly the average. To do this we resort to what is termed a "give-and-take line," as C D; by which those portions of the ground on the top side of C D are ignored, as their area is considered to be equivalent to that of those portions below the line, which are really out of the property.

The same principles apply in the case of a slanting boundary, whence it is necessary to measure to get the mean length between

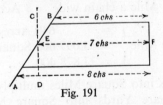

Fig. 191

two parallel boundaries, as in Fig. 191. Here, on the left of the property, is a fence running diagonally, whose length on the

top side is 6 chains, and on the bottom side 8 chains. To get
the mean length of course we can say $\dfrac{6+8}{2} = 7$ chains, but in
practice a little judgment will enable one to arrive at a fairly
accurate result.

By triangles – The most simple, and indeed most satisfactory,
method of computing areas is by means of triangles. Thus,
if upon the plan to be measured a sheet of tracing-paper is
spread and securely fastened, then, with a fine pencil, let the
whole area be divided into triangles, each of which (beginning at
the top) should be consecutively numbered, and at the boundaries let the indentations of the fence be carefully treated on
the give-and-take principle. This being done, lines perpendicular
to the longest sides of each triangle should be dotted, and these,
together with the longest sides, should now be accurately
measured, and the dimensions scheduled as in the following
example, Fig. 192. Here we have a property – the internal fences

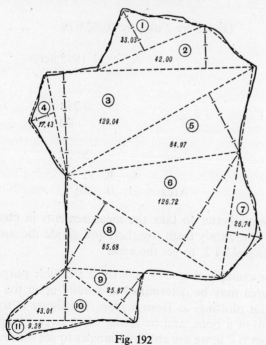

Fig. 192

being purposely left out – the area of which it is necessary to compute. It will be seen that it has been divided into eleven triangles, the sides of some of which have been arranged so as to "give and take" the inequalities of the boundaries. The dotted lines show the triangulation, while the perpendiculars are delineated by a dot and cross-stroke. The following is the schedule:

Triangle No.	1.	$9·05 \times 3·65 =$	$33·03$	sq. chains.
„	2.	$12·00 \times 3·50 =$	$42·00$	„
„	3.	$16·05 \times 8·04 =$	$129·04$	„
„	4.	$8·30 \times 2·10 =$	$17·43$	„
„	5.	$16·50 \times 5·15 =$	$84·98$	„
„	6.	$14·40 \times 8·80 =$	$126·72$	„
„	7.	$9·62 \times 2·78 =$	$26·74$	„
„	8.	$14·40 \times 5·95 =$	$85·68$	„
„	9.	$6·90 \times 3·75 =$	$25·88$	„
„	10.	$9·82 \times 4·38 =$	$43·01$	„
„	11.	$5·80 \times 1·60 =$	$9·28$	„

Divide by 2 and by 10)623·79   „

31·1895 acres.
4

0·758
40

30·32

A.   R.   P.
Area = 31   0 $30\frac{1}{4}$

It is always better to take the measurements in chains and decimals, to multiply them together, and divide the sum of the whole triangles by 2, to get the area.

Another example, Fig. 193, will serve a double purpose, viz. how the area may be determined as readily upon the ground and without plotting, as from a plan. The figure is somewhat in the form of a boot, and by laying out a large triangle A B E and another D C B, we are able by triangles to get the area of the

greater portion of the field without much trouble. Upon the
line A E of the larger triangle set up ordinates $a\,b$, $c\,d$, $e\,f$, $g\,h$,

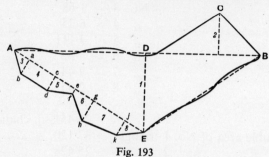

Fig. 193

and $j\,k$. Then the area of each space 3 to 8 may be obtained as
follows:

3.   A $a = 1\cdot40$
         $\times a\,b = 1\cdot20$
         —————
         $1\cdot68$ area.

4. $a\,b = 1\cdot20$
         $+c\,d = 1\cdot30$
         —————
         $2\cdot50$
         $\times a\,c = 2\cdot50$
         —————
         $6\cdot25$ area.

5. $c\,d = 1\cdot30$
         $+e\,f = 0\cdot40$
         —————
         $1\cdot70$
         $\times c\,e = 1\cdot83$
         —————
         $3\cdot111$ area.

6. $e\,f = 0\cdot40$
         $+g\,h = 1\cdot80$
         —————
         $2\cdot20$
         $\times e\,g = 1\cdot60$
         —————
         $3\cdot52$ area.

7. $g\,h = 1\cdot80$
         $+j\,k = 1\cdot40$
         —————
         $3\cdot20$
         $\times g\,j = 2\cdot95$
         —————
         $9\cdot44$ area.

8. $j\,k = 1\cdot40$
         $\times j\,\text{E} = 1\cdot75$
         —————
         $2\cdot45$ area.

All the foregoing are double areas, 3 and 8 being triangles, the
sides A a and j E are respectively multiplied by $a\,b$ and $j\,k$. The
areas 4, 5, 6, and 7 have their two ends *added* together, and the

sum multiplied by the distance apart. They may be tabulated as follows:

$$\begin{aligned}
\text{No. } 3 &= 1\cdot68 \\
\text{,, } 4 &= 6\cdot25 \\
\text{,, } 5 &= 3\cdot111 \\
\text{,, } 6 &= 3\cdot52 \\
\text{,, } 7 &= 9\cdot44 \\
\text{,, } 8 &= 2\cdot45
\end{aligned}$$

$$26\cdot451 \text{ sq. chains.}$$

Add double area of No. 1 triangle $= 87\cdot120$,,
,, ,, 2 ,, $= 25\cdot428$,,

Divide by 2 and by 10)138·999

6·94995 acres area.
4

3·7998
40

31·9920

Total area, 6 A. 3 R. 32 P.

The double area of No. 1 triangle is $14\cdot40 \times 6\cdot05 = 87\cdot12$; and No. 2 is $8\cdot15 \times 3\cdot12 = 25\cdot428$.

Ascertaining areas on ground – In Fig. 194 is illustrated Simpson's method of computing the area of an irregular piece

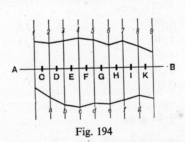

Fig. 194

of ground, either with or without plotting. In this case the line A B should be measured as near as possible in the middle of the plot, and marks should be left in the ground at the end of each chain: lines at right angles should be drawn through these points, and should be measured.

The following rule applies in this case:

1st. The first and last lengths should be added together separately.

2nd. Now add the 2nd, 4th, 6th, and 8th lengths together, and multiply the result by 4.

3rd. Take 3rd, 5th, and 7th lengths, and multiply their sum by 2.

4th. Collect all these sums together, multiply by the common distance, or 100 links, and one-third of the product will be the area.*

Example: (1st)   (2nd)   (3rd)

	(1st)	(2nd)	(3rd)
A = 300 links.		a 2 = 350 links.	b 3 = 400 links.
B = 300 ,,		c 4 = 450 ,,	d 5 = 430 ,,
		e 6 = 400 ,,	f 7 = 400 ,,
600 ,,		g 8 = 350 ,,	
(4th) 6,200 ,,			1,230 ,,
2,460 ,,		1,550 ,,	2
9,260 ,,		4	2,460 ,,
100		6,200 ,,	
3)926,000 ,,			
308,666 ,, = 3 A. 0 R. 13·87 P.—*Ans.*			

Another and simpler way, but at the same time somewhat approximate, is to mark every half-chain, so that an imaginary line through C, D, E, F, G, H, I, K, will give a mean length of the strips, 1 2, 2 3, 3 4, 4 5, 5 6, 6 7, 7 8, 8 9. If these lengths are

* This only applies to an even number of strips which must be numbered as in the figure.

added together and the result multiplied by 100, we shall have the area, as follows:

Example C = 325
,,   D = 375
,,   E = 425
,,   F = 440
,,   G = 415
,,   H = 400
,,   I = 375
,,   K = 325
          ——————
          3,075
          100
          ——————
          307,500 = 3 A. 0 R. 12 P.–*Ans.*

The slight discordance between this result and that gained in the same example above, shows the necessity of adhering to the previous and more accurate method, although it must be noted that neither of these is so simple nor so satisfactory as the method of computing areas by means of triangles.

Computation scale – This last example serves as an excellent introduction to the computation scale, for the principles involved are precisely the same. For this, it is customary to prepare a piece of tracing-paper with horizontal lines a certain distance apart, drawn in blue. This distance between the lines is so arranged that a scale divided especially for the purpose, and moved from left to right between any two lines, shall record the area of the strip according to the length traversed. Thus, as a simple illustration, suppose we have spans of one quarter of an inch, and use a scale of four chains to an inch, the span would thus represent one chain. If we apply the scale to the left end of the span, and read ten chains on our scale, we shall have obtained an area of one acre; and supposing we were to measure the whole length of a 12-inch scale, which would give 48 chains, then we should record 4 acres and $8\frac{1}{10}$ths of another acre, or 4 A. 3 R. 8 P.

Now, what is done is to place the sheet of tracing-paper upon the plan to be computed and carefully fasten it down, taking

care that one of the parallel lines cuts the most extreme point of the top of the plan; then, as each span will pass through the boundaries of the property, so may the area be computed.

Plate 3 is a practical illustration of the method of ascertaining the acreage by means of the computing scale. It represents a plan of an estate, drawn to a scale of 4 chains to an inch, over which is placed (and fastened down with drawing-pins) a sheet of tracing-paper, upon which have been carefully drawn blue lines $\frac{1}{4}$ inch apart. For convenience of illustration these parallel lines are shown dotted. It will be seen that the line A B impinges on the extreme north of the plan, and the vertical lines A and B have been judged to equalise the whole area of that portion of the property which lies between the lines A B and C D. That portion which is hatched is excluded from computation as being equal in area to the ground traversed by the line A B and which is exterior to the actual boundary. The same applies to the points at C D, E F, G H, I J, K L, etc.

The computing scale, which is fully illustrated in the plate, is shown in position upon the plan, having traversed from the line A B to J' K'. It consists of a boxwood scale – in this case – 1 ft. 7 in. long, 1 $\frac{1}{4}$ in. wide, and $\frac{1}{4}$ in. thick. It has an undercut groove along its centre in which travels the tongue A A (Fig. 195), to which is attached, by means of the screw-handles D D, the frame

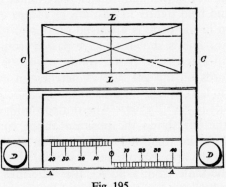

Fig. 195

C C, which passes over the side of the rule and lies flat upon the paper on which the rule is placed when in use. The handles D D enable the tongue and attached frame to be moved freely in the groove. The scale on the upper and lower side of the groove is divided into six equal parts of $2\frac{1}{2}$ in. each, representing 6 acres (10 chains a chain wide being an acre, will to the scale of 4 chains to 1 in. be $2\frac{1}{2}$ in. by $\frac{1}{4}$ in.), and each of these is subdivided into 4 parts representing roods. The scale as illustrated is divided into acres and roods, from 1 to 6 reading from left to right, and from 6 to 12 from right to left, so that when the tongue and frame have traversed the full length of the scale to 6 acres it may be moved back and will record acres, etc., from 6 to 12. Upon the tongue is an index drawn across its centre, and on each side of this index a distance equal to one of the subdivisions on the rule is divided into 40 equal parts to represent perches. These divisions are placed, those on the left side of the index to read with the divisions of the scale on the upper side of the groove, and those on the right of the index to read with the divisions on the under side of the groove.

In some scales the frame carries a piece of thin horn or perspex on which are ruled two lines parallel to the rule, at a distance apart which represents a chain, and the centre of this enclosure being determined by the intersections of its diagonals, a line L L, called the index line, is drawn through this centre at right angles to the parallel lines, and in the same straight line with the index on the brass tongue. But many scales are made with small holes pierced at L L, through which a piece of fine wire or thread is passed and held tightly in position by means of screws. The scale shown in the plate is arranged on this principle, and the index wire or line is shown to have passed from left to right, from zero to 2 acres and past 2 roods, whilst the index on the tongue records on the left side 21 perches (of course reading from right to left) so that the area of the space between the lines from J' to K' is 2 A. 2 R. 21 P. The dotted outline of the index frame on the left shows the position at the commencement, whilst that on the right shows its position at the end of the scale, so that the arm, having only traversed about one-half the length of the scale from J' to K', the scale must be carefully taken up and adjusted so that the index line cuts the "give-and-take" line of the next span from L' to M', and so on until the full length of the scale has been run. Referring to the plate, it will be seen that the progress of the index frame from A to B was 0 A. 1 R. 24 P., and having been moved to C it reads 1 A.

1 R. 0 P. at D, 2 A. 2 R. 1 P. at F, 3 A. 3 R. 26 P. at H, 5 A. 1 R. 18 P. at J, and we arrive at the extent of the scale before we can reach L, consequently when the index is at 6 A. 0 R. 0 P. as at *a*, we mark the point with a fine pencil-line.

Here I would say that in this, as in all surveying operations, I advise working from left to right, and consequently I should prefer the lower portion of the scale to be divided from 6 to 12, working left to right, instead of the way in which it is shown. It will be seen that I have used it in this case, as I advocate, instead of retracing our steps from 6 to 12, to do which I have added the readings on the upper scale to 6, 12, 18, 24, and 30 acres as the case has been, so that from *a* to N the scale recorded 0 A. 3 R. 21 P., therefore 6 A. +0 A. 3 R. 21 P. = 6 A. 3 R. 21 P., and so on until *b*, *c*, *d*, and *e*. Thus, in the position of the scale at J′ K′ we have had *five* changes of *six* acres, and a length from *e* to K′ of 2 A. 2 R. 21 P., or a total area from A B to J′ K′ of 32 A. 2 R. 21 P.

Various kinds of computing-scales – There are numerous types of computing-scales, some of a universal character, and others so constructed that instead of the frame working upon a tongue, the groove is made to receive strips of very thin box-wood, upon which are divided scales of from 1 to 6 chains to an inch, and the various Ordnance scales.

Areas by different scales to plan – The scale illustrated in the plate is of a simple and reliable character; and while it is advisable to have computing-scales of the various scales, yet it is quite possible to arrive at an accurate estimate of the area of property drawn to a different scale from that of the computer. For instance, suppose we have a plan 5 chains to an inch, the area of which it is desired to ascertain, but our computing-scale is 3 chains to an inch. As an example, we will assume that the operation of computation gives a result of 6 A. 2 R. 0 P. with the scale. Now, as 5 chains to an inch is much smaller than 3 chains, then the area will necessarily be greater, so that if we treat it as a rule-of-three sum we shall get the correct result, but the student should remember that as we are dealing with areas, it is as the square of three is to the square of five, so is the known area to that required. So that, having the area with the 3 chain scale of 6 A. 2 R. 0 P., we proceed as follows: $3^2 : 5^2 :: 6$ A. 2 R. 0 P. : 18 A. 0 R. 8 P. 26 yds. 8 ft. = area of the plan drawn to a scale of 5 chains to an inch.

Planimeter – Another method of ascertaining the areas of a plan is by means of an instrument known as the planimeter which is illustrated in Fig. 196. This instrument has two bars hinged together. At the extremity of one bar is a weight suspended over a needle point which is used to anchor the bar *outside* the area to be measured and about which all other points move.

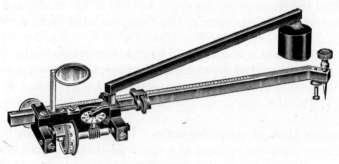

Fig. 196

The end of the second bar has a pointer which is moved around the boundary of the areas to be measured in a clockwise direction. At the other end of this bar there is a small roller which touches the paper and revolves as the pointer is moved. Coupled to this roller is a geared scale and fixed vernier on which the number of square inches can be read off when the area has been traversed by the pointer.

In order to use the instrument the needle weight is fixed outside the area and a pencil mark made at any point on the boundary from which the pointer is to commence and terminate. It is not necessary to set the scale to zero but merely to note the reading of the counter-disc, roller scale and vernier. The tracing point is then moved along the boundary in a clockwise direction, taking care to trace the boundary lines exactly, until it arrives at the starting point. The scales are then read again and the original reading deducted when the remainder will give the number of square inches enclosed within the area. In order to

determine the true area of the land in question it will be necessary to multiply this result by the scale to which the plan is drawn. For example, suppose the reading of the scales before use is 11·40 and 24·85 after tracing the boundary of the area of land. The area traced out is then $24·85 - 11·40 = 13·45$ square inches. If the plan is drawn to a scale of, say, 2 chains to 1 inch, then since 1 square inch of paper $= 2 \times 2$ chains (i.e. 4 sq. chains) the true area of the land will be:
$13·45 \times 4$ sq. chains $= 53·80$ sq. chains or 5·38 acres.

The accuracy of the planimeter should be tested regularly and this is carried out by carefully drawing a square of, say, 6 inch sides and tracing around the boundary with the instrument.

Averaging uneven fence lines with the parallel ruler – A knowledge of this simple process is often extremely useful when areas have to be scaled. Taking Fig. 197 as an example, the small irregularities are first of all averaged with a transparent set-square into a series of straight lines, the points at which these intersect each other being numbered as shown in the figure.

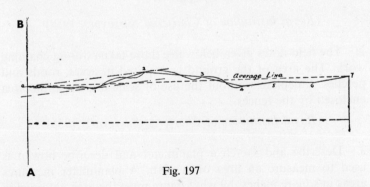

Fig. 197

One of the side fence lines is then produced as A B. The edge of the parallel ruler is now placed against the commencing point 0 and the point marked 2. It is then drawn back until the edge touches the point marked 1. Keeping it in this position, the pricker is inserted in the line A B, and against the edge of the ruler. Retaining the pricker here, the ruler is swung round until its edge lies against the pricker needle and the point numbered 3. It is then pushed forward until its edge touches the point 2, when the pricker is again inserted in the line A B. This process is repeated until the last point No. 7 is reached. When this occurs, the last point at which the pricker is inserted, *i.e.* after the parallel ruler has been placed against point 6, is connected with the point 7 and is the average line required.

Examination Questions

1. Find the area in square yards enclosed by the straight boundaries joining the points A, B, C, D, E, F, A whose co-ordinates are:

	Eastings ft.	Northings ft.
A	250	75
B	550	175
C	700	425
D	675	675
E	450	675
F	150	425
A	250	75

(*Royal Institution of Chartered Surveyors*, 1958)

2. The field notes given below are those taken during chaining work. The area of the ground is required in acres, roods and perches. Calculate, without the use of scale drawings, the area enclosed by the fences.

(*Royal Institution of Chartered Surveyors*, 1955)

3. Describe and sketch a planimeter and describe how it is used to measure an area on a plan. A planimeter measures areas in square inches, by what figure must the area obtained in square inches be multiplied to give the true area in acres if the scale of the plan is:

(a) 6 inches to 1 mile, (b) 1/500.

Describe briefly one other method of measuring an irregular area on a plan.

(*Institution of Municipal Engineers*, 1958)

Field notes for Question 2

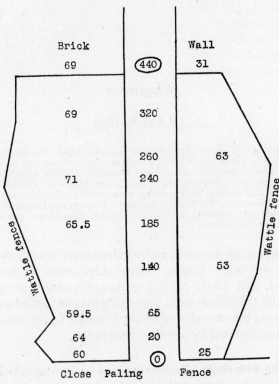

(All measurements in feet.)

4. Calculate the area in acres enclosed by the polygon A B C D E F A, using latitudes and longitudes derived from the data tabulated. The calculations may be made by slide rule.

Line	Latitudes (ft.)		Longitudes (ft.)	
	N	S	E	W
AB	150·5	—	146·4	—
BC	12·4	—	262·7	—
CD	—	201·7	120·7	—
DE	—	231·5	—	204·7
EF	208·4	—	—	120·9
FA	61·9	—	—	204·2

(*Institution of Municipal Engineers*, 1949)

Chapter 6

TRAVERSING

Traversing with chain—Traversing by included angles—Northings and southings in traversing—Closing a traverse—Necessity for care in checking—Relative positions of bearings—Magnetic variation or declination—Isogonic lines—Making and plotting a closed traverse—Field work—Internal and external angles—Office work plotting—Quadrant angle or reduced bearing—Whole circle bearings—Traverse calculation sheet—Methods of adjusting errors in traverse—Bowditch's method—Examination questions.

WHILE surveying proper is entirely dependent upon a system of triangles or other figures, whose sides must be accurately measured, and whose relative points of intersection must be tied in with the greatest care, traversing may be termed a method of following the meandering of any irregular figure, whose sides shall be determined by angular observation.

Traversing with chain – Traversing may be accomplished with a chain only, but this method is open to great objection, as inaccuracies may find their way into the work itself, and there is no real check upon its accuracy.

I illustrate by Fig. 198 the general principles of a chain traverse, and it will be obvious to those who have read the preceding chapters that little or no dependence should be placed upon the relative positions of lines to each other, which rely solely upon the measurement of a short length at the extremities of lines. Take the lines A B, B C, C D, D E, and E F (Fig. 198), whose directions are entirely dependent upon the care with which the triangles *a b* B, *c* C D, D *d e*, and E *f g* are taken, not only as effecting the measurement upon the ground, but more particularly the subsequent operation of plotting; for, unlike a chain survey of a series of triangles and check lines, there is nothing in an open chain traverse to guarantee the accuracy of the work. Upon fairly level ground, in the enforced absence of instruments, it may be admissible to ascertain the relative positions of diverging lines by some such method, but even so I should strongly advise the use of an optical square to establish the triangles, which, wherever practicable, should be *right angled;* but in undulating ground I do not hesitate to say that chain traversing is inadmissible.

Traversing by included angles* – Traversing may also be performed by taking the included angles A B C, B C D, C D E, and D E F (Fig. 198) either with a box-sextant or, preferably, a theodolite. These angles having been accurately observed, and

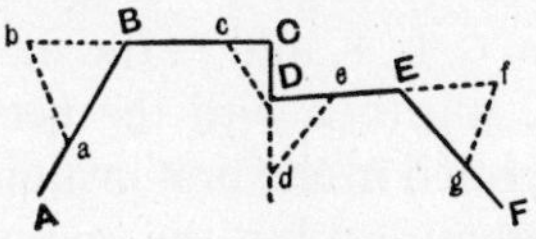

Fig. 198

the lengths, A B, B C, C D, D E, and E F carefully measured, the survey may be plotted with a straight-edge and protractor, but the greatest care is necessary, for it is only what is called an "unclosed" traverse.

One method of traversing is by taking the "bearing" of each line by observations from magnetic north, as is illustrated in Fig. 201, which shows an unclosed traverse; in other words, the survey has no means of being adjusted to its starting point, either from real cause or option. If we were to take such a figure as an octagon (Fig. 199), and work all round its eight sides at the points A, B, C, D, E, F, G, and H, then, if we had observed the necessary care in taking the angles, when we closed from H upon A we should find our work would prove itself. But in the case of Fig. 201, which is the traverse survey of a meandering road on either side of which are dense plantations, in terminating our work at F we have nothing to guarantee its

* This is known as the "back angle" method.

accuracy, as it is impossible to command the starting point A. If we could do so it would enable us to test our work.

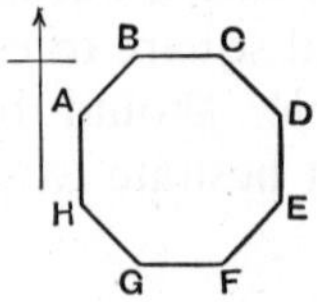

Fig. 199

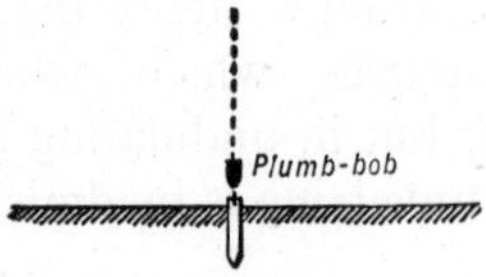

Fig. 200

Now, in commencing a traverse, or any operations in which the compass is used, it is imperative to guard against any metallic attraction, as even with the most studious care traversing is a very delicate process. It is necessary to carefully select your stations, and by means of pegs or other means to mark the various points, as A, B, C, D, E, and F; the measuring of the lines between these points, together with the necessary offsets right and left, may be performed in the first instance or subsequent to the instrumental observations, but the one operation should be distinct from the other. Possibly it would be more convenient to have the survey made first, so that the angles and other information may be neatly entered in the book in their proper order and place. It should be noted that after the instrument has been adjusted, the upper and lower plates being clamped at zero (and duly levelled, care having been taken to firmly plant it exactly over the point of intersection of the line*), and when the zero of the upper and lower plate has been made to coincide with magnetic north, that the lower plate should be firmly clamped, and on no account must it be touched either by accident or intent, otherwise the work will be in error. Now having taken all these necessary precautions, the instrument being placed at A (Fig. 201), direct the telescope to a rod held on the peg at B, being careful that the wires intersect the spike of the rod. In the illustration the angle which B makes with magnetic north at A is 50 deg. on the A vernier and 310 deg. on that at B;† now remove the instrument to B, with the upper plate

---

* This is best accomplished by driving a brass-headed nail in the centre of the peg, and let the point of the plumb-bob be coincident with it. See Fig. 200.

† Most theodolites have their verniers marked A and B, the former being used to take the angle proper and the latter as a check.

still clamped at 50 deg., and, after having adjusted it, direct the telescope back to A, and by means of the tangent-screw see that the wires exactly cut the bottom of the rod.

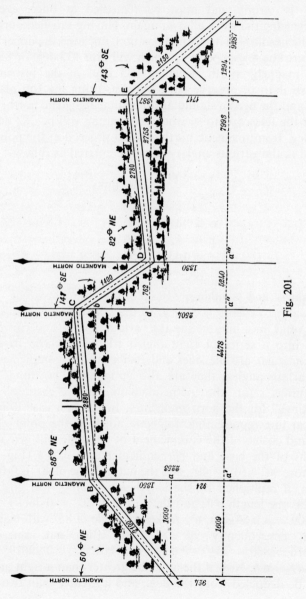

Fig. 201

Having intersected the point A, unclamp the upper plate and bring it to zero; the result should be that the needle will record magnetic north, if not, something is wrong and must be remedied at once, even to commencing the work all over again. Having satisfied ourselves that the needle is in its normal position, unclamp the upper plate and turn the telescope to C, which will give 135 deg. or 85 deg. from magnetic north. Keeping 135 deg. in the instrument, remove it to C, observe back upon B, bring the top plate to zero, and the needle should again assume magnetic north. Next direct the telescope to D, when the reading will be 282 deg. or 147 deg. from magnetic north, and so proceed at the points D, E, and F; the various angles should be entered as follows:

$$
\begin{aligned}
A &= 360° \\
B &= \ \ 50°
\end{aligned} \Big\} \ 2100 \text{ links.}
$$

$$
\begin{aligned}
C &= \ \ 85° & 2880 & \quad ,, \\
D &= 147° & 1400 & \quad ,, \\
E &= \ \ 82° & 2780 & \quad ,, \\
F &= 143° & 2150 & \quad ,,
\end{aligned}
$$

Northings and southings – In plotting the foregoing it is necessary, to ensure accuracy, to draw a series of vertical and horizontal lines intersecting the various points, and converting them into a series of right-angled triangles, whose base and perpendicular are the sines and cosines of the complements of the various angles; they are also designated "northings" and "southings" for the perpendiculars, and "eastings" and "westings" for the horizontal lines. In the first case draw the vertical line representing magnetic north at the point A. The sine and cosine of the complement of an angle will give us the lengths of the base and perpendicular as A a, a B (Fig. 201), therefore $90° - 50° = 40°$, and the natural sine of 40° is 0·64279, which, if multiplied by the length A B = 2100, will give 1350 links as the length a B; and the cosine of $40° = 0·76604 \times 2100 = 1609 = $ A a. Again, B C makes an angle of 85° with magnetic north, consequently $90° - 85° = 5°$, then nat. sin. $5° = 0·08716 \times 2880 = 251 = b$ C, or nat. cos. $5° = 0·99619 \times 2880 = 2869 = $ B b. Now if the angle be greater than a right angle it must be deducted from 180 deg., and if greater than two right angles then from 270 deg., and if greater than 270 deg. then from 360 deg. Thus in the case of D the angle being 147 deg., we must deduct it from 180 deg.; thus $180° - 147° = 33°$, and nat. sin. $33° = 0·54464 \times 1400 = 762 = d$ D, nat. cos. $33° = 0·83867 \times 1400 = 1174 = d$ C; and in like manner all the various sides may be calculated which are tabulated as under:

				HYP.	BASE	PER.
A B	$90°-$	$50° =$	$40°$	2100	1609	1350
C	$90°-$	$85° =$	$5°$	2880	2869	251
D	$180°-$	$145° =$	$33°$	1400	762	1174
E	$90°-$	$82° =$	$8°$	2780	2753	387
F	$180°-$	$143° =$	$37°$	2150	1294	1717

But these calculations are not alone sufficient to ensure accuracy, as it is necessary to treat an unclosed traverse somewhat in a similar manner to plotting a section. Referring again to Fig. 201, it will be seen that f E is 1717, and e E is 387, therefore ef is $1717 - 387 = 1330$; d D, D e are in one straight line, consequently $a'' d$ is 1330, and d C is 1174, whilst $d b$ is $1174 - 251 = 923$, and b B is parallel to A a, therefore $a'' d + d b = 1330 + 923 = 2253 = a'$ B; consequently if we mark on the line A' F the horizontal distances A' a', A' a'', A' a''', A' f, and f F, which are 1609, 4478, 5240, 7993, and 9287, and then plot A' A $= 924$, a' B $= 2253$, a'' C $= 2504$, a''' D $= 1330$, f E $= 1717$, we shall have satisfactorily accomplished our traverse, and assured ourselves as far as we are able as to its accuracy. If it be possible, with the instrument at F, to command a station at A', then taking the last angle, viz. $143°$ from $180° = 37°$, consequently E F A' $= 53°$; if, therefore, from F an angle E F A' of $53°$ be set out it should give a point 924 links below A, which is of course an important check equally as the length A' F could it be accurately chained, which would give 9287 links.

Closing a traverse – Whenever possible, it is essential to close a traverse, even to the extent of working back to your starting point by a circuitous route, as illustrated in Fig. 202. Having run from A to B, C, D, E, and F, (the work required to be done), it would be preferable to continue back to A by the zigzag route F G, G H, H J, J K, and K A; and although it would be more satisfactory to have the lengths of these lines as well as their bearings, yet it is not absolutely necessary, as the sum of the angles will give (if the observations be carefully taken), the result of working back on to A as we commenced.

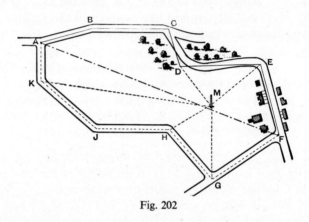

Fig. 202

Care in checking – In taking angles from magnetic north it is necessary to be very careful that the readings are correct; and as an additional check upon the work, especially in a close survey, it is desirable to take frequent objects, such as the chimney at M in Fig. 202, to which observations may be made at the points D, E, F, G, H, and K.

Relative position of bearings – In booking the bearings, it is desirable to have them in their proper order. For instance, all angles less than 90 deg. will be N.E.; between 90 deg. and 180 deg. S.E.; between 180 deg. and 270 deg. S.W.; and between 270 deg. and 360 deg. N.W. When it is possible to take the included angle between points such as E F G (Fig. 202), it is, of course, very desirable to do so.

Magnetic variation – It is necessary to make allowance for what is termed the magnetic declination or variation which alters each year. At the beginning of the century (1904) the magnetic declination at Greenwich was 16° 17′ W. In the year 1934 it was 11° 27′ W. In 1954 it was 8° 30′ W. and in 1974 it will be about 5° 20′ W. It will be seen that the declination decreases about 9′ per annum.

"Isogonic" lines are the irregular lines which pass through places of equal declination as, for instance, a line joining the Isle of Wight and the Humber which is about 1° more than at Greenwich. In fact the further west or north we go in the British Isles the greater becomes the declination. On a line through the Scilly Isles and Edinburgh it is some 3° more than at Greenwich.

It is necessary, therefore, when plotting to ascertain the correct declination for the date and place and when drawing the north point on a plan the magnetic north taken from the bearings of the survey is first of all drawn, followed by the true north meridian.

Making and plotting a closed traverse – The student often finds some difficulty in the field and office work when running a closed traverse. It is essential that he fully understands the procedure. In particular, examiners are very fond of setting questions on traversing in most professional examinations on surveying.

This chapter will, therefore, conclude with a more detailed description of the work that is necessary in this important branch of surveying.

A. Field work – It cannot be overstated that a traverse should always be closed wherever possible, even to the extent of running a number of additional chain lines in order to end at the starting point. An exception will sometimes arise when surveying between two points, both positions of which have been previously determined, since there will be a check on the work and to close the traverse in such a case would be unnecessary.

The two methods of conducting a traverse have already been referred to (i.e. (i) the "back-angle" method of reading the included angles and (ii) the "bearings" method of taking the angle contained by the survey lines and the magnetic meridian). Of the two methods the first is probably the most satisfactory because it allows for "repetition" of angles and other instrumental refinements which help to reduce errors and it also provides a perfect field check on the work by a well known geometrical proposition. Both methods, however, have their advantages and disadvantages and both are in general use.

The geometrical proof referred to above concerns the angles of any polygon and is as follows:

1. When the *internal* angles of a closed traverse are taken the sum of all the angles, *plus* four right angles = twice as many right angles as the figure has sides.
2. When the *external* angles of a closed traverse are taken the sum of all the angles, *minus* four right angles = twice as many right angles as the figure has sides.

As an example refer to Fig. 203 (A and B) which shows the chain lines of a simple closed traverse.

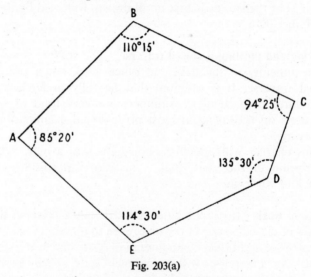

Fig. 203(a)

(a) Taking the internal angles (Fig. 203A) A, E, D, C, B.

B A E	85°	20'
A E D	114°	30'
E D C	135°	30'
D C B	94°	25'
C B A	110°	15'

	540°	0'
add 4 rt. angles	360°	0'
	900°	0'

Geometric proof: The figure has 5 sides so that twice the number of right angles = $10 \times 90° = 900°$ 0' which shows that the field work is correct.

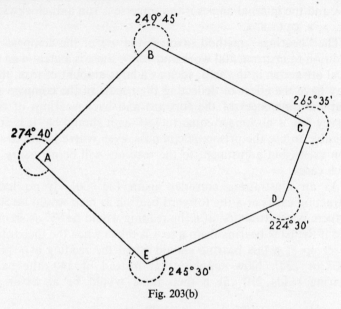

Fig. 203(b)

(b) Taking the external angles, A, B, C, D, E (Fig. 203B).

B A E	274°	40'
C B A	249°	45'
D C B	265°	35'
E D C	224°	30'
A E D	245°	30'

	1260°	0'
less 4 rt. angles	360°	0'
	900°	0'

It is seldom that the field work will come out exactly as the example above and the allowable error would depend upon the importance and size of the survey and the magnitude of the error. In general terms the error should not be more than $\sqrt{N}$ minutes where N is the number of angles taken in the traverse.

Since the scale of the ordinary theodolite reads in a clockwise direction it would be more convenient to read the external angles if the traverse is run in a clockwise direction A, B, C, D, E, A and the internal angles if the traverse is run anti-clockwise, viz, A, E, D, C, B, A.

The "bearings" method involves the use of the compass in addition to instrumental work and where there is a great deal of local attraction in the area, such as a large amount of iron, this may have the effect of deflecting the needle of the compass so that the differences of the forward and back bearings of the survey line is no longer equal to 180° as it should be. It is still possible to use the prismatic compass, even where local attraction exists, but adjustment to the readings will be necessary in such cases.

As an illustration, consider again Fig. 201. If no local attraction exists at A the forward bearing as read would be 50°. If there is no attraction at B the reading would be 85° as shown and if the back bearing from B to A is taken when the theodolite is set up at B this bearing should equal the reading at A plus 180° or 230°. Now suppose that instead of 230° the back bearing reads 210° at B then there would be an error of

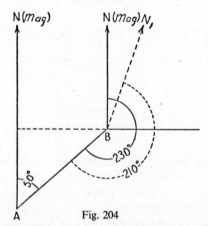

Fig. 204

230° − 210° = 20° N.E. and if a careful check does not show an error in manipulation, it is due to local attraction and adjustment at station B must be made accordingly. This is shown diagrammatically in Fig. 204 where N shows the true magnetic meridian at station A and B, N_1 the compass direction due to local magnetic attraction at B = 20° N.E.

B. Office work – Plotting – One method of plotting would be to use a protractor and a scale but this is inaccurate and is seldom undertaken. The almost universal method is plotting by rectangular co-ordinates.

It is usual to plot on squared paper but this is not essential although it helps considerably with the work if it is used. What is important is to work systematically throughout the whole operation of plotting and "reducing" a traverse. If this is kept in mind much of the initial difficulties usually experienced by the student will disappear.

The principle of plotting by rectangular co-ordinates expressed in its simplest form is the fixing of the survey lines in direction by trigonometrical calculation after the angles, taken in the field traverse, have been reduced to a standard form. As an illustration refer to Fig. 205. The survey line is shown in direction A B making an angle of 50° with the magnetic meridian A N. If A B chains, say, 350 links it will be clear that the direction could be readily calculated by trigonometry since the length A B is known and the angle N A B is also known. By erecting a right-angle triangle so that A B forms the hypotenuse and A N the base containing the right angle, the direction A B can be exactly fixed by calculation. The whole traverse is thus built up on a series of right-angle triangles as will be described.

The whole of a traverse is plotted from one base line, known as the *primitive line of direction*. This can be either a horizontal or vertical line. The *origin* of the traverse (i.e. point of commencement of the traverse) may be on this line or at any point to the east of it. The example given in Fig. 203 is again used in Fig. 205 to demonstrate the plotting of a closed traverse.

The line X Y is the "primitive line of direction" from which the Latitudes (i.e. the vertical lines) are worked out and plotted.

The point A is the Origin from which all Departures (i.e. lateral distances) are plotted. The position of B is obtained by calculation. Now the chain-line A B lies in a north-easterly direction and is the hypotenuse of the triangle A N B. In Fig. 203(b) the external angle B A E was shown as 274° 40′ but the angle required is the angle N A B (Fig. 205). In order to obtain this

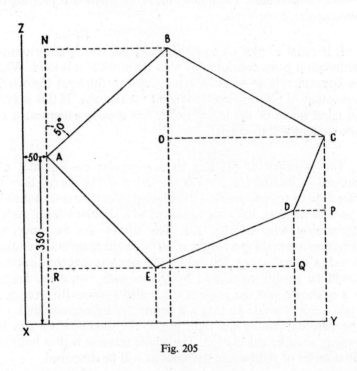

Fig. 205

angle (and the remaining angles required to plot the whole traverse) the following procedure is adopted:

The bearing of each line must be calculated as a *Quadrant Angle* or *Reduced Bearing* east or west of north or east or west of south. The reduced bearings are obtained from the *Whole Circle Bearings* which are the angular direction of the survey lines from magnetic north measured in a clockwise direction from 0° – 360°. (In Fig. 204 the angle N B A of 230° is the whole circle bearing. The angle N A B 50° is the quadrant bearing or reduced bearing).

In order to obtain the reduced bearing it is first necessary to determine the W.C.B. The bearing of A E = N 135° 20′ E. (Fig. 206). If to this is added the internal angle at E and 180° is

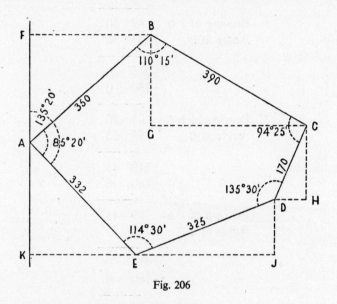

Fig. 206

subtracted the result is the bearing E D (i.e. bearing A E = 135° 20′+114° 30′ (internal angle A E D) = 249° 50′−180° = 69° 50′ which is the bearing of E D).

The general rule for obtaining the bearing of a line is to add the bearing of the previous line to the included angle between the two lines and subtract 180°. If, however, after adding the internal angle to the previous bearing the result is less than 180°, then 180° must be *added* and not subtracted.

The same rule applies where the *excluded* angles are taken but if the result of adding the bearing of the previous line to the excluded angle between the two lines is more than 360°, then 360° is deducted instead of 180°.

It is wise to tabulate the results as follows:

Bearing of A E	135°	20'
Angle at E	114°	30'

	249°	50'
	−180°	0'

Bearing of E D	69°	50'
Angle at D	135°	30'

	205°	20'
	−180°	0'

Bearing of D C	25°	20'
Angle at C	94°	25'

	119°	45'
	+180°	0'

Bearing of C B	299°	45'
Angle at B	110°	15'

	410°	0'
	−180°	0'

Bearing of B A	230°	0'
Angle at A	85°	20'

	315°	20'
	−180°	0'

Bearing of A E	135°	20'

It will be seen that the results obtained by tabulating the workings gives a check on the calculations.

The next step is to work out the Reduced (Quadrant) Bearings. The calculations are quite simple and are as follows:
  (a) If the W.C.B. is less than 90° the R.B. will be east of north and the same as the W.C.B.

(b) If the W.C.B. is between 90° and 180° the R.B. will be east of south and will be found by subtracting the W.C.B. from 180°.

(c) If the W.C.B. is between 180° and 270° the R.B. will be west of south and would be found by subtracting 180° from the W.C.B.

(d) If the W.C.B. is between 270° and 360° the R.B. will be west of north and would be found by subtracting the W.C.B. from 360°.

The following table summarises the above:

Quadrant	W.C.B.	R.B. (or Q.B.)
N.E.	0° to 90°	W.C.B.
S.E.	90° ,, 180°	180° − W.C.B.
S.W.	180° ,, 270°	W.C.B. − 180°
N.W.	270° ,, 360°	360° − W.C.B.

Before working out the traverse from the calculation sheet it would be better to tabulate the results obtained.

The student should work out and reduce the included angles of the traverse himself, compiling the Traverse Sheet and finding the error of closure. The following worked example shows the tabular forms and traverse calculation sheet of the same example but with the *excluded* angles and clockwise direction of traversing.

The working of the bearings is left for the student to practice. The following table shows one method of tabulating the results obtained.

Line	W.C.B.	R.B. (or Q.B.)	Length (links)
AB	50° 0′	N 50° 0′ E	350
BC	119° 45′	S 60° 15′ E	390
CD	205° 20′	S 25° 20′ W	170
DE	249° 50′	S 69° 50′ W	325
EA	315° 20′	N 44° 40′ W	332
			1,567

Note that the chainage lengths are shown in the last column.

Assume that the co-ordinates of station A to be 350 links N and 50 links E, the traverse sheet is prepared as shown in the following table (see Fig. 205).

TRAVERSE SHEET

Station	Line	R.B.	Working	N.	S.	E.	W.	Co-ordinates Lat.	Dep.
A								350	50
	AF	N 50° 0' E	Log 350 2·5441 / Log Cos 50° $\bar{1}$·8081 = 2·3522	225					
	FB		Log 350 2·5441 / Log Sin 50° $\bar{1}$·8843 = 2·4284			268·1			
B								575	318·1
	BG	S 60° 15' E	Log 390 2·5911 / Log Cos 60° 15' $\bar{1}$·6957 = 2·2868		193·6				
	GC		Log 390 2·5911 / Log Sin 60° 15' $\bar{1}$·9385 = 2·5296			338·6			
C								381·4	656·7
	CH	S 25° 20' W	Log 170 2·2304 / Log Cos 25° 20' $\bar{1}$·9561 = 2·1865		153·7				
	HD		Log 170 2·2304 / Log Sin 25° 20' $\bar{1}$·6313 = 1·8617				72·7		
D								227·7	584·0
	DJ	S 69° 50' W	Log 325 2·5119 / Log Cos 69° 50' $\bar{1}$·5373 = 2·0492		112				
	JE		Log 325 2·5119 / Log Sin 69° 50' $\bar{1}$·9725 = 2·4844				305		
E								115·7	279·0
	AK	N 44° 40' W	Log 332 2·5211 / Log Cos 44° 40' $\bar{1}$·8519 = 2·3730	236					
	EK		Log 332 2·5211 / Log Sin 44° 40' $\bar{1}$·8470 = 2·3681				233·4		
A								351·7	45·6
				461 / 459·3	459·3	606·7	611·1 / 606·7	351·7 / 350·0	50·0 / 45·6
				1·7			4·4	1·7	4·4

The closing error is 1·7 links in latitude and 4·4 links in departure. The closing error is thus $\sqrt{1\cdot7^2+4\cdot4^2} = \sqrt{22\cdot25} = 4\cdot72$ links.

This would ordinarily be too great in a traverse of this size – it is only shown here to demonstrate the method of finding and correcting the errors.

The degree of accuracy of the chainage of any traverse of importance should be about 1 in 1,000, so that the closing error in the above example should not be more than about 1·5 links. Since the angles were proved correct the chainage should be run again and the error rectified and adjusted in further calculation.

Methods of adjusting errors in traverse – The same example will now be used to illustrate how small closing errors are adjusted, although it must be emphasised that in actual practice this particular chainage error would have to be reduced before the work could be accepted as accurate.

1. The error is more likely to occur along the longest side of the traverse and where the closing error is small the line in question may be adjusted. The direction of the bearing may provide a clue as to the source of the error.

2. A more correct procedure would be to distribute the closing error proportionally in the lengths of the sides of the traverse. In the case under consideration the error in latitude is 1·7 links and in departure 4·4 links and these would be distributed as follows:

Latitude	Departure
$A F = \dfrac{350}{1567} \times 1\cdot7 = 0\cdot4$	$F B = \dfrac{350}{1567} \times 4\cdot4 = 1\cdot0$
$B G = \dfrac{390}{1567} \times 1\cdot7 = 0\cdot4$	$G C = \dfrac{390}{1567} \times 4\cdot4 = 1\cdot1$
$C H = \dfrac{170}{1567} \times 1\cdot7 = 0\cdot2$	$H D = \dfrac{170}{1567} \times 4\cdot4 = 0\cdot5$
$D J = \dfrac{325}{1567} \times 1\cdot7 = 0\cdot3$	$J E = \dfrac{325}{1567} \times 4\cdot4 = 0\cdot9$
$E K = \dfrac{332}{1567} \times 1\cdot7 = 0\cdot4$	$K A = \dfrac{332}{1567} \times 4\cdot4 = 0\cdot9$

Total error (latitude) 1·7 links Total error (departure) 4·4 links

Q

The results of the corrections may be tabulated thus:

Line	N.	S.	E.	W.	Lat.	Dep.
					350	50
AB	224·6				574·6	319·1
			269·1		380·6	658·8
BC		194				
			339·7		226·7	586·6
CD		153·9				
				72·2	114·4	282·5
DE		112·3				
				304·1	350·0	50·0
EA	235·6					
				232·5		
	460·2	460·2	608·8	608·8		

3. A third method of correcting the closing error is graphically. The traverse is plotted as shown in Fig. 207 (A and B) from the measured lengths and bearings, but because of the

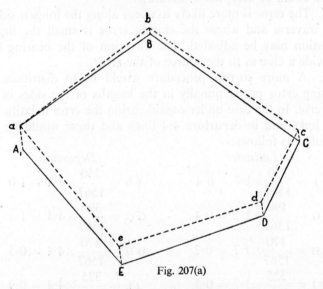

Fig. 207(a)

closing error the point A_1 does not close on the commencing point A as it should do if the traverse has been correct. It is therefore necessary to adjust all the lines in proportion so that A_1 and A will converge and the error will be properly distributed.

Draw a straight line A A₁ (Fig. 207(b)) to a smaller scale than the plotted traverse and mark off to represent the total length of the traverse. Mark off along this line the various lengths of the traverse sides A B, B C, C D, D E, E A. From A set off A-1 to a larger scale than the plotted traverse and to represent the length

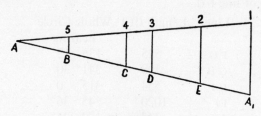

Fig. 207(b)

of the closing error. Draw parallel to this line B-2, C-3, D-4, E-5, cutting the lines A A₁ and A-1, then these distances are those by which the points B, C, D and E have to be moved to the correct scale as shown by the broken perimeter line on the plotted traverse.

4. Bowditch's method is similar to the graphical method described in (3) above.

The traverse is plotted as in Fig. 207(a) and as before A A₁ is the closing error. A A₁ is again joined by a broken line and the remaining intermediates B, C, D and E are drawn parallel to A A₁

$$\text{B } b \text{ is then equal to } \frac{\text{A B}}{\text{sum of lengths of all lines}}$$

$$\text{C } c \text{ to } \frac{\text{A B+B C}}{\text{sum of length of all lines}}$$

$$\text{D } d \text{ to } \frac{\text{A B+B C+C D}}{\text{sum of length of all lines}} \text{ and finally,}$$

$$\text{E } e \text{ to } \frac{\text{A B+B C+C D+D E}}{\text{sum of lengths of all lines}}$$

The dotted line A, B, C, D, E, A is then the corrected traverse.

Examination Questions

1. Describe, in relation to suitable diagrams, graphical methods of adjusting rough traverse surveys (a) by altering lengths and bearings of lines and (b) by altering lengths only.

(*University of London B.Sc. Estate Management*, 1957)

2. The following are the first three columns of a table for finding the latitudes and departures of a closed traverse. Apply the usual check to the angles, complete the table and calculate the latitudes and departures for each of the five lines. Show how to balance the survey and find the corrected latitudes and departures of line F G.

Line	Length (ft.)	Whole Circle Bearing
F G	525	136° 12'
G H	798	241° 30'
H I	554	315° 0'
I J	1020	45° 36'
J F	347	179° 24'

(*Institution of Municipal Engineers*, 1949)

3. The following lengths, latitudes and departures refer to a closed traverse A B C D E A;

	Length	Latitude	Departure
A B	3425·9	0	3425·9
B C	938·2	812·6	469·1
C D	4573·4	2287·1	−3961·0
D E	2651·3	−2295·7	−1325·9
E A	1606·4	−803·0	1391·1

Adjust the traverse by the Bowditch Method, finding the corrected latitudes and departures to the nearest 0·1 ft.

Discuss the merits and demerits of this method, with particular reference to its effect on lines C D and D E.

(*University of London B.Sc.(Eng.*), 1956)

4. The figures tabulated below refer to a theodolite traverse run from station A, 780·49 ft. west 2231·20 ft. north, to station B, 534·07 ft. west 2108·75 ft. north. Compute the traverse and give the adjusted co-ordinates of the traverse stations 1, 2 and 3.

Station	Corrected Bearing from North	Length, in feet
A-1	82° 49'	121·2
1-2	77° 51'	92·6
2-3	33° 17'	85·2
3-B	182° 48'	228·6

(*Institution of Civil Engineers*, April 1958)

5. A boundary line A B of length 2,000 ft. is to be set out in a direction N. 75° E. Station A has been set out in the field but as B cannot be set directly from A a traverse A X Y Z has been run, the observations being as follows:

Line	Length – ft.	Bearing
A X	652	113°
X Y	876	86°
Y Z	803	32°

Compute the required bearing and distance for setting out B from Z.

(*Royal Institution of Chartered Surveyors*, 1955)

6. From the information given below determine the rectangular co-ordinates of the points B, C and D with relation to A distributing any errors systematically. Point B lies N. 42° 30′ E. of A, and C is to the East of B.

Included Angles		Length in feet	
A B C =	120° 40′ 30″	A B	915
B C D =	92° 29′ 30″	B C	765
C D A =	81° 15′ 00″	C D	939
D A B =	65° 35′ 00″	D A	1290

(*Institution of Civil Engineers, April* 1957)

7. A theodolite and chain traverse resulted in the records given below. If the bearing of A B was S. 57° 16′ E. and the co-ordinates of A 10,000 ft. N. 5,000 ft. E., determine the co-ordinates of the points B, C and D.

Side	Length-ft.	Clockwise angles	
A B	569·2	A B C	293° 03′
B C	918·3	B C D	307° 52′
C D	630·2	C D A	228° 39′
D A	321·1	D A B	250° 26′

(*Royal Institution of Chartered Surveyors*, 1957)

8. The following table gives a summary of the observations extracted from a field book for a closed traverse survey.

Prepare a table of co-ordinates to enable the survey to be plotted. The whole circle bearing of the line A B is 10° 26′ east of north.

Line	Length-ft.	Internal angles	
A B	413	A B C	149° 57′
B C	164	B C D	54° 17′
C D	859	C D A	38° 13′
D A	489	D A B	117° 45′

(*Institution of Municipal Engineers*, 1958)

Chapter 7

TOWN-SURVEYING

Marking stations in streets—Taking angles—Objections to lamp-posts, &c.—Taking observations in crooked streets—The chain—When to take angles—Do not erase figures in book—Use arrows for counting—Buildings—Lamp-posts, gullies, etc.—Streams—Plotting—Photographic and aerial surveying.

To make a survey of a town or even a village is by no means an easy task, added to which it is a very tedious proceeding, for it seldom happens that lines of any great length can be arranged. It is desirable, however, that when possible a base-line should be taken through the town from end to end, in order to tie all the other lines on to it. Triangulation is almost impossible owing to the irregularity of the streets. It is equally out of the question to do town-surveying without an instrument for taking the angles of the various lines.

The surveyor should provide himself with a skeleton plan of the principal thoroughfares, upon which he should lay out such lines as appear to him feasible and then proceed to examine them upon the ground. Having determined upon some of the chief lines, he should establish stations, where possible using hydrants or manhole covers to mark the spot. In the absence of such, he will have to drive down iron spikes or "dogs" into the pavement, for which purpose he should be provided with a small steel bar and a fairly heavy hammer. Wherever possible the base-lines should be run along the kerbs so as to avoid traffic. The spikes should be of $\frac{3}{8}$-in. iron and from $2\frac{1}{2}$ in. to 4 in. long, pointed at one end. They should be driven well home and their position very carefully observed by means of a detail sketch, with several measurements from well-defined points, as in Fig. 208, taking distances from the four angles of Cross Street and Dale Street; or, as in Fig. 209, with two distances from the

angles of Church Lane and High Street, and from the end of
the "Crown Inn" and from a point measured along the face of

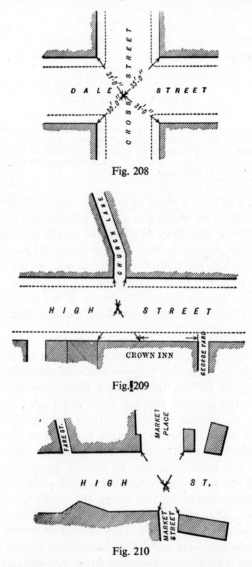

Fig. 208

Fig. 209

Fig. 210

the hotel from George Yard; or, in Fig. 210, from the two angles
of the Market Place and those of Market Street.

Town-surveying requires great care and patience, with a very considerable amount of methodical organisation. It resolves itself into three distinct operations after the lines and stations have been determined: 1, the observation of the angles; 2, the chainage of the lines between these points; and 3, the detail measurement of the yards, gardens, buildings, etc.

Taking angles – There are two ways of taking the angles. First by taking (with theodolite or prismatic compass) the angle which a street or road makes with the magnetic meridian; but this cannot be recommended in towns (although in villages it may be more practicable), in consequence of the numerous sources of attraction to the needle, such as electrical interference, lamp-posts, hydrants, man-holes, iron railways, etc. By the second and most reliable method the included angles of one or more lines are taken with the theodolite as illustrated in Fig. 211, where a line along Station Road terminates at the junction of three streets. Here the theodolite should be planted, and after being carefully adjusted, the angle between Station Road and

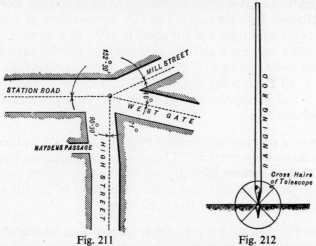

Fig. 211   Fig. 212

High Street (90° 30'), between High Street and West Gate (71°), and between West Gate and Mill Street (46°), should be observed; the sum of which should be 207° 30'. Now take the angle between Station Road and Mill Street, which should be 152° 30', or the difference between 360° and 207° 30'.

Objection to lamp-posts, etc. – Observations should not be taken onto lamp-posts, corners of houses, etc. In the first place they can only be of a temporary character, and a lamp-post is not sufficiently defined for the purpose. If spikes are driven in the streets or roads at points of intersection, it is more accurate for a chain-man to hold the point of the rod upon the spike, and observations are taken at the centre of this point only. I cannot impress upon the student too strongly the necessity of observing the bottom of the rod as in Fig. 212 in *all* surveying operations, whether it be simple chain-surveying or with a theodolite. By this means we have an absolute point upon which our instrument will in turn be placed, so that with necessary care all our observations should be accurate, and judgment (often very misleading) as to which is the actual centre of a far distant lamp-post is obviated.

In consequence of the circuitous nature of many streets in European towns – which, unlike American cities, were evidently never laid out with any idea that it would be necessary to survey them – it is often impossible to get a straight line from end to end. Take the case of Fig. 213. Here we have, at A, to take the two angles right and left equal to 180°. At B we should take the angle between A and Bemer Street, and that between Bemer Street and C, whilst to test our work we must observe the angle C B A, all three being equal to 360°; at C, the included angle B C D and its supplement; at D, all four angles, which should equal 360 deg.

Now a very natural question might be asked: "Yes, I see how you do such a street, and if I have taken the angles and distances between the points correctly, all well and good: but how do I know that it will all fit on to the other parts of the survey?" I will endeavour to clear this question up.

In Fig. 214 we have a sketch map of part of the town of Leatherhead, of which it was desired to make a detailed survey. It was found impossible to run a larger base-line through the principal streets than the line A B, about 1,200 ft.; but C D, 2,050 ft., could be tied on to the other portion of the survey outside the town, and as it is always best to take the longest line for a base we adopted C D. It so happened that A B is so situated that it was possible to set out the line at right angles to C D, which of course was of immense advantage. But with the

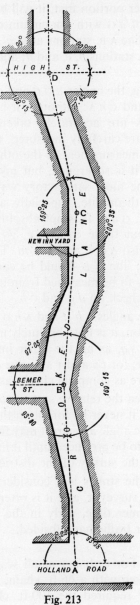

Fig. 213

exception of the short line $g\,h$, this is the only case in which it was possible.

Taking the upper portion first, it will be seen that G C at the ends of C D and of a G with A B circumscribed this portion of the town; on the line A B, stations at a, a', b', c', e', and n were left, whilst on G C, stations b, c, and d; and on the upper part of C D, h and l.

Strictly speaking, the angles a G C and G C D should be taken as well as G a B and C n A; although it is argued that if these latter two angles are accurately taken, and the distances G a, $a\,n$, and n C are carefully measured, then by calculation in the one case and measurement in the other the length G C will be proved. I say it is so argued, but my own opinion is that whilst about it the most satisfactory way will be to take the angles with the theodolite, especially as we must take the angles G $b\,e$, G $c\,f$, G $d\,g$. It is not absolutely necessary to take the angle $b\,e\,f$, but those $c\,f\,j$, $f\,j\,g$, $g\,j\,k$, and $k\,l$ C are imperative; as are also A b' E and A c' m. The angle A a' E is not necessary, but the line a' E should be carefully measured as a tie; $g\,h$ needs only to be measured from its two terminal points and will act as a check on $d\,g$ and C h.

Similarly, if the angles A $b'\,t$ and A n D be carefully observed in the lower portion, it is not absolutely necessary to take more than $b'\,t\,n$ and $u\,s\,q$, as all the other lines tend to check the trapesium b' F D n; for $t\,n$ and $v\,x$ in one direction and $r\,y'$ and $x\,z$ in the other are as complete checks as can be wanted.

Thus will be seen the relative systems to be adopted in street surveying, but let it never be forgotten that there should be no question about the angle any street may form with another. The line C D was able to be produced until it fitted into the system of triangulation for the survey of the district around the town.

The traffic in the streets is a considerable drawback to the operations of the surveyor, and it is often necessary to arrange the work in summer time, early in the morning or after the evening rush-hour traffic has subsided.

As to the chain – For ordinary small scale plans the measurements may be taken with a 66-ft. chain, but when great detail and accuracy are required the 100-ft. chain is the best. The offsets should be taken in feet and inches with a tape; those at right angles to the chain-line require the greatest care and are

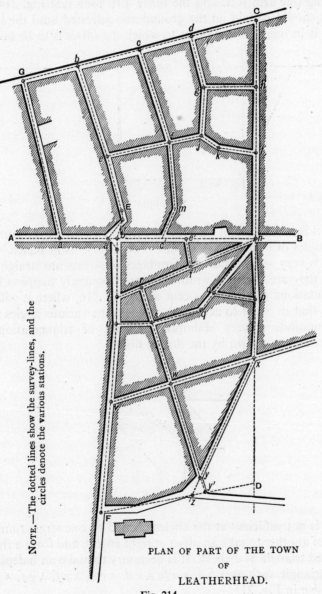

PLAN OF PART OF THE TOWN

OF

LEATHERHEAD.

Fig. 214

NOTE.—The dotted lines show the survey-lines, and the circles denote the various stations.

best set out with an ordinary square (as it is seldom from the narrowness of the streets, that an optical square can be used) having one arm 6 ft. and the other 4 ft. long (see Fig. 214A). This should be laid on the ground and adjusted until the long arm is in line with the point to which the offset is to be taken.

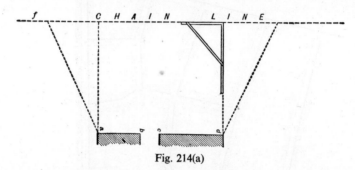

Fig. 214(a)

But it is not sufficient to trust to such offsets to fix the corners or angles of buildings. A tie-line is necessary, as in sketch.

It is very seldom that the frontages of streets are straight or that they are of equal width. It more frequently happens that indentations of all kinds occur as in Fig. 216, where it will be seen that in order to accurately take up the various angles and indentations a very elaborate network of triangulation is necessary, as shown by the dotted lines.

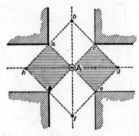

Fig. 215

It is not sufficient at the angles formed by one street running out of another to take an offset at right angles, and form a right-angled triangle as a check. It is necessary to make an independent triangle such as A *b c*, A *a b*, A *c d*, A *e d*, A *e f*, A *g f*, A *g h*, or A *h a* in Fig. 215.

The diamond formed by those triangles which are hatched need not necessarily be taken, but it is quite as well to have the thing complete, especially at important points.

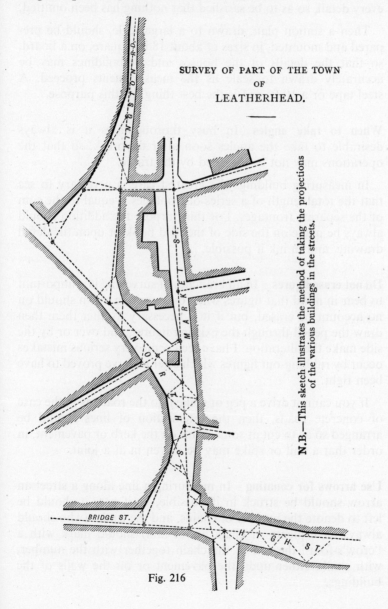

SURVEY OF PART OF THE TOWN
OF
LEATHERHEAD.

N.B.—This sketch illustrates the method of taking the projections of the various buildings in the streets.

Fig. 216

When the outlines of the streets have been surveyed and plotted, the surveyor should make a careful tracing of sections of the work, and then carefully walk over the route to examine every detail, so as to be satisfied that nothing has been omitted.

Then a station plan, drawn to a large scale, should be prepared and mounted, in sizes of about 18 in. square, on a board, so that the details of the houses and outbuildings may be accurately drawn to scale as the measurements proceed. A steel tape or a 10-ft. rod is the best thing for this purpose.

When to take angles – In busy thoroughfares it is always desirable to take the angles soon after daybreak, so that the operations may not be impeded by the traffic.

In measuring buildings the greatest care is necessary to see that the total length of a series of frontages is equal to the sum of the separate frontages. For this purpose the addition should always be made on the side of the field book or upon the detail drawing, and in ink if possible.

Do not erase figures – In all branches of surveying it is important to bear in mind that figures when once written down should on no account be erased, but if it is necessary to alter them then draw the pencil through the existing figures, and over or by the side make the alteration. I have seen some very serious mistakes occur by rubbing-out figures which after all have proved to have been right.

If you cannot drive a peg or spike into the road, as in the case of concrete roads, then the intersection of lines should be arranged so as to cut at some point on the kerb or pavement, in order that a nail or spike may be driven in at a joint.

Use arrows for counting – In measuring a line along a street an arrow should be struck in if possible, or if not, it should be left to denote the number of chains, and the leader (who should always have plenty of chalk about him) should mark with a "crow's-foot" the end of the chain together with the number, with chalk, either upon the pavement or on the walls of the buildings.

As to buildings – Outhouses should be specified in the field book. Churches, chapels, schools, and all public buildings should be carefully noted. Also public-houses, inns, etc.

Lamp-posts, gullies, etc. – The position of lamp-posts, gullies, ventilators, sluice-valves, hydrants, manholes, etc., must be taken *en route* and carefully plotted on the plan.

Streams – Should a street or road cross over a river or stream the full particulars thereof must be noted; and by an arrow the direction of the flow should be indicated. Or in the case of a railway crossing over or being crossed by a street, the direction of its commencement and termination, should be ascertained and marked upon the plan. The nature of the street or road should be observed – whether gravel, macadam, granite-pitched, wood, asphalte, concrete, etc. And the pavement, whether York paving, artificial stone, asphalte, concrete, brick-on-edge, gravel, etc. The boundaries of the various parishes must be ascertained and carefully plotted. The parliamentary or municipal boundaries, or those of wards, must also be shown. Each road or street must be plainly marked with its name, and the thoroughfares at the outside of the survey should have written in italics the places to or whence they lead.

Plotting – The survey of a town or parish should *always* be plotted so as to be north and south; in other words, the top of the sheet is north and the left and right sides are west and east respectively.

Photographic and aerial surveying – Photogrammetry is briefly dealt with in Chapter 12 under the heading "Geodesy and specialised surveying" to which the student is referred.

R

Chapter 8

LEVELLING

Definition—Curvature of the earth—Allowance for the earth's curvature—Refraction—Necessary adjustments—Simple levelling—Compound levelling—Datum—Plotting levels—Ordnance datum—Ordnance bench marks—Flying levels—Bench marks—Position of Bench marks—Different kinds of levelling—Level-book—Foot-plates—Keeping the level-book—Making up the level-book—Collimation method—Levelling-staff, how to use it—Distances—Measuring across streams—Levelling on hills, etc.—Instructions to staff-holder—Plenty of information—Taking level of water—Levelling with theodolite—Permissable error in levelling—Levelling with aneroid—Cross-sections—Precise levelling—Examination questions.

LEVELLING is the art of finding the difference between two points which are vertically at different distances from a plane parallel with the horizon. Take the ocean or a sheet of water, the calm surface of which is in a plane parallel with the horizon, then the bank or beach that is above the water-line at certain points is relatively higher in level than the water itself. Thus in Fig. 217,

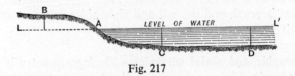

Fig. 217

where A represents the impingement of the water upon the slopes of the stream, B is relatively higher, and C and D lower, than the horizontal line L L'.

This is a very primitive description of what levelling means, but it is nevertheless a true one.

The earth's curvature – There is a very important consideration in reference to this question, and that is, that the earth being spherical in form, strictly speaking two points are only truly level when they are equidistant from the centre of the earth.

Also, one place is higher than another, or out of level with it, when it is further from the centre of the earth; and a line equally distant from that centre, in all its points, is called the *line of true level*. Hence, because the earth is round, that line must be a curve, and make a part of the earth's circumference, or at least be parallel to it and concentrical with it, as the line P F D B C E Q (Fig. 218), which has all its points equally distant from A, the centre of the earth considered as a perfect globe.

But the line of sight F′ D′ B C′ E′, given by the operation of levels, is a tangent or right line perpendicular to the semidiameter of the earth at the point of contact B, rising always higher above the true line of level the farther the distances, and is called *the apparent true level*. Thus C′ C is the height of apparent above the true level, at the distance B C from B; also

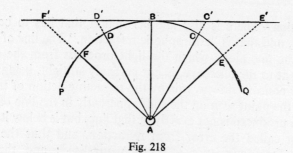

Fig. 218

E′ E is the excess of height at E. The difference between the true and the apparent level, it is evident, is always equal to the excess of the secant of the arc of distance above the radius of the earth.

Now the difference C C′ between the true and apparent level, at any distance B C or B C′, may be found thus: by a well-known property of the circle 2 A C + C C′ : B C′ :: B C′ : C C′; or, because the diameter of the earth is so great with respect to the line C C′ at all distances to which the operation of levelling commonly extends, that 2 A C may be safely taken for 2 A C+ C C' in that proportion, without any sensible error, it will be, as

$$2\,\text{A\,C} : \text{B\,C}' :: \text{B\,C}' : \text{C\,C}'; \quad \text{C\,C}' \text{ therefore } = \frac{\text{B\,C}'^2}{2\,\text{A\,C}'} \text{ or } \frac{\text{B\,C}^2}{2\,\text{A\,C}}$$

nearly; that is, the difference between the true and apparent level is equal to the square of the distance between the places, divided by the diameter of the earth; and consequently is always proportional to the square of the distance.

Taking the mean diameter of the earth (2 A C), as 41,781,097 feet = 501,373,164 inches, and the distance B C = 1 mile = 63,360 inches:

$$\frac{\text{B\,C}^2}{2\,\text{A\,C}} = \frac{63,360^2}{501,373,164} = \frac{4,014,489,600}{501,373,164} = 8 \text{ inches in one mile,}$$

which is the difference between the apparent and the true level.

Refraction – There is also another matter that has to be considered, and that is "atmospheric refraction." The line of sight, being the line along which the light proceeds from the object looked at to the telescope, is not perfectly straight, being made slightly concave downwards by the refracting action of the air. Hence the point seen on the staff apparently in the line of collimation produced is not exactly in that line, but is below it by an amount called the error from refraction, and thus the error arising from curvature is partly neutralised; and the correction to be subtracted for curvature and refraction usually is somewhat less than the correction for curvature alone.

The error produced by refraction varies very much with the state of the atmosphere, having been found to range from one-half to one-tenth of the correction for curvature, and in some cases to vary even more. Its value cannot be expressed with certainty by any known formula; but when it becomes necessary to allow for it, it may be assumed to be on an average 0·154 of the correction for curvature; so that the joint correction for curvature and refraction to be subtracted from the reading of the staff is as shown in the following table:

Distance, or B C	Deduct	Distance, or B C	Deduct
Feet	Decimals of a foot	Miles	Feet Dec.
300	0·002	¼	0·035
600	0·007	½	0·141
900	0·016	¾	0·318
1200	0·029	1	0·564
1500	0·046	1½	1·270
1800	0·066	2	2·258
2100	0·089	2½	3·528
2400	0·117	3	5·081
2700	0·148	3½	6·914
3000	0·182	4	9·032
3300	0·220	4½	11·431
3600	0·262	5	14·112
3900	0·308	5½	17·077
		6	20·322

Thus, if the staff be 600 feet from the instrument, and the cross-wires cut 10·50 feet, we must deduct for correction of curvature and refraction 0·007 of a foot from this reading, which should now be 10·493 feet.

Professor Rankine expresses an opinion that "the errors produced by curvature and refraction are neutralised when back and fore sights are taken to staves at equal or nearly equal distances from the level. At distances not exceeding ten chains they are so small that they may be neglected. The uncertainty of the curvature and refraction makes it advisable to avoid, in exact levelling, all sights at distances exceeding about a quarter of a mile."

Adjustments – Before proceeding to level it is necessary to attend to the temporary adjustments, which require to be made each time the instrument is set up, as follows:

1. To plant the legs of the instrument firmly in the ground, taking care that the parallel plates are made as horizontal as possible.

2. To level the instrument, that is, to place the vertical axis truly vertical.

3. To adjust the telescope for the prevention of "parallax," that is, to bring the foci of the glasses to the cross-wires, look through the telescope, and shift the eye-piece in and out until the cross-wires are seen with perfect distinctness. Then direct the

telescope to some well-defined distant object, and by means of the milled-head screw, adjust the focus until the image of the object is seen sharp and clear, coinciding apparently with the cross-wire. This latter part of the adjustment must be made anew for each new object at a different distance from the preceding one. The nearer the object the further the inner tube must be drawn out.

A good test of the adjustment for parallax is to move the head from side to side while looking through the telescope. If the adjustment is perfect, the image of the object will seem steadily to coincide with the cross-wires; if imperfect, the image will seem to waver as the head is moved. If the image seems to shift to the opposite direction to the head, the inner tube must be drawn out further; if in the same direction, it must be drawn inwards.

Levelling is of two kinds, simple and compound. Simple levelling has only one line of collimation, whilst compound levelling entails constant changes of collimation, and hence the necessity for extreme accuracy in the work and care in the adjustment of the instrument. In the case of Fig. 219 the instrument is placed equally between A and B, and the telescope being directed towards A, the line of collimation cuts the staff at 5·70 (this being the first reading is called the "back-sight");* the telescope is then reversed, and the reading appears 11·68, consequently, by the invariable rule that if the intermediate or fore-sights are greater than the back-sights they are "falls," and if less "rises;" in the present case it is a fall of 5·98 feet from A to B. Here I would refer to a query which is frequently put by students: "How does the height of the instrument affect the result?" The height of the instrument has nothing whatever to do with the operation of levelling. For instance, in the case of Fig. 219, the line of collimation being an imaginary line parallel with the horizon, the heights which are taken at A and B are in reality the depths of the surface of the ground at those points below the line of collimation, consequently it does not matter whether the instrument is 4 or 40 feet above the surface of the ground.

---

* In levelling, the first sight after the level has been planted and adjusted is always the "back-sight," and the very last sight before the instrument is removed is the "fore-sight:" all others are "intermediates."

Compound levelling consists of following the undulation of the ground along a line of section, by means of varying lines of collimation, according to the rise or fall of the ground.

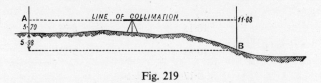

Fig. 219

Fig. 220 is a simple illustration of my meaning. The instrument is placed equidistant between A and B, and the reading of the staff at A is 4·10, while that at B is 10·15, showing a fall of 6·05. Next remove the level to *b* and establish a new line of collimation. Now where in the previous case was a fore-sight 10·15, the instrument now reads on the same staff 5·30 as a back-sight, consequently the line of collimation is 4·85 lower than that from A to B. Now turn the telescope towards C for a fore-sight 10·63, and then move the instrument to *c*. Here again

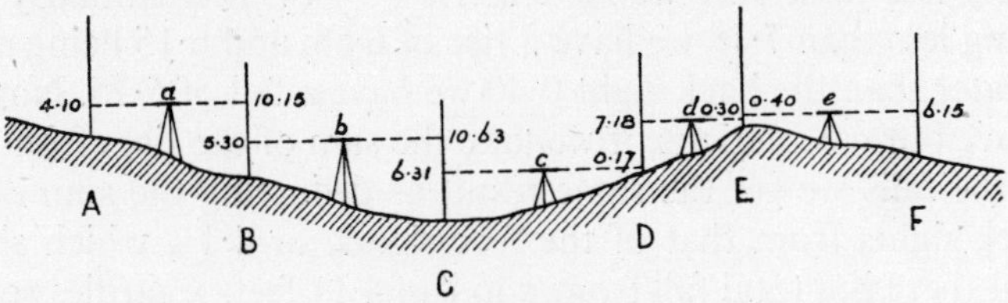

Fig. 220

our line of collimation is lower, its exact depth being determined by reading off the staff at C a back-sight of 6·31, which gives a fall 4·32. Reverse the telescope for a fore-sight at D of 0·17, now move the level to *d* on higher ground, and we find that the line of collimation cuts the staff at D for a back-sight at 7·18, or a rise of 7·01. At E the fore-sight is 0·30, whilst a back-sight from the level at *e* to E is only 0·40, showing the last line of collimation to be only 0·10 higher than the one from D to E, the staff at F showing a fore-sight of 6·15 shows a fall of 5·75 from E to F. We will now tabulate these results, and for the moment I shall only deal with two columns for the readings of back- and fore-sights, and the ordinary "rise" and "fall" columns.

Back-sight	Fore-sight	Rise	Fall
4·10			
	10·15		6·05
5·30			
	10·63		5·33
6·31			
	0·17	6·14	
7·18			
	0·30	6·88	
0·40			
	6·15		5·75
———	———	———	———
23·29	27·40	13·02	17·13
	23·29		13·02
	———		———
	4·11		4·11

We see that by taking the less from the greater we get rises or falls, as follows: 10·15 being greater than 4·10 is a fall of 6·05, 10·63 being greater than 5·30 gives a fall of 5·33, while 0·17 being less than 6·31 we have a rise of 6·14; and similarly 0·30 being less than 7·18 we have a rise of 6·88, and 6·15 being again greater than the back-sight 0·40 we have a fall of 5·75. Now, to prove our calculations, if we take the sum of the rises from that of the falls we get the same result as deducting the sum of the back-sights from that of the fore-sights, or 4·11, which shows that there is a total fall from A to F of 4·11 feet, regardless of the fact that the ground rises at D and E.

Before proceeding to elaborate the subject of compound levelling, I think it advisable to deal with two primary questions, which may well be introduced at this point. I refer to datum and bench-marks.

Datum – First, as to datum. It is an imaginary line parallel with the horizon, and with the several lines of collimation. Its object is to simplify all calculations in levelling operations by referring all the observations to one fixed standard, which is fixed at some convenient depth below a well-known and clearly defined mark (called usually a bench-mark), and from this standard line all heights are relatively adjusted.

As an illustration refer to Fig. 221. It will be seen from the
level book that c is the lowest level that was read. In order to
select a datum line all heights should be above this line for
simplicity in "reducing" the levels and plotting sections. If, in
this case, a datum of 20 feet below A is selected it will provide
ample margin. The selected datum is entered under the
"Reduced Levels" column of the level book on the line opposite
the first back-sight reading of 4·10 ft. The remaining readings
are now reduced as shown in the level book page repeated
below thus:

Back-sight	Fore-sight	Rise	Fall	Reduced levels	Remarks
4·10				20·00	Below A
	10·15		6·05	13·95	At B
5·30					
	10·63		5·33	8·62	„ C
6·31					
	0·17	6·14		14·76	„ D
7·18					
	0·30	6·88		21·64	„ E
0·40					
	6·15		5·75	15·89	„ F
23·29	27·40	13·02	17·13	20·00	
	23·29		13·02	15·89	
	4·11		4·11	4·11	

Beginning with the selected datum of 20 feet the calculated
heights entered under the "Rise" column are added and those
under the "Fall" column deducted. Finally, the last level is
subtracted from the first (or vice versa if the last point at F
happened to be higher than A) and the difference should agree
with the difference between Fore-sight and Back-sight and
Rise and Fall columns as shown.

Plotting levels – In order to plot the levels based on the above
example, the method usually employed is to draw a section,
the datum thus forming the horizontal reference line from which
all the levelled points above are related. The result will be a
sectional view of the undulations of the land that has been
levelled, as if the earth had been sliced down vertically and we

were viewing this "slice" from a horizontal plane. This is
illustrated in Fig. 221 although it is usual to connect the points
obtained in levelling by *straight* lines as shown in Fig. 235.

First draw a horizontal line which will form the datum line
and to a convenient scale mark off the distances chained between
the levelled points A B, B C, C D, D E, E F. Set up vertical lines at

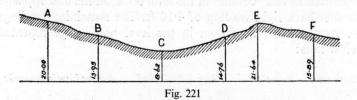

Fig. 221

these points and mark off the heights from the "Reduced Levels"
column of the level book. Now join the extremities of these
points by straight lines and the section is complete.

It is generally convenient to plot the vertical heights to a larger
scale than the horizontal distances in order to emphasise the
irregularities of the surface. If the same scale is used for both
vertical and horizontal plotting it is said to be drawn to a
"natural scale."

Ordnance datum – Originally the ordnance datum of this
country was determined by the ordnance authorities to be "the
approximate mean water at Liverpool," and all the levels
marked upon the ordnance maps are the "altitudes in feet above
this datum."

Certain discrepencies were later discovered, however, and a
new Ordnance Datum has been fixed as the result of the
determination of the mean sea level, but at Newlyn (Cornwall),
which differs slightly from the old one at Liverpool.

The whole country is being re-levelled and wherever Ordnance
Maps are revised the new levels, corrected and referred to the
Newlyn Datum, are included. Along roads the levels are
marked with a small cross, thus **X**, with a figure printed in
italics in a convenient position near it. These levels are only
given in round numbers, thus, 556, which indicates that the
point at which the small cross is shown is 556 feet above
ordnance datum. Bench marks are indicated on the map with a

crow's foot, the height of the same being shown thus, B.M. 611·7. In all levelling operations it is essential, wherever possible, to refer all heights to *ordnance* datum by selecting a datum line at a convenient height above or below it, and at the same time below the lowest point in the section.

Ordnance bench marks – Every endeavour should be made to commence and end a series of levels on an O.B.M., even if this entails carrying the section some considerable distance further than is required. By the use of the established O.B.M's. not only will it be possible to check the accuracy of the work by taking readings on these B.M's. in passing and thus avoiding the necessity of taking "flying levels"* back to the point of commencement, but it will also be possible to refer the reduced levels and plotted section to ordnance datum which should be the aim wherever possible.

The old type of bench mark shown in Fig. 222 is being supplemented but it will be many years before they are completely replaced. The new types are of three classes – primary, secondary and ordinary.

Fig. 222

The primary class are some 25 miles apart and consist of granite or reinforced concrete pillars set solid in rock, on the top of which gunmetal bolts are fixed. They are for use by the Ordnance Survey in particular.

The second class of B.M. about 1 mile apart are fixed to walls

---

* "Flying Levels" are a series of levels taken back to the point of commencement in order that the accuracy of the work can be checked. These flying levels are booked in the usual way and when 'reduced' the last flying level fore-sight reading should agree with the first back-sight reading taken on the section. When taking flying levels the object is to return to the starting point as speedily as possible, consistent with accuracy, thus all changes of gradient usually taken when levelling a section may be ignored and long readings are made.

of important buildings. These consist of small bronze face plates to which a portable support bracket can be attached on which the foot of the levelling staff is rested. Fig. 223 shows the elevation and section of this type of B.M.

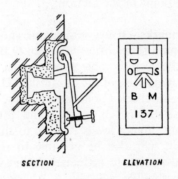

SECTION　　ELEVATION

Fig. 223

The ordinary type, about 400 yards apart, have copper rivets let into horizontal surfaces, such as the top of stone or brick walls.

Bench-marks – Where it is impossible to use the ordnance bench-mark, it is necessary to establish ones own. It is then essential to find some clearly defined and immovable point for this purpose. In other words, the top of a mile-stone, a corner of the top step of some well-known building, a boundary stone, the hinge-post of a gate, the trunk of a tree, or a mark cut on a wall, should represent the commencement of a series of levels, and this should be accurately described and located as to enable a stranger to easily determine its whereabouts.

In selecting a bench-mark, if on a mile-stone or a gate-post, the highest point is always to be taken; or, in the case of a stone post, whose top may be uneven, then select the extreme point, as shown in Fig. 224; and in the case of iron or round stone posts the apex, as in Fig. 225. Driving nails into the trunks of trees (Fig. 226) is by no means satisfactory, and should be avoided except under most exceptional circumstances. It may be necessary to utilise a tree in close proximity to the work, in which case it is always advisable to cut a cross or crow's foot on the root, as in Fig. 227. Again, it is usual to advise students to make bench-marks of gate-posts, the favourite expression being

Fig. 224

Fig. 225

the "top hook of the hanging post," as in Fig. 228. I can only say that this is a mistake, as the constant opening and shutting of the gate must loosen the hook and destroy the identity of the

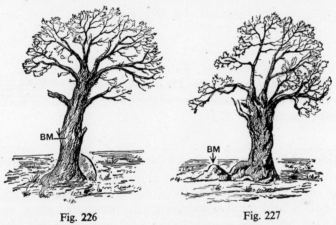

Fig. 226

Fig. 227

mark. The hanging post of gates, in the absence of any more suitable fixtures, may do very well, but instead of the hook, as in Fig. 228, it should be on the top of the post itself, as in Fig. 229. The door-steps of churches, chapels, public-houses,

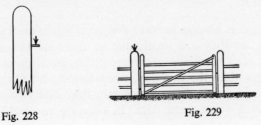

Fig. 228

Fig. 229

farmhouses, etc., are frequently adopted for bench-marks, in which case it is always usual to take the top step (Fig. 230), and to be extremely careful to describe whether it is north, south, east, or west. Ordnance bench-marks are invariably cut

Fig. 230

in the walls of buildings, public or private, or in stone or wooden mile- or gate-posts. Their positions may be accurately determined by an examination of the 25 inch Ordnance Survey map of the district.

Position of bench-marks – Bench-marks need not necessarily be exactly on the line of section, nor is it essential that they should be at the commencement of the work. In starting to take levels the staff is held upon some convenient permanent mark, such as I have mentioned, as near to the work as possible, but I have known cases where the only fixed point suitable for a bench-mark has been a considerable distance away, in which case it has been necessary to level expressly from this point to that of the commencement of the section, even if it be a mile off or more.

My advice is always to have frequent bench-marks (besides O.B.M's.), as they are invaluable at the time the section is plotted or afterwards for reference. If the operation of levelling takes longer than the one day, when leaving off always do so upon a bench-mark, from which you may safely resume your levelling at a subsequent date. In entering the position of a bench-mark in the level-book it needs to be described very minutely, somewhat thus: "B M on top of doorstep, N E corner of Coach and Horses P H" or "B M on top of sixth mile-post from Dover;" or "B M on top of hanging post of gate leading from main road to Cedar Farm."

Different kinds of levelling – Levelling may be done in several ways: 1st, by taking observations of altitude at measured points upon a given line, which is called a section; 2nd, by taking observations of altitude at points along a road; 3rd, relative levels at points of an estate, whose positions are fixed, upon plan, and whose relative values to the datum are marked thereon.

First, as to a line of section. It is necessary to determine the various features of undulation, commenced at a fixed point, as A. After having held the staff upon a bench-mark at A, it is removed to the point which is the commencement of the section.

Level-book – Before going into details, however, it is necessary for me to say a few words about the level-book and the method of taking observations. The following is known as the "rise and fall" method. It consists of six columns on the left page and one column and a large space on the right page. The first three columns, viz. "back-sight," "intermediate," and "fore-sight," are exclusively for the observations with the instrument; and these, together with the whole of the right page for "distance," and "remarks," have reference only to field operations, while the fourth, fifth, and sixth columns, for "rise," "fall," and "reduced levels," need not necessarily be worked out in the field, but it is always as well to do so if time and circumstances permit.

Now referring to Fig. 234 and to the level-book just described, the instrument is planted in some convenient position to command the ordnance bench-mark on the wall of house, marked A on plan (note that the 1st line of collimation is not shown in Fig. 234). Direct the staff to be held thereon, and direct the telescope towards it. Carefully observe the reading

"RISE AND FALL" METHOD LEVEL-BOOK

Back Sight	Inter- mediate	Fore Sight	Rise	Fall	Reduced Levels	Distance	Remarks
6·30					50·00*		O.B.M. on wall of house at A on plan.
	1·60		4·70		54·70		On peg at end of line 5.
	1·45		0·15		54·85		On peg No. 2.
	0·55		0·90		55·75		Centre of road.
		0·59		0·04	55·71		Peg No. 3.
9·80					—		
	2·20		7·60		63·31	000	Commencement of section.
	4·30			2·10	61·21	100	At peg.
	5·90			1·60	59·61	150	,,
	8·30			2·40	57·21	180	,,
	10·00			1·70	55·51	200	,,
	7·30		2·70		58·21	300	,,
	4·90		2·40		60·61	400	,,
	3·50		1·40		62·01	500	,,
	0·10		3·40		65·41	600	,,
	10·50			10·40	55·01	700	,,
		12·53		2·03	52·98	—	,,
5·02					—	—	,,
	4·70		0·32		53·30	800	,,
	8·60			3·90	49·40	900	,,
	11·80			3·20	46·20	1000	,,
	13·50			1·70	44·50	1100	,,
		5·02	8·48		52·98	—	,,
7·30					—	—	,,
	7·40			0·10	52·88	1200	End of section.
		10·27		2·87	50·01*		O.B.M. on wall of house.
28·42		28·41	32·05	32·04			

* See p. 265.

where the cross-wire cuts the staff – in this case it is 6·30. This is a back-sight. And here let me again impress upon the student that the *first sight* he takes after fixing the instrument is always a *back-sight*, and *the last* he takes before he removes the instrument is always a *fore-sight*, and all other sights are intermediate. Again, a back-sight signifies the commencement of a series of levels and fore-sight its termination. Now 6·30 is the first reading, therefore book it in the first column, and having entered it take another look to satisfy yourself that the reading is correct.* Now there are three points at which it is desirable to have readings before moving the instrument – 1·60, 1·45, and 0·55. These being connected with the same line of collimation will appear in the second or "intermediate" column, and for convenience of sight it is arranged that the chain-man should hold the staff at a point the reading of which is 0·59, which, being the last, will appear in the third or "fore-sight" column, and we have now done with this line of collimation, and must proceed to establish another. *But the staff must remain at the last point.* Be careful, in turning the figures towards the new position of the level, that it is exactly upon the same spot. To illustrate further, refer to Fig. 231. The instrument is at A

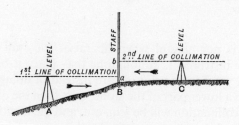

Fig. 231

(for the first line of collimation), and B is the point deemed desirable for a change of collimation, the staff being held on some fixed point at B and the sight taken at *a*, the reading of which is 0·59. The second line of collimation is established by

---

* To carefully observe a reading and make a mental note thereof enables the leveller to accurately record it in the book; and looking again, after having booked it, will prove a corroboration of the observation.

S

planting the level at c, and reading the staff still held at B but cutting it at *b*, which reads 9·80. Now the 0·59 goes in the third column and 9·80 in the first, but whilst the readings are different the point B is just the same, the staff never having moved (except to turn its face towards c). The difference lies in the alteration of the lines of collimation, and it is most important to impress this fact, that the accuracy of the levels is entirely dependent upon the care with which the changes of collimation are made, so that if there is the slightest alteration in the point at B, where the sights *a* and *b* are observed – in other words, if the staff in the process of turning has shifted only slightly – the accuracy of the work is destroyed. Let me further emphasise this. According to the reading of the staff at B the value of *a* is 0·59 when the staff is held on a stone (as *a*, Fig. 232). Now if the

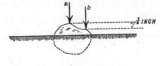

Fig. 232

chain-man is not careful when he raises the staff to turn it towards the instrument, although he may place it back on the same stone, yet if from want of care instead of doing so at *a* he puts it upon a lower part of the stone, as *b*, then the difference of the lines of collimation will be ½ in. out, and the identity of *a* and *b* at B, in Fig. 231 is destroyed, for by this error of ½ in. they are not taken on the self-same spot.

Foot-plates – To obviate this difficulty the chain-man may carry an iron foot-plate, such as Fig. 233, for soft ground.

Proceeding with the second line of collimation, with 9·80 as the back-sight. By reference to the level-book it will be seen that the real commencement of the section is not until the first intermediate in the second line of collimation, viz. 2·20, and it is here that the seventh column is brought into use, and three cyphers are booked to notify the zero of the horizontal measurement. At 1 chain occurs the second intermediate 4·30, and following at 150, 180, 200, 300, 400, 500, 600, and 700 links are eight intermediate sights, 5·90, 8·30, 10·00, 7·30, 4·90, 3·50, 0·10, and 10·50; and for the convenience of shifting the instrument we

Fig. 233

now make a fore-sight (12·53) on a peg put in for that purpose only, having no chainage because it is not intended to be plotted. This ends the second line of collimation. The third line of collimation begins with a back-sight of 5·02, has four intermediates, 4·70, 8·60, 11·80, 13·50, at 800, 900, 1000, and 1100 links, and is terminated by a fore-sight (5·02) also on a peg not to be plotted. The fourth line of collimation begins with a back-sight (7·30) on that peg, has an intermediate (7·40) at 1200 links of chainage, and terminates with a fore-sight (10·27) on the bench-mark from which we started: this also forms no part of the plotted section, and therefore has no chainage. I have given this illustration, taken from actual practice over a portion of a section of a railway, which by being for the first 1200 links round a very sharp curve, gave the section the form in which it appears in Fig. 234, and also enabled us to tie upon our original bench-mark.

Keeping the level-book – On p. 250 I explained that if the "intermediate or fore-sights are greater than the back-sights they are falls, and if less rises," and thus in the present case we shall have no difficulty in making up our book as follows (see p. 260). Working diagonally downwards from left to right,

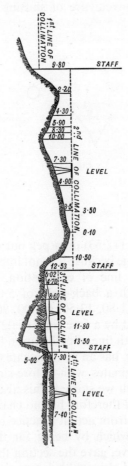

Fig. 234

1·60 being less than 6·30, is a rise of 4·70; 1·45 being less than 1·60 is also a rise; 0·55 being less than 1·45 is a rise; but 0·59 being greater than 0·55 is a fall of 0·04. We have now done with the first series; and although the fore-sight 0·59 and the back-sight 9·80 are taken on the same point, I prefer to start a fresh line, as a better illustration that each series is independent of the other. Thus 9·80 back-sight being greater than 2·20 (inter-mediate) is a rise, but 2·20 being less than 4·30 shows a fall of 2·10, and 4·30 less than 5·90 a fall of 1·60, and so on until 10·00 being greater than 7·30 we have a rise of 2·70, 2·40, 1·40, 3·40, a fall of 10·40, and finally the fore-sight 12·53 being greater than the last intermediate (10·50) shows a fall of 2·03. Now a new line of collimation, with a back-sight of 5·02, we have a rise of 0·32, the three intermediates showing falls of 3·90, 3·20, 1·70 respectively, whilst the fore-sight gives a rise of 8·48, and the fourth and last line of collimation has a fall of 0·10 from the back-sight, and also on to the O.B.M. a fall of 2·87.

Making up level-book – We have seen that, commencing with a back-sight of 6·30 on the bench-mark, we terminate upon the same point with a fore-sight of 10·27, and that we have four back-sights of 6·30, 9·80, 5·02, and 7·30, giving a total of 28·42 ft., and also four fore-sights of 0·59, 12·53, 5·02, and 10·27, in all 28·41 ft. Thus the back-sight being greater by 0·01 than the fore-sight shows a discrepancy of $\frac{1}{100}$th of a foot, or $\frac{1}{8}$th of an inch. In so short a distance this should not occur, but I have purposely shown it to illustrate my meaning. Now if we have correctly reduced the intermediate and fore-sight from the back-sight, the rises and falls if added together should give the same difference as that existing between the back- and fore-sights, or 32·05 rise $-$ 32·04 fall $=$ 0·01. On p. 254 I have spoken about ordnance datum, and in the present case the ordnance datum is 50 ft. The value of this B.M. appears in the sixth column, opposite the 6·30 in the first, and it will be necessary to carry forward the system of reduced levels by adding or deducting the consecutive rises or falls as follows: 50·00+4·70 = 54·70, 54·70+0·15 = 54·85, 54·85+90 = 55·75, 55·75−0·04 = 55·71. This last being a fall must be deducted. There is no reduced level opposite 9·80 in the back-sight column, as being identical with 0·59 in the fore-sight column;

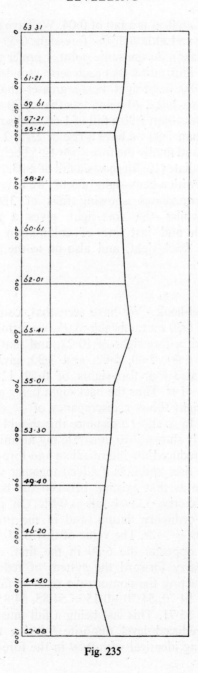

Fig. 235

its value is just the same* above datum of 55·71, and to save confusion I simply draw a dash across the space. Then to 55·71 must be added 7·60 = 63·31; from 63·31−2·10 = 61·21; from 61·21−1·60 = 59·61; 59·61−2·40 = 57·21; 57·21−1·70 = 55·51; 55·51+2·70 = 58·21, and so on until the last fall of 2·87, opposite the last fore-sight 10·27, gives a result of 50·01, from which should be taken the height above datum, viz. 50·00 = 0·01, or $\frac{1}{100}$th of a foot. Having thus obtained all our reduced levels, we now proceed to plot our section, as shown in Fig. 235. To avoid complications or inaccuracies with the level-book in cases where there are a large number of intermediate sights which continue on to the next page, the following procedure is recommended.

In the first case at the bottom of Example No. 1 is an intermediate 4·90, and at top of page No. 2 is also an intermediate immediately following, of 3·50, so that the fore-sight 12·53 does not occur until the fifth line. It is necessary to make each page of the level-book balance, so that the difference between the back- and fore-sights, rise and fall, and reduced levels, correspond. But page No. 1 (Example 1) will prevent this, for there is only one fore-sight, 0·59, as compared with two back-sights (16·10) a rise of 15·51; and if the falls are deducted from the rises down to 4·90, then 18·45−7·84 = 10·61. This is not only confusing (although not incorrect), but may lead to serious errors. If, however, as in Example 2, at the bottom of the page, 4·90 is made into a temporary fore-sight (taking care that what has been borrowed on page 1 is repaid on page 2, so that 4·90 appears there as a back-sight) each page can be made to balance, and the making up of the book is facilitated. It may be asked how is it that the total back-sights in case No. 1 are 28·42 and the fore-sights 28·41, whilst in case No. 2 they are

---

* Some surveyors prefer to place their back- and fore-sights upon the same line, as in example A; but I prefer to devote a separate line to each observation as in example B, which shows more clearly the various lines of collimation. The back-sight 9·80 is placed one lower than fore-sight 0·59, being taken on the same spot, for the new collimation-line.

A

B. S.	Inter.	F. S.
9·80		0·59

B

B. S.	Inter.	F. S.
		0·59
9·80		

33·32 and 33·31 respectively? The reason is because we have added one more back- and fore-sight: thus $28·42+4·90 = 33·32$, and $28·41+4·90 = 33·31$; but the difference between the back- and fore-sight is exactly the same in both cases, or $\frac{1}{100}$th of a foot. The foregoing example may seem hardly a matter of much importance, but in fact it helps considerably and prevents errors in casting up creeping in unawares which would not occur if each page is made to properly balance. On no account should figures be rubbed out in the back-, intermediate, fore-sight, or distance columns; any alteration can be made by drawing the pencil through the figures that are to be amended and the corrected figure re-written over.

Collimation method – A method of keeping the level-book without "rise" and "fall" columns is termed sometimes the "height of instrument method" and sometimes the "collimation method." The principle is, that all sights taken at the first "set" of the instrument are referred to the height of its collimation above the first starting-point; and those taken at each successive "set," to the height of such new collimation above the spot on which the fore-sight of the previous "set" was taken, the new collimation-height being determined by adding to the reduced level of that fore-sight the reading of the back-sight taken after the shift of the instrument. From each collimation-height, the intermediates and the fore-sight taken at that "set" are deducted, the remainders being the reduced levels of the several points. As the intermediates in some "sets" are numerous, each successive collimation-height is entered (on the same line as the new back-sight) in a column so headed, without which it would have to be either noted on a slip of paper or carried in the memory. The subjoined version of the level-book (see page 270), when kept according to the collimation method explains the procedure. It will be observed that the collimation-height, unlike the reduced levels, is not entered at each sight, but given only at the commencement of the "set" to which it relates, thus effecting a saving of trouble and of possible confusion with the reduced levels of the several points.

The O.B.M. of 50·00 feet as before is entered under the reduced level column; and back-sight 6·30 is added thereto and

TWO METHODS OF KEEPING THE LEVEL-BOOK

(USUAL METHOD)

Page No. 1			Page No. 2		
Back-sight	Inter-mediate	Fore-sight	Back-sight	Inter-mediate	Fore-sight
6·30	1·60		16·10	3·50	0·59
	1·45			0·10	
	0·55	0·59		10·50	
9·80	2·20		5·02	4·70	12·53
	4·30			8·60	
	5·90			11·80	
	8·30			13·50	
	10·00		7·30		5·02
	7·30			7·40	
	4·90				10·27
16·10		0·59	28·42		28·41

Example No. 1

(AUTHOR'S METHOD)*

Page No. 1			Page No. 2		
Back-sight	Inter-mediate	Fore-sight	Back-sight	Inter-mediate	Fore-sight
6·30	1·60		16·10	3·50	5·49
	1·45		4·90	0·10	
	0·55	0·59		10·50	
9·80	2·20		5·02	4·70	12·53
	4·30			8·60	
	5·90			11·80	
	8·30			13·50	
	10·00		7·30	7·40	5·02
	7·30	4·90			10·27
16·10		5·49	33·32		33·31

Example No. 2

* See Note, p. 267.

entered as collimation-height for the sights of the first "set." From this, the intermediates are one by one deducted, and finally the fore-sight 0·59 at peg No. 3 leaves the reduced level of that peg 55·71. The instrument is then shifted, and the back-

COLLIMATION METHOD LEVEL-BOOK

Back sight	Inter-mediate	Fore sight	Collima-tion height	Reduced level	Distance	Remarks
				50·00		O.B.M. on wall of house A on plan.
6·30			56·30	—		
	1·60			54·70		On peg at end of line 5.
	1·45			54·85		On peg No. 2.
	0·55			55·75		Centre of road.
		0·59		55·71		Peg No. 3.
9·80			65·51	—		
	2·20			63·31	000	Commencement of section.
	4·30			61·21	100	At peg.
	5·90			59·61	150	,,
	8·30			57·21	180	,,
	10·00			55·51	200	,,
	7·30			58·21	300	,,
	4·90			60·61	400	,,
	3·50			62·01	500	,,
	0·10			65·41	600	,,
	10·50			55·01	700	,,
		12·53		52·98	—	,, (not for plotting).
5·02			58·00	—	—	,,
	4·70			53·30	800	,,
	8·60			49·40	900	,,
	11·80			46·20	1000	,,
	13·50			44·50	1100	,,
		5·02		52·98	—	,,
7·30			60·28	—	—	,,
	7·40			52·88	1200	End of section.
		10·27		50·01		O.B.M. on wall of house.
28·42		28·41				

[NOTE – The discrepancy of 0·01, to which attention is drawn on p. 267, is here purposely retained.]

sight 9·80 (on peg No. 3) is added to 55·71 the final reduced level of the previous "set," giving a new collimation-height of 65·51. As a back-sight has no reduced level, a line is there drawn

across the reduced level and the distance columns. The intermediates and the fore-sight throughout the second "set" are
then one by one deducted from the new collimation-height
65·51; and the like procedure is followed at each shift, and so
on, to the end of the section. It will be noticed that each sight –
back, intermediate, or fore – is entered on a separate line, and
that a new collimation-height always stands on the same line as
a new back-sight.

The collimation-method is preferred by many surveyors to
the "rise" and "fall" system; since by keeping the "distance"
and "remarks" columns on the right-hand page, the level-book
can be reduced to a width of $3\frac{5}{8}$ inches (a considerable gain in
handiness) without cramping the space available for the several
entries, while at the same time all risk of confusing the chainage
figures with those of the staff-readings is avoided.

It is further claimed that the surveyor can reduce his levels as
he proceeds, and thus save time in office-work. The actual gain
on this score, however, is at best only slight, and seems to be
more than counterbalanced by the fact there is no complete
check on the work in the absence of the rise and fall columns.

Levelling-staff – The staves in general use are those upon the
telescopic principle in three pieces – 5 ft., 4 ft. 6 in., and 4 ft. 6 in.
for the 14-ft.; and 6 ft., 5 ft. 6 in., and 4 ft. 6 in. for the 16-ft.
staff. At the bottom of the two upper members there is a
spring-clip which, upon the member being drawn out, closes
accurately over the top of the lower portion, as in Figs. 236 and
237. Some surveyors prefer the folding staves, some 10 ft. in
length, which are hinged in one or two sections. It is necessary
for the chain-man to be carefully instructed in the use of the
staff before commencing operations. He should see that each
length of the staff is drawn out to its proper length and the
spring-clips are secure, and in carrying it he should be careful
not to injure it by allowing it to strike the boughs of trees or
buildings. In open country he may carry it with the lowest
portion over his shoulder, but in woods, orchards, etc., it is better
to carry it trailing with the top joint in front of him; in crossing a
ditch or brook he should either get some one to hold it whilst he

gets over, or should lay it gently across with the bottom in the direction in which he is going, and upon no account use it as a jumping-pole! The staff must always be held perfectly plumb, and the chain-man should hold it by standing immediately behind with his fingers on the top of the first joint. When once

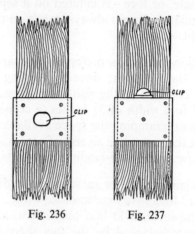

Fig. 236   Fig. 237

upon a back- or fore-sight he must never move until so instructed by the surveyor. To avoid any chance of an error in booking by reason of the staff not being exactly perpendicular, it is as well to instruct the holder to gently wave the top backwards and forwards. There should be a code of intelligible signals, arranged between the surveyor and his assistant, which can be extremely useful at long distance or in windy weather.

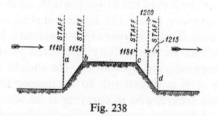

Fig. 238

Distances – Across open ground there is little need for taking sights oftener than at the end of each chain, unless the ground is very undulating. In crossing a bank similar to that in Fig. 238, it is necessary to take the tops and bottoms – thus, 1140*a*, 1154*b*, the near bottom and top of slope, 1184*c* the foretop; whilst 1200 comes part of the way down the slope, the bottom of which *d* is 1215, but in a case of this kind it is not absolutely necessary to take a level at 1200, being so near to 1215. In the case of Fig. 239, in crossing a ditch and fence levels are required at *e*, *f*, *g*, and *h*, but distances must be taken at those points such as 1310, 1312, 1317, and 1319, and it is as well to make a sketch in the level-book similar to Fig. 239. In crossing a river, whose width admits of both banks being observed from

Fig. 239

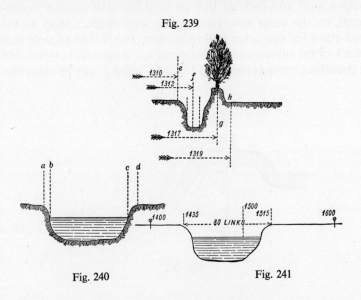

Fig. 240   Fig. 241

the same station, it is usual to take the edge of each bank and the impingement of the water on the shore, as *a*, *b*, *c*, *d* in Fig. 240; and if sufficiently shallow to allow the staff to be read with the bottom upon the bed, so much the better; if not, the depth of the surface of the water above the bed must be ascertained by sounding either with the levelling staff, or, if not long enough, with a line and lead.

Measuring across streams – If the river is too wide to measure with a chain, one of the methods of calculating the width described in Chapter 4 will have to be adopted. It sometimes happens, as in Fig. 241, that the end of a chain comes near to the edge of a river, in such a case it is unnecessary to resort to calculation, if the exact width is taken with the chain. Supposing it to be not wider than 100 links, by care it is possible to connect and to continue the chainings. In this case the near edge of the river is 1435, and the width to the opposite edge is 80 links, thus 1435+80 = 1515, and if 15 links is held at that point, then the end of the chain will be 200 links from the last arrow at 1400. In the case of a wide river, of say 3 or 4 chains' width, it is desirable to establish a bench-mark and send a man across with a staff and instruct him to hold the staff upon a bench-mark on the other side, then take a long-distance sight across and allow for curvature and refraction. This would be only as a check of the subsequent operation of levelling round by possibly a circuitous route as shown in Fig. 242, when it may be necessary

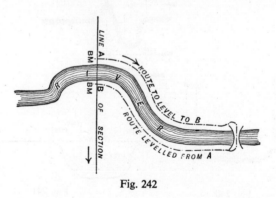

Fig. 242

to sight for $1\frac{1}{2}$ miles or more round by a bridge; or across some convenient ford, in which case, having levelled from A to B, it is essential to check back from B to A before continuing the section. In taking the level of water of a tidal river it is necessary to ascertain the level of high and low water.

Levelling on hills, etc. – It will have been noticed that, in speaking about curvature and refraction, I said it was seldom considered in modern practice, as by equalising the distance between the staff at each end and the instrument, the necessity for making the allowance would be obviated. If only back- and fore-sights are required it will not be difficult to arrange for the equidistance of the staff, except in levelling on steep hills, but it does not necessarily follow that the instrument must be exactly in line with the staves, and this is a means of overcoming the difficulty of levelling up a steep hill when the line of collimation will cut the staff low down when the level is quite close on fore-sight but on taking back-sights it will be possible to have the staff some distance from the level. This will be clear from Fig. 243. By offsetting the instrument as in Fig. 244 the fore-sight and back-sight can be more approximately equalised.

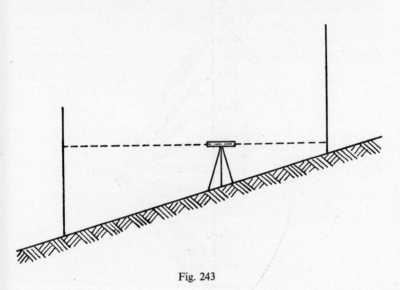

Fig. 243

Always select some suitable position upon which to plant your level, so as to command as large a range of your work as possible consistent with the necessity to have the back- and fore-sights equidistant.

In Fig. 244 I give a simple illustration, which really deals with the whole question, however complicated. In the line of section from A to D it is assumed that we commence at A with the staff

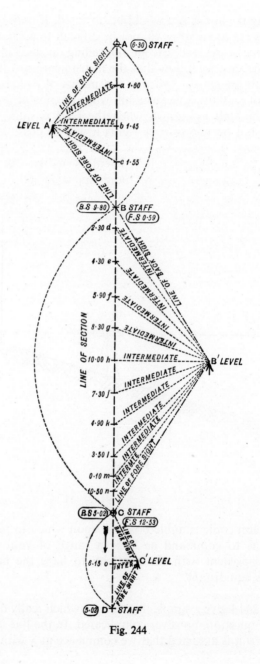

Fig. 244

reading 6·30, the instrument being at A': the staff is then held at a (1·60), at b (1·45), and c (1·55), all three intermediates, and finally at B for a fore-sight, the same distance (or thereabouts) as from A. Now by keeping A and B the same distance from A' we have fulfilled the condition required by curvature and refraction, and if the instrument is in perfect adjustment the depths of the intermediates a, b, c, below the line of collimation A B, although of different radii to A and B, yet for all practical purposes will be sufficiently accurate. This will be possibly better understood by reference to Fig. 245. Here let me say that, whilst it is absolutely essential that the back- and fore-sights should be most accurately observed, because the difference of their sum will be the actual rise or fall from the commencement

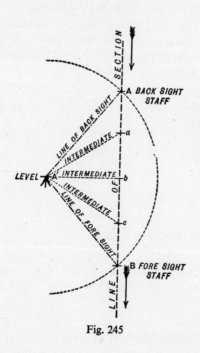

Fig. 245

to the termination, yet for all practical purposes it is not necessary (except in the case of the level of water, existing railways, or road crossings) to read intermediates nearer than

T

tenths. Thus 1·43 would be booked 1·40, and 1·47 would appear as 1·50. By so doing a great deal of unnecessary labour and complication in making up the book is avoided, and seeing that with even the largest scale in practice it is impossible to plot less than $\frac{10}{100}$th of a foot, it is a needless waste of time to observe so minutely in the field.

Passing back to consideration of Fig. 244. Having observed the fore-sight at B (0·59), and previously taken care that the staff is held upon some firm place, the face thereof being now turned towards B′, to which point the instrument has been transplanted, and duly adjusted, the reading of the back-sight at B is 9·80; and now follow the various points along the line, d (2·30), e (4·30), f (5·90), g (8·30), h (10·00), j (7·30), k (4·90), l (3·50), m (0·10), and n (10·50), all intermediates, whilst C (12·53) is the fore-sight. The same principle as previously explained equally applies, and so on *ad infinitum*, showing at the finish of the section—

Back-sight.	Fore-sight.
6·30	0·59
9·80	12·53
5·02	5·02
——	——
21·12	18·14
18·14	
——	

2·98 rise from A to D.

This is only a very simple illustration, but it may be adopted either for a great length of section or for a few chains.

Instructions to staff-holder – It is desirable that the surveyor should direct the staff-holder as to the points at which it is necessary to take readings, especially for back- and fore-sights, and unless he has some trustworthy person to read the distances on the chain-line he should ascertain the longitudinal measurements himself; certainly he must personally superintend the establishment of bench-marks, and see that the staff is not only held on the highest point, but that it is the same place which is described in the "remarks" column.

Plenty of information – Another point is that the remarks should be in as much detail as possible, accompanied by neat and graphic sketches of any important features met with in the section, especially with regard to the bench-marks. A sight should certainly be taken at the end of every chain except under exceptional circumstances. It may be well here to explain, that it is not by any means necessary that there should be any longitudinal measurements at either a back- or a fore-sight, but if it be found convenient to change at a point on the line of section which is to be determined by measurement, then the distance will appear opposite the fore-sight. Opposite the next back-sight (which represents the same spot), there will be no

Back-sight.	Inter-mediate.	Fore-sight.	Dis-tance.
6·30			000
	1·60		100
	1·45		200
	1·55		300
		0·59	400
9·80			—
	2·30		430
	4·30		500

and so on.

Fig. 246

distance, but it will help if a dash is drawn across the column. Thus, referring to Fig. 244: if with the level at A' the surveyor had intended to take an intermediate at B, but found that the rise of the ground would hardly justify his continuing further; instead of entering 0·59 as an intermediate he would book it as a fore-sight, and put the distance upon the chain-line opposite, as in Fig. 246; and having moved the level to B', in sighting the staff held at the same place (viz. B) would read and enter in the first column the back-sight 9·80, so that at 1·60 the distance was 1 chain (100 links), at 1·45 = 200, at 1·55 = 300, at F s 0·59 = 400, at B s 9·80 = 400, at 2·30 = 430 links, and so on. I should explain that in Fig. 244 the back- and fore-sights A, B, C, and D are (for the purpose of this particular illustration) shown upon the line of section but, if they are not needed as part of the section when plotted, and are kept equidistant from the instrument, they may be at any point right or left of the line. Again, I have been frequently asked if the first back-sight is the commencement of the section? The answer is, no. The first back-sight must necessarily be upon a bench-mark, in as near proximity to the commencement of the section as possible; but invariably the zero of the chainage is an intermediate. The same applies to the last fore-sight, which may be some distance from the termination of the section, involving a number of back- and fore-sights before the bench-mark is reached. And when this has been done, then the difference between the sum of the back-sights and fore-sights will represent (or should do) the difference between the levels of the first and last bench-mark.

Again, as the intermediate sights are the depths below the varying lines of collimation (which are regulated by back- and fore-sights alone), then so long as they have been accurately observed they are disregarded in making up the field-work, and are only affected in the rise and fall columns, as connected with the reduced levels. But it should be emphasised that the accuracy of the section so far as its minor details are concerned depends entirely upon the care with which the intermediates are observed, especially in reading long distances, as a IX may be easily taken for XI,* which involves an error at this particular point on the section of two feet, but does not in any way affect the whole section. Patience and care will obviate such an unpardonable error.

Taking the level of water – In taking the level of the surface of

---

* In most cases the modern levelling staff is marked N in place of a or IX.

water, it is best to so place a stone on the fore-shore that it is only just covered with a film of water, and then hold the staff upon the stone. This applies only to standing water; but for a tidal stream the exact time of the observation should be recorded, and, from a nautical almanack or by other means, the exact position of high and low water may then be determined.

Levelling with theodolite – Except under circumstances which are unavoidable, the use of the theodolite for levelling purposes should be confined to ascertaining inaccessible points or for the heights of mountain sides, for which the ordinary operations are inadmissible. In such cases the procedure is in accordance with the principles described in Chapter 10 (pp. 308 – 315). When, however, a section has to be taken where, owing to steepness or loose shifting surface, a level cannot be properly planted, or where configuration of the ground would necessitate too many shifts of the instrument and sights of inconvenient shortness or objectionable inequality of length: the theodolite will be found useful. The operation presents varieties of detail too numerous to be all worked-out here; but the following example illustrates the mode of procedure, and, with due modification according to circumstances, will enable the student to solve all other cases.

The last point to which levelling by the ordinary means can be carried, is marked by a peg at H (Fig. 247). The theodolite is here planted, and the height of its axis A above the peg is measured. The points on the slope at which sights are to be taken, B, C, D, E, are then selected and marked, and the straight-line distances from point to point, on the slope, A B, B C, C D, D E, are measured: these measurements must be made with the utmost possible accuracy. A vane or mark is fixed on the levelling-staff at the reading corresponding to the height A H of the axis above starting-peg; and the angles of elevation of this mark are observed at each selected point on the slope.

Let the data thus obtained be:

Length on ground A B $=143\cdot5$; angle of elevation B A B$'=26°$

    ,,   ,,   B C $=172\cdot4$;   ,,   ,,   C A C$'=34° 45'$

    ,,   ,,   C D$=129\cdot0$;   ,,   ,,   D A D$'=38° 10'$

    ,,   ,,   D E$=154\cdot8$;   ,,   ,,   E A E$'=40°$

            Angle C A B $= 34° 45' - 26°$ $= 8° 45'$

        ,,   D A C $= 38° 10' - 34° 45' = 3° 25'$

        ,,   E A D $= 40° - 38° 10'$ $= 1° 50'$.

The observations are then worked out as follows:

From obtuse angle B let fall perpendicular B F on base A C, dividing triangle A B C into two right-angled triangles A F B, C F B.

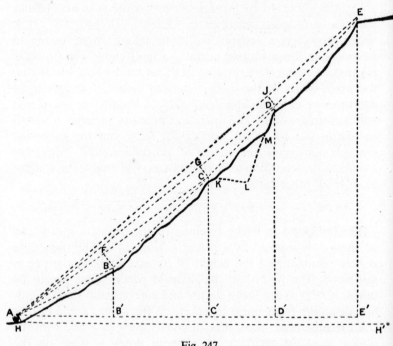

Fig. 247

From obtuse angle C let fall perpendicular C G on base A D, dividing triangle A C D into two right-angled triangles A G C, D G C.

From obtuse angle D let fall perpendicular D J on base A E, dividing triangle A D E into two right-angled triangles A J D, E J D.

In triangle A B′ B are given

$$\text{angle } \text{B}' = 90°$$
$$\text{,, } \quad \text{A} = 26°$$
$$\text{side } b' = 143\cdot5$$

To find sides b and a.

$$b = \cos 26° \times 143\cdot5 = 128\cdot9591$$
$$a = \sin 26° \times 143\cdot5 = 62\cdot9063.$$

In triangle A F B are given

$$\text{angle } \text{F} = 90°$$
$$\text{,, } \quad \text{A} = 8°\ 45'$$
$$\text{,, } \quad \text{B} = 90° - 8°\ 45' = 81°\ 15'$$
$$\text{side } f = 143\cdot5$$

then $\sin 90° : 143\cdot5 : : \sin 81°\ 15' : b = 141\cdot8299$

and $\sin 90° : 143\cdot5 : : \sin 8°\ \ 45' : a = 21\cdot8297.$

In triangle C F B are given

$$\text{angle } \text{F} = 90°$$
$$\text{side } f = 172\cdot4$$
$$\text{,, } \quad c = 21\cdot8297$$

then $172\cdot4 : \sin 90° : : 21\cdot8297 : \sin \text{C} = 9\cdot1025106$

$$= \sin 7°\ 16'\ 28''$$

and $90° - 7°\ 16'\ 28'' = 82°\ 43'\ 32'' = \text{B}$

whence $\sin 90° : 172\cdot4 : : \sin 82°\ 43'\ 32'' : b = 171\cdot0124$

and $\text{A C} = \text{A F} + \text{F C} = 141\cdot8299 + 171\cdot0124 = 312\cdot8423.$

In triangle A C′ C are given

$$\text{angle } \text{C}' = 90°$$
$$\text{,, } \quad \text{A} = 34°\ 45'$$
$$\text{side } c' = 312\cdot8423$$

then $c = \cos 34°\ 45' \times 312\cdot8423 = 257\cdot0458$

and $a = \sin 34°\ 45' \times 312\cdot8423 = 178\cdot3190.$

In triangle A G C are given

$$\text{angle } \text{G} = 90°$$
$$\text{,, } \quad \text{A} = 3°\ 25'$$
$$\text{,, } \quad \text{C} = 90° - 3°\ 25' = 86°\ 35'$$
$$\text{side } g = 312\cdot8423$$

then $\sin 90° : 312\cdot8423 : : \sin 86°\ 35' : c = 312\cdot2861$

and $\sin 90° : 312\cdot8423 : : \sin \ 3°\ 35' : a = 18\cdot6448.$

In triangle D G C are given

$$\text{angle } G = 90°$$
$$\text{side } g = 129\cdot0$$
$$\text{,, } d = 18\cdot6448$$

then $129\cdot0 : \sin 90° : : 18\cdot6448 : \sin D = 9\cdot1599581$
$= \sin 8° 18' 36''$
and $90° - 8° 18' 36'' = 81° 41' 24'' = C$
whence $\sin 90° : 129\cdot0 : : \sin 81° 41' 24'' : c = 127\cdot6434$
and $A D = A G + G D = 312\cdot2861 + 127\cdot6434 = 439\cdot9294.$

In triangle A D′ D are given

$$\text{angle } D' = 90°$$
$$\text{,, } A = 38° 10'$$
$$\text{side } d' = 439\cdot9294$$

then $d = \cos 38° 10' \times 439\cdot9294 = 345\cdot8898$
and $a = \sin 38° 10' \times 439\cdot9294 = 271\cdot8549.$

In triangle A J D are given

$$\text{angle } J = 90°$$
$$\text{,, } A = 1° 50'$$
$$\text{,, } D = 90° - 1° 50' = 88° 10'$$
$$\text{side } d = 439\cdot9294$$

then $\sin 90° : 439\cdot9294 : : \sin 88° 10' : d = 439\cdot7041$
and $\sin 90° : 439\cdot9294 : : \sin 1° 50' : a = 14\cdot0671.$

In triangle E J D are given

$$\text{angle } J = 90°$$
$$\text{side } j = 154\cdot8$$
$$\text{,, } d = 14\cdot0671$$

then $154\cdot8 : \sin 90° : : 14\cdot0671 : \sin E = 8\cdot9584343$
$= \sin 5° 12' 50''$
and $90° - 5° 12' 50'' = 84° 47' 10'' = D$
whence $\sin 90° : 154\cdot8 : : \sin 84° 47' 10'' : d = 154\cdot1595$
and $A E = A J + J E = 439\cdot7041 + 154\cdot1595 = 593\cdot8636.$

In triangle A E′ E are given

$$\text{angle } E' = 90°$$
$$\text{,, } A = 40°$$
$$\text{side } e' = 593\cdot8636$$

then $e = \cos 40° \times 593\cdot8636 = 455\cdot0369$
and $a = \sin 40° \times 593\cdot8636 = 381\cdot7282.$

Where any considerable break occurs in the general ground-line between two selected points, as shown by the dotted line K L M, and the point L cannot be observed with the theodolite and levelling-staff, it may be determined either by measurement from the two nearest selected points C and D, or by separate observation with a hand-level or a clinometer.

The heights B B', C C', etc., added to the reduced level of peg H, will give the reduced height of the several selected points above datum.

Permissable error in levelling – In precise levelling the error should not exceed $0·116\sqrt{\text{length of section in miles}}$ and this is the accuracy expected by the Ordnance Survey. For general levelling purposes the error should not exceed 0·02 feet on a section not exceeding 10 chains, increasing as the square root of the distance. Thus a distance of 90 chains should be accurate within $0·02 \times \sqrt{\frac{90}{10}} = 0·06$ feet.

Levelling with aneroid – The aneroid barometer has been fully described in Chapter 2, and it is necessary only to explain its manipulation in the field. The larger the size, the more satis-factory the observations. The surveyor should provide himself with an accurate plan or map of the district through which he proposes to take the levels, and at the points of observation he should mark with a small dot, and place letters as A, B, C, etc., so that he may identify their relative positions from his note-book in which he records the readings. The temperature at starting should be noted, and the index or zero of the movable scale "should be set to where the hand of the instrument points." "On ascending a mountain the hand travels backward, and as each division represents 100 ft. (on the movable scale), an approximate indication of the ascent is thus readily obtained." The aneroid should be held perfectly horizontal, and gently tapped during an observation. "Subtract the reading at the lower station from that at the upper station; the difference is the height in feet."

Cross-sections – Cross-sections in their general acceptance mean a line of levels taken at right angles to the longitudinal section at every chain, or oftener if necessary. Their length is regulated by circumstances; for railways from 1 to 5 chains on each side, at points right and left at all changes of contour. They are set out either with a cross-staff or preferably an optical square. The most satisfactory and accurate method is to treat the sections at each chain as consecutive members – 0, 1, 2, 3, 4, etc., starting at the commencement of the longitudinal section – and, looking in direction of its termination, to treat all observations either of height or distance as being right or left of the centre line (or line of section), as in Fig. 248; and having set out three sight-lines, commence to measure from the centre, right

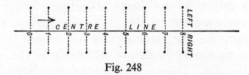

Fig. 248

and left in each separate case, noting any irregularity in the surface of the ground. These measurements should be personally made by the surveyor, who should be provided with a quantity of pieces of white paper (about $1\frac{1}{2}$ in. square), upon which he writes the number of the cross-section, and the measurement in feet (all cross-sections should be measured in feet); and after these particulars have been carefully written upon the paper, it should be placed in a slit of a stick or twig, pointed at the other

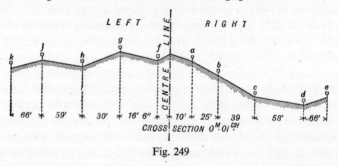

Fig. 249

end, and stuck in the ground at the point to be observed. Thus, as in Fig. 249, it will be observed that the cross-section is at $\overset{\text{M. CH.}}{0\cdot01}$ (no miles, 1 chain), and on the right-hand side there are five points, a, b, c, d, e, of 10 ft., 25 ft., 39 ft., 58 ft., and 66 ft.

from the centre, whilst on the left there are also five points, f, g, h, j, k, of 4 ft., 16 ft. 6 ins., 30 ft., 59 ft., and 66 ft. respectively. Take the point b on the right and g on the left, they would be marked on the paper (as in Figs. 250 and 251), No. 1 section, 25 ft. right and 16 ft. 6 in. left. The chief advantage obtained by this process is, that not only does the surveyor personally superintend these preliminary operations, but after a series of eight or a dozen cross-sections have been set out and measured

Fig. 250   Fig. 251

all the higher points of the series may be taken from one point, so that the change of instrument is minimised. The staff-holder, who should be properly instructed as to his duties, proceeds to each of the points, and holding the staff thereat, he picks up the ticket, and at a signal from the surveyor he reads out in a clear, loud voice, "Cross-section number one, 16 feet 6 inches left," the surveyor booking this repeats it, and if correct the ticket should be destroyed, so as not to be taken again.

In conclusion, I recommend the surveyor to make his assistants thoroughly understand their duties and his requirements, and, by a code of signals mutually understood, a great deal of unnecessary shouting can be avoided.

Precise levelling is a term applied to a system of levelling for the purpose of ascertaining, with the closest possible approach to absolute accuracy, the elevation of bench-marks pertaining to great territorial surveys such as the Ordnance Survey of the United Kingdom, the Government surveys of the United States of America, and similar works executed for national purposes. It is highly complex and requires extreme delicacy and minuteness of detail. It requires a course of special study and instruction which cannot be adequately set forth within the limits of the present volume, but the subject is touched on briefly in Chapter 12. The student will find a number of excellent text books which deal fully with the subject.

Examination Questions

1. The following figures are the staff readings taken in order on a particular scheme, the back-sights being shown in brackets:

(2·67), 7·12, 9·54, 8·63, 10·28, (12·31), 10·75, 6·23, 7·84, (9·22), 5·06, 4·18, 2·11.

The first reading was taken on a bench-mark 129·80 O.D.

Enter the readings in level book form, check the entries and find the reduced level of the last point. Comment on your completed reduction.

(*University of London B.Sc. Estate Management*, 1957)

2. Two pegs, x and y, are driven into the ground 200 ft. apart. Readings on to staffs at x and y by a Dumpy level, set up midway between them are 4·32 ft. and 4·27 ft. respectively. The level when placed near x gives a reading of 4·48 ft. for the staff at y and 4·53 ft. for the staff at x. Determine:

(i) The error of the instrument.
(ii) The reduced level of the peg at y if the reduced level of the peg at x is 64·03 ft.

(*Royal Institution of Chartered Surveyors*, 1955)

3. Show by clear diagrams the effects of curvature of the earth and refraction on long level sights, and give an estimate of the effect in terms of length of sight. How may errors due to curvature and refraction be minimized? Mention particularly the precautions taken to avoid refraction errors.

(*Institution of Municipal Engineers*, 1950)

4. Calculate the gradients between the following points which have been observed by level and measured on the uniform surface between them.

Back-sight	Intermediate	Fore-sight	Distance (slope) ft.
10·61			
8·76	—	4·36	112
7·21	—	6·21	87
4·22	—	8·32	68
		6·41	90

(*Royal Institution of Chartered Surveyors*, 1954)

5. Describe the faults that one might find in a dumpy level and explain, with the aid of diagrams, how you would check for and correct these faults.

The following is an extract of the bookings in a level book; copy it and reduce the levels using the rise and fall method. Show a check on your reduction.

Fore-sight	Intermediate	Back-sight	Reduced level
1·46			231·76 OBM
5·71		13·89	
13·66		2·83	
5·89		3·59	
	3·25		MH1
	8·91		MH2
	12·68		MH3
10·71		7·65	
	3·25		MH4
11·31		9·31	
		11·45	OBM as above

(*Institution of Municipal Engineers*, 1957)

Chapter 9

CONTOURING

Vertical intervals and horizontal equivalents—Hypotenusal allowance—
Table of horizontal equivalents—Keeping the field-book—Contouring
by squares—Examination questions.

CONTOURING is the art of delineating upon a plan a series of
lines which represent certain altitudes parallel with the horizon,
or, in other words, "lines of intersection of a hill by a horizontal
plane." The simplest illustration is the high and low water
marks along the sea-shore, where the fringe of seaweed marks
the extreme boundary of high water, and its zig-zag outline is
due to the water finding out the inequalities of the level of the
shore, so that whatever form this fringe may take, all round
the coast of this "sea-girt island" will be found a line approximately parallel to the horizon.

Another and very primitive illustration: if varying quantities
of different coloured liquids, commencing with the lightest
colours in the largest quantities, were poured into some basin-
shaped vessel whose sides would absorb some of the colours,
so as to leave the mark of their highest level, and smaller
quantities of colour of graduating darkness were successively
poured in and emptied out, the defined lines made by those
different colours would represent concentric circles on the sides
of the basin, whose distance apart would be governed by the
varying quantities of the different coloured liquids, and these
lines would be the contours of the sides of the vessel.

Vertical intervals and horizontal equivalents – It is the province
of the modern surveyor to practically show upon his plans
these lines of contour. The known differences of height thereof
are called the *vertical intervals*, and their distances apart upon

the survey are termed the *horizontal equivalents*, as will be seen
by Fig. 252. In Figs. 253 and 254 we have a simple illustration
of contour lines upon the truncated cone (Fig. 253) at points
A, B, C, D, E, F, G, H, which in plan are represented by the concentric circles in Fig. 254, so that in the former case the relative

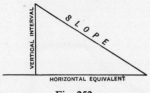

Fig. 252

heights B over A, C over B, etc., represent the vertical intervals,
whilst in Fig. 254 the distances B from A, C from B, etc., are the
horizontal equivalents.

Fig. 253

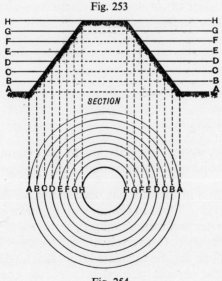

Fig. 254

In Figs. 255 and 256 we have examples of the form contour
lines will show on plan whose planes are projected from a section

of irregularity. The contours will occur in smaller horizontal distance, in proportion to the steepness of the ground. The contour lines in Fig. 256, besides giving the relative altitudes explain the form and flexure of every slope; thus A A′ and B B′ (Fig. 255) show the exact concavity and convexity of the slopes A A′, B B′ in Fig. 256.

Fig. 255

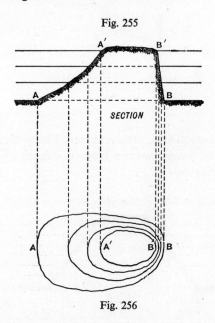

Fig. 256

Now these vertical intervals are to be determined by two methods; 1st by angular observations, 2nd by means of levelling.

As to the first of these: it has been shown, in the chapter on "Chain Surveying," that in chaining up or down a slope allowance for hypotenusal measurements can be made by observing its angle of elevation. Conversely, the difference of level between points on a slope may be calculated from that angle. If A =angle of slope, V the vertical interval between the contours, H the horizontal equivalent, and L the length of slope from contour to contour; then—

$$H = \cot A \times V,$$
$$L = \sec A \times H.$$

Fig. 257 shows the slope of a hill having in profile three different lines, A C, C D, and D E, their angles of elevation being respectively 10°, 35°, and 65°; whence, if V be put = 25, the

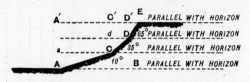

Fig. 257

horizontal equivalent of A C is 141·78 and its hypotenusal length 143·97. Of C D, these are respectively 35·70 and 43·59; and of D E, 11·66 and 27·58. The following table will facilitate computation.

TABLE OF HORIZONTAL EQUIVALENTS OF VARIOUS ANGLES OF SLOPE FOR A VERTICAL INTERVAL OF 25

< A	L sec A × H	H cot A × V	< A	L sec A × H	H cot A × V	< A	L sec A × H	H cot A × V
1°	1432·47	1432·25	16°	90·70	87·19	31°	48·54	41·61
2°	716·34	715·91	17°	85·51	81·77	32°	47·18	40·01
3°	477·68	477·03	18°	80·90	76·94	33°	45·90	38·50
4°	358·39	357·52	19°	76·79	72·61	34°	44·71	37·06
5°	286·84	285·75	20°	73·10	68·69	35°	43·59	35·70
6°	239·17	237·85	21°	69·76	65·13	36°	42·53	34·41
7°	205·14	203·61	22°	66·74	61·88	37°	41·54	33·18
8°	179·63	177·88	23°	63·98	58·90	38°	40·61	32·00
9°	159·81	157·84	24°	61·46	56·15	39°	39·73	30·87
10°	143·97	141·78	25°	59·16	53·61	40°	38·89	29·79
11°	131·02	128·61	26°	57·03	51·26	41°	38·19	28·76
12°	120·24	117·62	27°	55·07	49·07	42°	37·36	27·77
13°	111·14	108·29	28°	53·25	47·02	43°	36·66	26·81
14°	103·34	100·27	29°	51·57	45·10	44°	35·99	25·89
15°	96·59	93·30	30°	50·00	43·30	45°	35·36	25·00

For smaller vertical intervals, the tabular number divided by 25 and multiplied by the new V, will give the L and H value.

For sketch surveys this method is useful; and Figs. 258 and

U

259 show how sections thus obtained may enable contour lines (lines of equal altitudes) to be sketched-in.

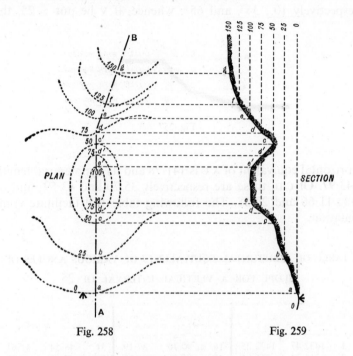

Fig. 258   Fig. 259

Contouring by angle of slope, however, is not suitable for cases where much accuracy is required: for this purpose the work must be done by actual levelling, the two usual methods being that of cross-sectioning, and that of setting out the contour lines on the ground.

In the first of these, cross-sections are taken along lines normal (as nearly as can be judged) to the general curves formed in plan by principal salient and retiring features of the ground, as shown in Fig. 260 by the lines D E, F G, H J, K L. These lines being set out, levels are taken along them, from which, when plotted, points answering to the reduced levels of the intended vertical intervals are marked-off on the plan and determine the figure of the contour lines. Or, alternatively, the reduced level of the first contour line having been settled by reference to a bench-mark, the levelling-staff is shifted along the line of each cross-section in succession until it stands on a spot where its reading gives that reduced level: a peg is driven at each such spot, the positions of these pegs marking the several points of the contour lines.

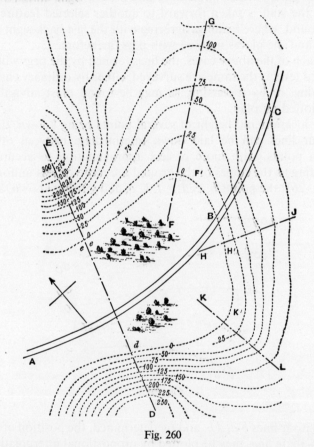

Fig. 260

In the second method, the reduced level of the first contour line having been determined as before, the staff is held at a salient or retiring feature in the estimated run of the contour line, and there shifted up or down the slope until the desired reading is obtained. A peg is driven at the spot: the staff is then removed to a suitable point further along the estimated contour line, and a peg driven where the reading is the same; and so on.

The staff remaining at the furthest point along the contour line which the surveyor chooses to read with that set of the level, he enters the reading as a fore-sight, the level is then planted at a suitable place further in advance and a back-sight taken; after which the staff is taken forward to another selected feature of the ground, where readings agreeing with the last back-sight are taken and the places marked with pegs, as before.

In each of the above cases, the lines formed by the pegs whose reduced level is the same are surveyed, either by ordinary chain-surveying, or by traversing, as may be found most advisable, and plotted on plan.

The location and height of several points being known, their contour lines can be laid down intermediate between other known points, with more or less approximation to accuracy according as the slopes of the ground are more or less uniform. In Fig. 261, the points b, c, d, e, f, h, a, and g being known, and

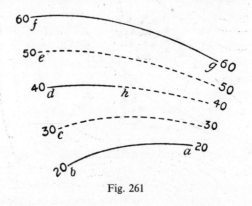

Fig. 261

the contour lines $b\,a$, $d\,h$, and $f\,g$ determined, the position of the intermediate ones may be plotted by proportional interpolation. The horizontal equivalent of $b\,f$ being 640 ft. with a total rise of 40 ft. and a nearly uniform slope of 1 in 16, the horizontal equivalent of each contour is 160 ft. and its vertical interval 10 ft. The horizontal equivalent of $a\,g$ is 360 ft. with a total rise of 40 and a slope of 1 in 6·75, the horizontal equivalent of each contour being 90 feet. A cross-section of the slope through the point h has a horizontal equivalent of 540 feet, and the contour lines there will be 135 feet apart. The completed contours in the figure are shown in full lines and the interpolated ones by dotted lines.

Contouring by "squares" – This method is in general use by many surveyors and consists of setting out a series of equal squares in the field by means of laths or ranging rods and taking spot levels at the corners of each square. The best method is to level first in one direction and follow back on the next parallel line of squares in reverse direction, and so on. The whole area is thus covered by a series of equidistant spot levels and after deciding the vertical intervals for the contours these can be sketched in by eye or, if a more exact method is desired, by proportional interpolation.

Examination Questions

1. It is required to plot the actual contour lines at 5 ft. vertical intervals of an area of pasture land 400 yds. by 400 yds. containing the usual trees and hedges. Describe how you would do this using a plane table, telescopic alidade with stadia hairs, a quickset level and a Sopwith staff. The variation in height is from 160 ft. at a stream which forms one boundary and where there is a B.M., to 200 ft. at another B.M. on a road forming the opposite boundary.

The plan is to be drawn to a scale 1/1,250.

(Institution of Civil Engineers, April 1956)

2. Describe how to set out contour lines of specific reduced level on the site of a proposed reservoir. Show how to estimate the volume of the reservoir below a given contour.

(Institution of Municipal Engineers, 1941)

3. An area of approximately 300 acres is to be developed as a housing site and a contoured plan to a scale of 1/500 is required. Compare the advantages and disadvantages of having the survey made by aerial survey and a team of land surveyors. At what intervals would you consider it desirable that contours should be drawn on the finished plan? With what degree of accuracy can these be obtained by aerial survey methods?

(Institution of Municipal Engineers, 1958)

Chapter 10

THEODOLITE-SURVEYING

THE theodolite, its construction, adjustments and usages has
been fully described in Chapter 2. Examples of the field work
and the practical application of the instrument is described
below. In Chapter 4 I have endeavoured to show how surveying
may be accomplished with the chain only; and for small surveys
in open country, perhaps the base-lines are most accurately
connected by chain measurements; but in the present chapter I
propose to demonstrate how any large or complicated survey
can be checked and considerably expedited by means of the
theodolite.

Check-lines reduced – In the first place we have seen that in the
simple case of a four-sided figure, whose sides may have been
carefully chained, it is impossible to plot the same except by
diagonal or other check-lines – the only means of testing the
accuracy of the work – whereas with a theodolite check-lines can
be reduced in number, and in the field the accuracy of the
relative positions of the four stations is made absolute by the
addition of the four angles together, the sum of which should
give 360 deg.

Accurately mark station – In commencing a theodolite survey,
it is necessary to establish the chief stations in the first place,
and at these points to drive stout pegs well into the ground, and

298

into the centre of each should be driven a nail to mark the exact point of intersection of the lines. This is absolutely necessary.

When to take angles – It is a matter entirely of choice whether the angles be taken at the commencement of the survey or not; but it will be found most convenient to take them altogether (and possibly it is preferable to do so the last thing), as it is not desirable to keep the instrument knocking about in the field, where accidents, often of a serious nature, easily happen.

The necessary number of angles – The number of angles necessary to be taken depends so much upon configuration of the ground, extensiveness of the survey, and complexity or otherwise of the system of survey-lines and the tie-lines needful for checking them, that only a general rule can be laid down, viz.: In all cases, the taking of angles serves as a useful check, but ought not to be employed to the exclusion of tie-lines where these can be run without undue increase of time and expense.

In the case of Fig. 262, if the side A C and the angles at A and C are given, it is possible to calculate the sides A B and B C; or if the angle B and the sides A B and B C are given, so may A C be found.

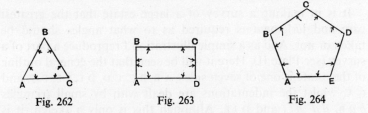

Fig. 262   Fig. 263   Fig. 264

Therefore in the field it is not absolutely necessary to take more than the angle B in the one case, or the angles A and C in the other, to check the accuracy of the sides A B, B C, A C; but this is a very primitive illustration, and really to do the thing properly I should recommend that *all* the angles be taken. Again, in Fig. 263, if the angles A and B are taken, then it will be possible to test the accuracy of the line B C; but it would be better to take the angles at A and C and run a tie-line from B to D. In the case of a five-sided figure (Figs. 264 and 265), tie-lines B D and B E and the angles at A and C would answer as well as taking all the five angles. In a figure such as Fig. 266, by taking the angles B A G, B C D, C D E, D E F, and F G A, some of the tie-lines shown might be omitted. And in Fig. 267, even if the seven angles at A, B, C, D,

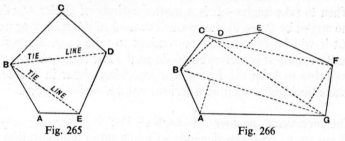

Fig. 265   Fig. 266

E, F, and G were taken, this would not dispense with the need of tie-lines from C to G and from G to D, or angular observations by which their length could be calculated.

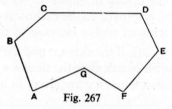

Fig. 267

It is in making a survey of a large estate that the greatest care and judgment is required as to what angles should be taken or not. And as a simple illustration I reproduce a part of a survey (see Plate II). Here it will be seen that the general outline of the estate is one of seven sides, A B, B C, C D, D E, E F, F G, and G A, whilst the indentations are dealt with by small triangles *b a* B, *d d″ d‴*, and D J E. Although this is only a sketch, it is fairly proportional, and serves to illustrate how the long offsets on lines A B, C D, and D E were avoided. I do not say that the angles of these small triangles should not be taken – indeed, if time permitted, it would be very desirable to do so – but I offer this sketch as a type of those angles which should be taken and those which may be avoided.

Angles necessary – Thus angles 1, 2, 3, 4, 5, 6, and 7 are indispensable to the accuracy of the survey, whilst the triangles may be treated in the ordinary way. So in the survey of an estate, large or small, a similar treatment will be found desirable.

Examination requirements – In the instruction to candidates issued by the Royal Institution of Chartered Surveyors, each candidate for Corporate Membership in certain sub-divisions is required to make a survey with the chain, level and theodolite. The whole of the work has to be executed from actual survey by the candidate, unaided by any other surveyor or skilled assistant. His general knowledge in surveying is thus tested in making the survey complete with the chain alone, and his acquaintance with the use of the theodolite by taking the angles.

What to avoid – In Fig. 268 I reproduce an example given in an

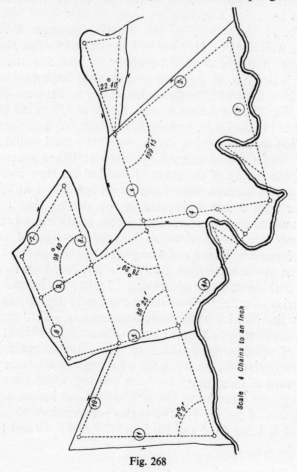

Fig. 268

old work upon surveying which, I think, will illustrate what to avoid in theodolite-surveying. It will be seen that by a more judicious use of the instrument the irregular boundaries of this property might have been more accurately determined than by the system illustrated.

We have an estate consisting of three large fields and one small one, irregularly formed, and encompassed by fourteen main survey-lines. I have reproduced (Figs. 269 and 270) the field-book of lines 1, 2, 3, and 4. Now, commencing line 1, we have the angle which line 11 makes with it, viz. 73 deg.; and at 490 we have line 5 making an angle of 86 deg. 25 min. with line No. 1; and at 910 line No. 9 makes an angle of 78 deg. 20 min. with line No. 1; but at 980, the station for line No. 4 on the right, it is not deemed necessary to take this angle, nor indeed is line No. 4A regarded as sufficiently important to have its position fixed with the theodolite. It is true that from 490 and 980 in line No. 1 the lines 4A and 4 have at 175 in the former, and at 222 in the latter, a check-line of 160; but the importance of having the meandering stream accurately fixed would surely justify, whilst the instrument was fixed at 490 to observe line No. 5, the taking of the angle of the line 4A. Now instead of forming two stations close together on line No. 1 at 910 and 980 for lines 9 and 4 respectively, by slewing line 9 round (which would be more convenient for the small fence) we should have only one instead of two stations for lines 9 and 4, and the angles formed by lines 9 and 4 respectively with line No. 1 could be taken at the same time. At 1335 in line No. 1 we have line No. 2 making an angle of 109 deg. 15 min., but instead of the small triangular field being fixed by the line 22 deg. 40 min. from 1335 in line No. 1 it would have been quite as well to check the actual position by finding the intermediate angle, without which I am of opinion the position of this triangular field is not sufficiently reliable. So much for what angles have been taken. I now turn to those that have been omitted, which lines in my judgment are essential to the satisfactory and indeed accurate completion of the survey. The angles between lines Nos. 2 and 3, 3 and 4, 4 and 4A, 5 and 10, 5 and 6, 7 and 8, 10 and 11, and 1 and 4.

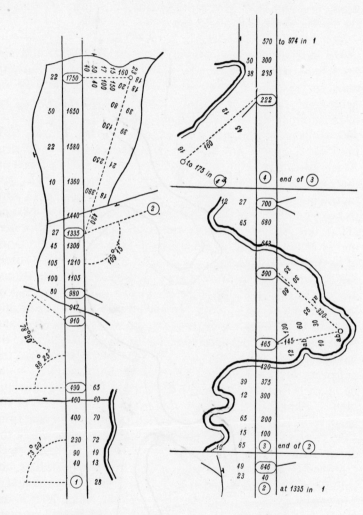

Fig. 269   Fig. 270

Surveying a river – In surveying a river, I cannot suggest a better method of recording its course, than that shown in Fig. 271. Here, we have line No. 2 forming an angle of 95 deg.

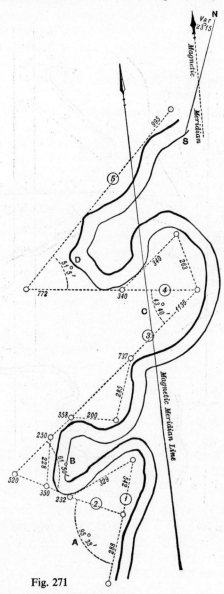

Fig. 271

38 min. with No. 1, line No. 3 forming an angle of 61 deg. 50 min. with No. 2, line No. 4 forming an angle of 43 deg. 40 min. with No. 3, and line No. 5 forming an angle of 51 deg. 5 min. with No. 4. The various small triangles on lines Nos. 2, 3, and 4 required for the purpose of taking up the bends of the river will serve as additional checks to the work.

Don't spare the use of the theodolite – I hope I have established a rule that the theodolite, when once called into requisition on a survey, should not be used sparingly, but all the chief lines, constructing as it were the main network, should be systematically connected by means of ascertaining their various included angles.

Corroboration of observation – What can be more satisfactory, to take a simple illustration, than to find the sum of three observed angles of a triangle make 180 deg. Much greater satisfaction of work in the field will result when a large number of angles are taken with similar accuracy.

There are cases, as in Fig. 272, where it is quite unnecessary to take more than the six angles, A, B, C, D, E, and F, which govern the lines that absolutely affect the external boundaries of

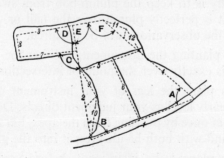

Fig. 272

the estate, such as 1, 2, 3, 4, 7, and 8. The truncated cone formed by lines 1, 2, 3, and 4 should give by the sum of the angles A, B, E, and F 360 deg., while the angles C and D serve to determine the exact position of a portion of line 3 and line 7.

Line 5, by reason of each of its extremities being fixed by the chainage on lines 2 and 4, should by its length be an additional check of the accuracy of the survey, while it serves to pick up the fence which runs alongside it. The same applies to line 6, while if the angles C and D and the lines 3 and 7 have been accurately taken and plotted, then line 8 should exactly fit in at their extremities.

Plate No. I illustrates the method of testing a chain-survey. The estate, bounded on the east and south by a wood, on the west by roads, and the north by a plantation, has been surveyed by chain only, on the lines 1, 2, 3, 4, 5, 6, 7, 8, and 9 with the various check-lines as shown. If, in addition, a theodolite was used, the following angles would be necessary: D A B, A B C, C B E, B C D, J H D, and C D A. By this method the tie-lines D B, a A, E e, C G, and H h would be obviated. Under the head of "Traversing" and "Town Surveying" further traverse work is dealt with in more detail.

Hints on the use of the theodolite – 1. It is of little use attempting to use the theodolite on a foggy, rainy, or windy day. Fog prevents clear reading, wet gets into the lens and the constant necessity to take them out and wipe them is not only a source of delay but a very great tax on patience; and with regard to wind, not only does it affect the steadiness of the telescope, but the chief difficulty is to keep the plumb-bob from swaying about, and unless it is perfectly plumb over the nail or cross-cut the accuracy of the observations will be impaired.

2. Before planting the instrument, see that the point of the plumb-bob is exactly over the point of intersection of the line.

3. Always plant the legs of your instrument firmly in the ground as nearly level as your judgment directs. Don't force all three legs in at once by pressing from the apex, but take each leg separately, and with both hands press it into the ground.

4. Having planted the instrument, before you proceed to level it take care to clamp the upper plate to the lower one at zero.

5. Now level the instrument by means of the parallel screws, having previously attended to the adjustments for collimation, parallax, etc. (referred to in Chapter 2).

6. Now direct the telescope in direction of the extremity of the first line which forms the angle as B (Fig. 273), and when as

near upon the point as is possible, clamp the lower plate, and bring it exactly to allow the cross-wires to intersect the point B by means of the lower tangent or slow motion. NOTE – Do not on any account touch any other than the lower clamp and tangent screws in this operation.

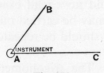

Fig. 273

7. Now (having entirely done with the lower clamp and tangent-screws) unclamp the upper plate and gently turn the telescope in direction of C, then clamp it at as near the point as possible, and with the upper tangent or slow-motion screw bring the cross-wires until they exactly intersect the point C.

8. Proceed to read the number of degrees and subdivisions of degrees on the lower plate, and the number of minutes and subdivisions in the vernier.

9. Always take the lowest point of a rod, and preferably the point of it, or an arrow held upon the nail or cross-cut in the peg. In the case of a church steeple it is advisable to take the apex.*

10. The observer should not talk or be listening to conversation during instrumental observations, as the distraction of his attention often leads to serious mistakes.

11. Most theodolites are graduated in the direction of the motion of the hands of a watch. When an angle has to be taken in the opposite direction, it has to be deducted from the instrumental reading at which it starts: from 360° if that reading is zero. Thus, if at starting the instrument is set at zero, an angle of 10° 25′ to the left of the direction in which the telescope points will read $360° - 10° 25' = 349° 35'$. If the instrument is set at (say) 195°, an angle of 12° 40′ will read $195° - 12° 40' = 182° 20'$. If at 11° 25′, an angle of 32° 56′ to the left will read $360° + 11° 25' - 32° 56' = 338° 29'$. Working to the left is often a difficulty to a beginner; but it is really a simple affair, requiring only care and attention.

* Chesterfield church excepted.

12. It is never wise to depend on one reading and the method of "repetition" should always be used in taking each angle. The angle is read as before (7 and 8): on station C keep top and bottom plates clamped and re-direct the telescope again to B. Clamp the bottom plate, unclamp the top plate and again direct to C. The vernier should now read exactly twice its previous reading. "Repetition" may be carried out a number of times if desired, but each angle should be repeated at least once.

Heights and distances – The trigonometrical measurement of height and distance of an object is a not unimportant part of surveying, and involves various problems arising out of the special conditions of different cases: of these we shall now consider the principal ones.

In the following examples, the angles of triangles are denoted by capital letters, and the sides by italic small ones; it being understood, in order to avoid multiplicity of lettering, that where two or more angles meet in the same point, the angle and the side or sides referred-to are those belonging to the triangle specified. Thus, in the triangle A B C (Fig. 274), the angle A is

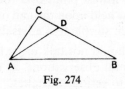

Fig. 274

C A B, the side *a* being B C; whereas in the triangle A B D the angle A is D A B, the side *a* being B D; and so on. The position of the theodolite or other instrument of observation is represented by a little tripod.

It is further to be noted, that in practice all linear and angular measurements must be made with the most scrupulous care and precision, the correctness of the result depending upon the accuracy of measurement of a line or an angle of sometimes very small dimensions.

Problem I – To find the height of an object having a vertical face B D, accessible to the observer; the ground line E D being horizontal (Fig. 275).

Measure E D = A C, and the angle of elevation B A C. Then, in the right-angled triangle A C B, the side b and the acute angle A are given, and $a = \tan A \times b$.

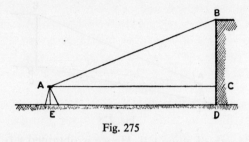

Fig. 275

To this add A E = C D. Then $a + C D = B D$ the height required.

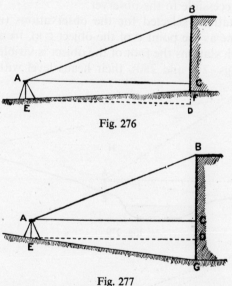

Fig. 276

Fig. 277

Note – If the ground slopes, as E F or E G (Figs. 276 and 277), the difference of level C F or C G can be ascertained by levelling, and the length of slope E F or E G measured. Then, in the right-angled triangle E D F (or E D G), the sides e and d are given, whence E D = $\sqrt{d^2 - e^2}$, and the required height of building = B C + C F (or B C + C G).

X

If the ground slopes upwards as E H (Fig. 278) so that the foot of the building is above the horizontal A C, ascertain the difference of level between E and H = D H by levelling, and

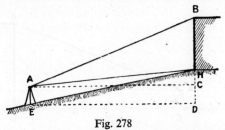

Fig. 278

measure length of slope E H. Hence is obtained E D = A C; and A C × tan B A C−(A C × tan H A C) = B H the height required.

Problem II – To find the height of an object having a vertical face C B inaccessible to the observer.

At the stations selected for the observations (in the same vertical plane as the point C of the object C B), from the nearer one of which stations the foot of the object is visible, drive pegs E and F (Figs. 279 and 280), their heads level with surface of

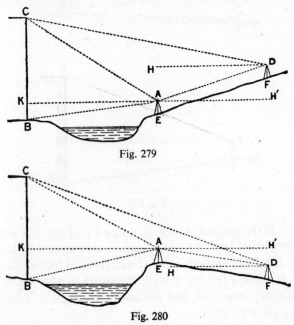

Fig. 279

Fig. 280

ground; and measure the length of base E F.* Set up theodolite over peg F, measure F D, the height of its horizontal axis D, and from D observe the angle of elevation H D C. Remove theodolite to station E; and from A observe the angle D A H′ between the reading F D on a levelling-staff set on peg F and the horizontal A H′.

H D and A H′ being horizontal and therefore parallel lines, H D A and D A H′ are equal; and C D H+H D A (Fig. 279) or C D H−A D H (Fig. 280) = C D A.

From A, observe angles C A D, K A C, and K A B.

Then, in the triangle A C D, $180° - (A+D) = C$;
and $\sin C : c :: \sin D : d$.

In the right-angled triangle A K C, $C = 90° - A$;
and $\sin K : k :: \sin A : a(= C K)$.

In the right-angled triangle A K B,
$$b \tan A = a(= K B),$$
whence $C K + K B = C B = $ the height sought.

In the above two examples, the foot of the object is visible from the nearer station. When it is visible from the further one only (Fig. 281) the problem may be solved as follows:

From D, observe the angles C D B and C D H; and measure D F the height of instrument above peg F. Remove instrument to station E; and from A observe the angles C A D and D A H′.

$$C D H + H D A = C D A.$$

Then, in the triangle A C D, $180° - (A+D) = C$;
and $\sin C : c :: \sin D : d$.

In the right-angled triangle C H D, $90° - D = C$.

---

* The height of a theodolite above the ground varies according to the spread given to the legs, and it is difficult to place it accurately in position over two pegs in succession with its axis at the same height above each. A usual and an unusual spread occasion a difference in height of about 7½ inches, corresponding to a difference of 0·00196 per cent. between the length of base as measured on the ground and that of a line joining the axis of the instrument at the two stations, the length of the latter being that whereon the triangulation is founded. To avoid prolixity in working the problems, the correction for this difference has been omitted in the examples, the two lines being taken as parallel and equal.

In the triangle C B D, $180° - (C+D) = B$,
and $\sin B : b : : \sin D : d$;
and $d = C B$, the height sought.

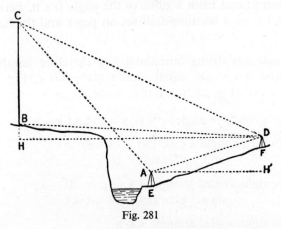

Fig. 281

Problem III – To find the surface-length of an inaccessible slope C D, as that of a steeple on a tower (Fig. 282).

Set out and measure base-line E F, and place theodolite at E and F successively. From A observe angles C A D, C A H, and

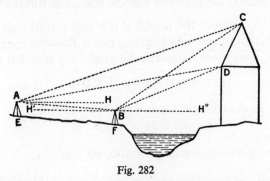

Fig. 282

D A H; and from B the angles C B D, C B H″, D B H″, C B A, and A B H′.

$$D B H'' - D A H = A D B,$$
$$C B H'' - C A H = A C B,$$
$$C A H + A B H' = C A B.$$

In the triangle A B C,

$$\sin \text{C} : c : : \sin \text{A} : a \, (= \text{B C}),$$
$$\sin \text{C} : c : : \sin \text{B} : b \, (= \text{A C}).$$

In the triangle A D B,

$$\sin \text{D} : d : : \sin \text{A} : a \, (= \text{B D}),$$
$$\sin \text{D} : d : : \sin \text{B} : b \, (= \text{A D}).$$

In the triangle C B D we have given

$$\text{side } d \, (= \text{B C}),$$
$$\text{side } c \, (= \text{B D}),$$
$$\text{and angle B;}$$

then

$$d + c : d - c : : \tan\left(\frac{\text{D} + \text{C}}{2}\right) : \tan\left(\frac{\text{D} - \text{C}}{2}\right),$$

whence

$$\tan\left(\frac{\text{D} + \text{C}}{2}\right) + \tan\left(\frac{\text{D} - \text{C}}{2}\right) = \tan \text{D},$$

$$\tan\left(\frac{\text{D} + \text{C}}{2}\right) - \tan\left(\frac{\text{D} - \text{C}}{2}\right) = \tan \text{C},$$

$$\sin \text{C} : c : : \sin \text{B} : b,$$

and $b = \text{C D} =$ the length of slope sought.

In all the foregoing examples the base-line is assumed to be set out in the same vertical plane as the point or points of the object. When, owing to configuration of the ground, or to other circumstances, this cannot be done, as in Fig. 283, where the base-line has to be set out on a narrow road bounded by precipitous cliffs on one hand and a river or lake on the other:

From A observe the vertical angles C A D, D A H, and the horizontal angle H A B. From B observe the horizontal angle H B A.

The angle A H B $= 180° - (\text{H A B} + \text{H B A})$.

In the triangle A H B,

$$\sin \text{H} : h : : \sin \text{B} : b \, (= \text{H A}).$$

And with H A as base, the heights C D and D H are ascertained, as in Problem I.

The measurement of inaccessible distances is performed on the same principle as that of inaccessible heights. Thus, if the heights in Figs. 275 to 281 are known, or ascertained, their dimension serves as a base-line, and the distances are obtained by a process the converse of that followed in the examples. Fig. 283 illustrates a case wherein the height of the observed object does not enter into the calculation, the distance H A (and thence D A) being obtained independently of it. In fact, by far the

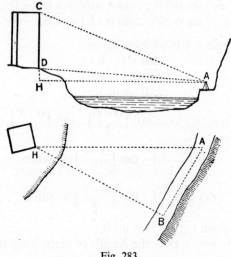

Fig. 283

greater number of such cases are solved by a base-line on the ground, and thus by angles in azimuth only.

Suppose it be necessary to ascertain the length between two trees C D, but it is impossible to approach them by reason of the river. Having measured the base-line A B very accurately, the

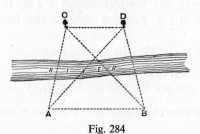

Fig. 284

angles C A B, C B A, D B A, and D A B must be observed; from which, by preceding problems, the sides C A, D B, C B, and D A must be calculated together with the angles A C D, B D C, C D A, and D A C. With these, as has been shown, the length C D may be calculated.

Examination Questions

1. Observations are taken from a point O to three stations A, B and C, the theodolite readings, graduated clockwise, being 30° 12′ 0″, 79° 43′ 0″, and 122° 11′ 0″. From an Ordnance sheet the distances A B and B C were found to be 973 ft. and 821 ft. respectively and the angle A B C nearest to O was 131° 14′ 0″. Calculate the lengths O A and O B.

(University of London B.Sc.(Eng.) 1956)

2. To settle a dispute which arose over the height of a chimney C, a base-line A B was set out 300·0 ft. long.

A theodolite set up at A with a horizontal telescope gave a reading of 4·38 on a staff held on the foundation block. The angle of elevation to the top of the chimney was 21° 15′ and the horizontal angle anti-clockwise from the centre of the chimney to B was 54° 12′.

With the theodolite at B and a horizontal telescope the staff reading on the foundation block was 10·07 and the horizontal angle clockwise from the centre of the chimney to A was 48° 36′.

Calculate the height of the chimney above the foundation block. What should the angle of elevation to the top of the chimney be, as measured from B?

(University of London B.Sc. Estate Management, 1956)

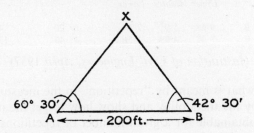

3. In order to measure the height of a building X (Fig. 1), a base-line A B was measured and the horizontal angles X A B and X B A measured. The angles of slope by theodolite from A and B respectively to X were +20° 15′ and +15° 00′. If the height

of the theodolite was 4′ 6″ at A and 4′ 3″ at B, determine the mean height of X.

(*Royal Institution of Chartered Surveyors*, 1954)

4. Write a specification for the accurate measurement of a horizontal angle, using a transit theodolite having two verniers on the horizontal plate, and explain briefly the significance and effect of each step in the procedure.

It may be assumed that the instrument is accurately centred and levelled on firm ground and that parallax has been eliminated.

(*Institution of Municipal Engineers*, 1950)

5. State which errors of adjustment in a theodolite are eliminated by taking the mean of face right and face left readings. Assume all readings are the mean of both verniers or both micrometers.

Describe how you would test for, and adjust, any two of these errors.

(*Institution of Civil Engineers*, April 1958)

6. The data given are observations made with an anallatic tacheometer. If the ground slopes evenly from B to C, what is the gradient of the slope?

Ins. station	Observing to	Stadia readings on vertical staff			Vertical angle to centre reading	Bearing from north
		Upper	Centre	Lower		
A	B	9·68	5·91	2·14	+ 6° 20′	43° 20′
	C	8·42	4·99	1·56	− 4° 40′	133° 20′

(*Institution of Civil Engineers*, April 1957)

7. State what is meant by "repetition" in the measurement of an angle by the theodolite, and show how to get the maximum accuracy obtainable for a given number of repetitions.

A straight line is to be set out making, very accurately, a specified angle with a line already set out on the ground. Show how repetition may be used very advantageously in setting out the line.

(*Institution of Municipal Engineers*, 1946)

Chapter 11

SETTING OUT CURVES

General principles—Limit of radii—Preliminary operations—Tangent points—Tangential angle—Length of curve—Impeded point in curve—Apex inaccessible—Setting out with two theodolites—Formula for curves—Table of tangential angles—Curves of different radii—Curves of contraflexure—Setting out by offsets—Curve offset rule—Setting out from same tangent—Setting out by means of ordinates—Degree curve system—Examination questions.

PRACTICAL surveyors are nowadays required to perform so many more duties than heretofore, that any work upon the subject of their duties would be incomplete if it did not treat upon the setting out of curves. It does not necessarily follow that these curves are only for railway work, as in the development of property it is often required to lay out new roads and boundaries, which, for economical and other reasons, frequently are required to take the form of regular curves.

The most accurate and satisfactory method of laying out curves is by means of a theodolite, but for approximate results the operation may be performed by tangents and offsets, or chords and ordinates.

In most cases a curve is used to connect two straight lines, whose relative positions are such that one forming an angle with the other they intersect each other at some given point. In Fig. 285 it will be seen that the lines A *a* and C *c* intersect at the point B. It matters not how acute or obtuse the angle of intersection may be, there is some curve, great or small, which will connect these two lines, to which they will be tangential.

In considering a railway, as an illustration, it simply consists of a series of straight lines, whose directions form angles with each other, whereby it is necessary to connect each with the

317

other by means of curves, as is illustrated in Fig. 286, by the
five lines A B, B C, C D, D E, E F, and four curves $a\,a'$, $b\,b'$, $c\,c'$,

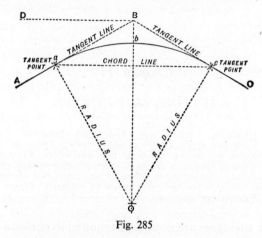

Fig. 285

and $d\,d'$. Here we have the angles A B C, B C D, C D E, and D E F,
without knowing the value of which it is impossible to set out
the curves upon the ground.

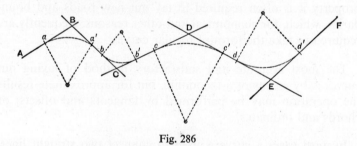

Fig. 286

It may be well here to mention that for railway work it is
better to lay out these straight lines and make them the base-
lines of the survey. This may be done either by traversing or,
preferably, by taking the included angles with the theodolite.
It need hardly be explained that for the purpose of taking up the
features on the right and left hand of these lines a complete
system of triangulation must be adopted.

Having obtained an accurate record of the relative positions
of these straight lines, which should be plotted to as large a

scale as possible, together with the details of the survey, it will then be possible to determine the various radii of the connecting curves.

Limit of radii – In speaking of the radii of curves, I may say that curves of less than 12 chains' radius are not desirable for railway work. I have known less, but for many reasons sharp curves are to be avoided. It is a very mistaken theory that curves of small radius enable the engineer to economise in the design of his work, or in other words to avoid undue severance of property; and it is a very questionable policy, for against a small saving in the purchase of the necessary land (which is settled once for all) must be placed the constant wear and tear of the permanent way and rolling stock, which, if capitalised at a period of years, will prove a very formidable amount. Again, in these days of high speed it is absolutely out of the question to adopt sharp curves. There is no fixed rule to govern the limit of radius of curves, as so much depends upon local and other circumstances, which it is not the province of this work to consider.

Preliminary – Now to take a simple illustration, we will assume that in Fig. 285 the ∠ of intersection A B C is 135°; bisect this = 67° 30′, which deducted from 90° = 22° 30′ the ∠ of deflection B a c = D b a = B O a. The line B O is at right angles to the line a c.

We will assume the radius of the curve = 30 chains, and it is required to find its centre. Multiply the natural secant of the ∠ of deflection (= 22° 30′) by the radius; then

Nat. sec. 22° 30′ = 1·08239 × 30 = 32·4718 chains,

which is the distance from the intersection B of the tangents to the centre O of the curve; and 32·4718 − 30 = 2·4718 chains = the distance B b from the point of intersection to the point b where the arc is bisected.

To determine the points of commencement and termination of the curve (the "tangent-points"), multiply the natural tangent of the ∠ of deflection by the radius; this gives the length of tangents B a and B c. Thus

Nat. tan. 22° 30′ = 0·41421 × 30 = 12·4264 chains = B a and B c.

When the point of intersection is not accessible, the length of tangents is set out as follows (Fig. 287). Run any line E F from tangent to tangent; then

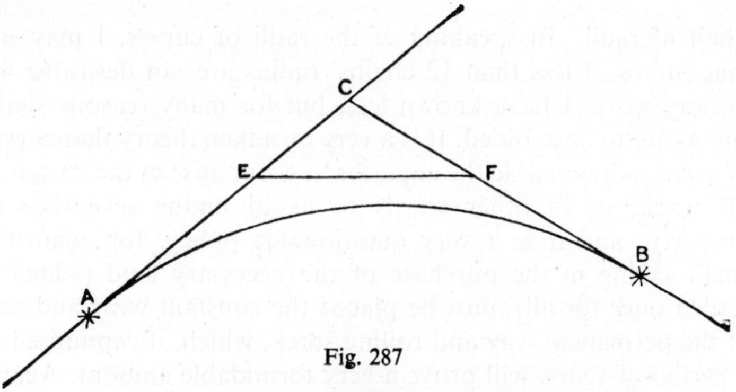

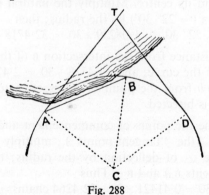

Fig. 287

$$\angle\,C\,E\,F = 180° - \angle\,A\,E\,F$$
$$\angle\,C\,F\,E = 180° - \angle\,B\,F\,E$$
$$\text{therefore }\angle\,A\,C\,B = 180° - (\angle\,C\,E\,F + \angle\,C\,F\,E)$$
$$\text{and side }E\,C = \frac{E\,F\times\sin C\,F\,E}{\sin A\,C\,B}$$
$$\text{and side }F\,C = \frac{E\,F\times\sin C\,E\,F}{\sin A\,C\,B}.$$

When a portion of the curve itself is inaccessible (Fig. 288), a point B in it from tangent-point A is set out as follows. The chord of any arc = twice sine of half the ∠ subtended by that chord at centre of curve. Thus

$$\angle\,T\,A\,B = \tfrac{1}{2}\,\angle\,A\,C\,B;\text{ whence }A\,B = 2\sin T\,A\,B\times\text{radius.}$$

Fig. 288

The tangents having been produced to their intersection B (Fig. 285), a stout peg is driven there, and the exact point of intersection marked by a spike driven into the top of the peg. The theodolite is adjusted over this mark; the ∠ of intersection A B C observed; the distance B *b* calculated; and the point *b* fixed by bisecting ∠ A B C and driving a peg lined-in by the theodolite on the line of bisection at the distance B *b*. The length of tangents is then set-off from B, a peg is lined-in by the theodolite and driven at their ends *a* and *c*, and distinguished by a peg driven at each side on a line transverse to the tangent (some prefer to drive four pegs, as shown in Figs. 289, 290, 291).

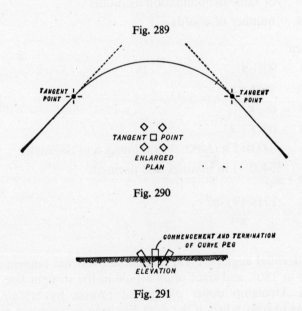

Fig. 289

TANGENT POINT

TANGENT POINT

TANGENT ☐ POINT

ENLARGED PLAN

Fig. 290

COMMENCEMENT AND TERMINATION OF CURVE PEG

ELEVATION

Fig. 291

The data assumed and calculated as above described, being adopted for illustration, we are now prepared to set out the curve by one or other of several methods, the most useful being: By Tangential Angles; by Offsets from Chords produced; by Offsets from Tangents; and by Ordinates from Chords.

The symbols and formulae are as follows:

R = radius of curve

I = half $\angle$ of intersection

F = $\angle$ of deflection ($=$ half $\angle$ at centre of curve)

D = distance from centre of curve to intersection of tangents

X = external secant of F

T = length of tangents

L = length of curve

C = tangential $\angle$ in minutes and decimals for each chord of same denomination as radius

N = number of chords

Then

$$F = 90° - I$$

$$D = \sec F \times R$$

$$X = D - R$$

$$T = \tan F \times R$$

$$L = \cdot000582 \, R \, (5400 - I \text{ in minutes and decimals})$$

$$N = \frac{5400 - I \text{ in minutes and decimals}}{C}$$

$$C = \frac{1718 \cdot 873387}{R}.$$

By tangential angles – Plant theodolite over first tangent-point, clamp at 180°, and sight upon a pole in the straight line backwards. Unclamp upper plate, and reverse by bringing the reading to zero, when, if the work has been correctly set out, the cross-wires should sight the spike in the intersection peg; and, with the vernier set to $\angle$ of deflection, the cross-wires should sight upon the second tangent-point. The radius of curve being 30 chains, the tangential $\angle$ for a 1-chain chord $= 57'$ $17\cdot7468''$. With one end of chain at the tangent-point, a pin at the other end, ranged to that $\angle$, marks the first point on the curve. Point No. 2 is marked by a pin 1 chain from point No. 1, ranged by a reading of double the first ∠. For the third point, the ∠ 57′ 17·7468″ is multiplied by 3, and a pin 1 chain from point

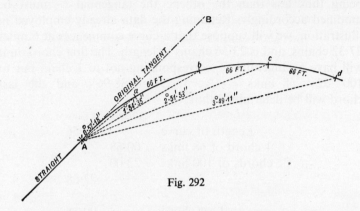

Fig. 292

No. 2 is ranged at that ∠, and so on (Fig. 292): the record of the several angles at the points being as follows:

1st tangential ∠ =   57′ 17·7468″ =   57′ 18″ =   57·296′
2nd   „   „   = 1° 54′ 35·4936″ = 1° 54′ 35″ = 1° 54·592′
3rd   „   „   = 2° 51′ 53·2404″ = 2° 51′ 53″ = 2° 51·887′
4th   „   „   = 3° 49′ 10·9872″ = 3° 49′ 11″ = 3° 49·183′
5th   „   „   = 4° 46′ 28·7340″ = 4° 46′ 29″ = 4° 46·479′

In the above example, the fractions of seconds are given to four places of decimals to show the reason of the apparent irregularity in the additions. As theodolites for ordinary railway and survey work seldom read to smaller angles than 20 seconds = one-third of a minute, tables of tangential angles are rarely carried to smaller subdivisions. Excess or defect in any one ∠ is too small to be of any practical account in setting out a curve, and, being in the table adjusted to the nearest half or one-third of a minute, it is not cumulative. Decimals are easily converted into thirds by the following table:

From 0·0000 to 0·1666 both inclusive = $\frac{0}{3}$
  „   0·1667 „ 0·4999   „   „   = $\frac{1}{3}$
  „   0·5000 „ 0·8333   „   „   = $\frac{2}{3}$
  „   0·8334 „ 1·0000   „   „   = $\frac{3}{3}$.

It is not often the case that a curve commences or terminates at even chainage; and, the initial or the terminal chord, or both, being thus less than the others, the tangential $\angle$ must be modified accordingly. Retaining the data already employed in illustration, we will suppose that a curve commences at 6 miles 27·32 chains, and is 23·56 chains in length. The first chord on it will have a tangential $\angle$ corresponding not to 1 chain but to $100-32 = 68$ links $= \frac{68}{100} \times 57\cdot296' = 38\cdot96'$; and the last chord will be determined thus:

	Chains	Chains
Length of curve =		23·56
1 chord of 68 links =	00·68	
22 chords of 100 links =	22·00	
		22·68
Last chord =		00·88

Its tangential $\angle$ will be $\frac{88}{100} \times 57\cdot296 = 50\cdot53'$; and the curve ends at 6 miles 50·88 chains.

Before commencing to set out, it is advisable to make a complete list of the tangential angles of the curve, from the first tangent-point to the last: it saves much trouble in the field, where the surveyor has his mind occupied and his hands full. For the curve we have taken as an illustration, the list of tangential angles will be as follows:

1st chord =	0° 38·96′		13th chord =	12° 6·51′
2nd ,, =	1° 36·26′		14th ,, =	13° 3·81′
3rd ,, =	2° 33·55′		15th ,, =	14° 1·10′
4th ,, =	3° 30·85′		16th ,, =	14° 58·40′
5th ,, =	4° 28·14′		17th ,, =	15° 55·69′
6th ,, =	5° 25·44′		18th ,, =	16° 52·99′
7th ,, =	6° 22·74′		19th ,, =	17° 50·29′
8th ,, =	7° 20·03′		20th ,, =	18° 47·58′
9th ,, =	8° 17·33′		21st ,, =	19° 44·88′
10th ,, =	9° 14·62′		22nd ,, =	20° 42·17′
11th ,, =	10° 11·92′		23rd ,, =	21° 39·47′
12th ,, =	11° 9·22′		24th ,, =	22° 30·00′

If the curve is to the left, the tangential angles above given would be deducted from 360° and the pegs set accordingly. Thus for the first chord the instrumental reading would be 360°−38·96′ = 359° 21·04′, for the second 360°−1° 36·26′ = 358° 23·74′, for the third 360°−2° 33·55′ = 357° 26·45′; and so on.

Curves of less radius than 15 chains should be set out in half-chain chords, for which the tangential angles of whole-chain chords of curves double the radius can be used.

Save in curves of radius exceeding 30 chains, it is not desirable to set out more than from five to eight chords from the same station, because the tangential ∠ becomes too large to ensure the placing of the pegs exactly on the line of curve. There may thus be one or more shifts of the theodolite; and sometimes trees, buildings, or other obstacles may prevent even that number being set.

After a shift, it is necessary to resume by sighting on some one or other of the back pegs, as follows:

Bring vernier to 180°+tangential ∠ of the peg from which the setting-out is to be resumed, and sight upon that peg. Clamp lower plate, and bring vernier to whole tangential ∠ of the forward peg next to be set out.

Thus, on the curve already used as an illustration, 30 chains radius and curving to the right, five chords having been set out from tangent-point A (Fig. 293), and the setting of any more being impeded by an obstacle, the theodolite is removed, and planted at peg No. 5 (A′). Tangent-point A being No. 0, its tangential ∠ is 0° 0′; and to resume from it the vernier is brought to 180° and the cross-hairs sighted upon it. Clamp lower plate, bring vernier to 5° 25·44′, the whole tangential ∠

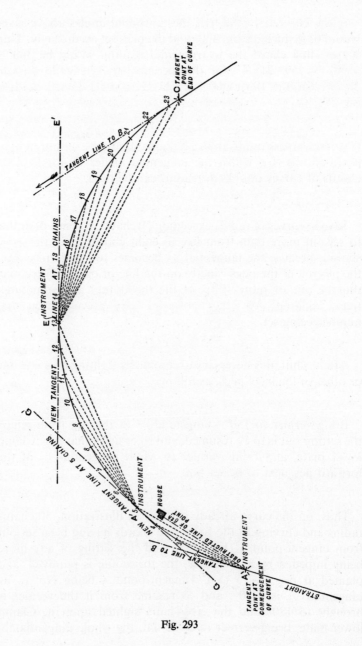

Fig. 293

of peg No. 6, set out peg No. 6 on that bearing, and the succeeding ones each on its own whole tangential ∠, *i.e.* peg No. 7 on 6° 22·74′, No. 8 on 7° 20·03′, etc. When peg No. 13 is set out perhaps another obstacle may oblige another removal of theodolite. Plant it at peg No. 13 as a fresh station. Bring vernier to 180°+tangential ∠ of previous station (peg No. 5) = 180°+4° 28·14′ sight on peg No. 5, and clamp lower plate. Bring vernier to read 13° 3·81′ the whole tangential ∠ of peg No. 14, and set out that peg; and so on.

Observe that in a curve to the left the vernier is to be brought to 180°−tangential ∠ of the peg from which the setting-out is to be resumed.

As a check upon the work as it proceeds, it is well to occasionally bring the vernier to 180°+(or − as the case may be) the tangential ∠ of the furthest visible back peg, and sight upon that peg, clamp lower plate, and bring vernier to whole tangential ∠ of second tangent-point if visible; the cross-hairs should then cut this point. If they fail to do so, some error has crept into the setting-out.

At the close of the work, the tangential ∠ of the final chord ought to cut upon the second tangent-point.

It is best not to drive the stumps until the whole curve has been set out; not only because chain-pins can be more accurately set out at first, but because they may need shifting, and also because driving the stumps may shake the theodolite.

Setting-out curves with two theodolites – This is in some respects the most satisfactory instrumental method: the points on the curve may be found without measurement, and it is especially suitable in cases where a river, a part of a lake, or other obstacles prevent the use of the chain; also in very hilly ground, where the measurement of the chord-lines would be attended not only with difficulty but also with liability to inaccuracy.

Fig. 294 is an illustration of this method. The straight lines if produced to B would intersect in the bay, and it is required to set out the points of the curve at 1, 2, 3, 4, 5, and 6. By the method explained and illustrated in previous pages, the ∠ of intersection may be obtained and the tangent-points A and C fixed. At each of these points a theodolite should be planted and adjusted to its tangent-line A B or C B.

In this example we will assume the curve to be to the right, the radius 8 chains, the ∠ A B C 92° 30' and the chords 2 chains each. The ∠ of deflection is 43° 45', the tangential ∠ for each of the 2-chain chords 7° 9·72', the length of the curve 12·24 chains, and the number of chords 6·11.

Bring vernier of theodolite at A to 180° and sight a mark on the straight line A D backwards towards D. Clamp lower plate, and bring vernier to 7° 9·72', the tangential ∠ of 1st chord.

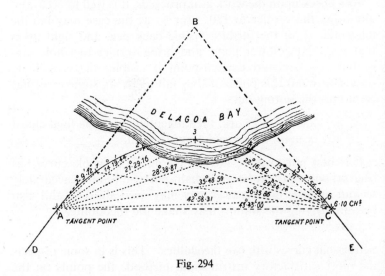

Fig. 294

The number of chords being 6·11, and the bearing of the first of them being thus set off from A, the tangential ∠ from C corresponding to peg No. 1 of the curve will be (6·11 − 1 = 5·11 × 7° 9·72') = 36° 35·86'. Bring vernier of theodolite at C to 180° and sight a mark on the straight line C E forwards towards E. Clamp lower plate and bring vernier to 360° − 36° 35·86' = 323° 24·14'; and at the intersection of this bearing with the bearing from A, put down the pin for first point of the curve.

The tangential $\angle$ at A for chord No. 2 is 14° 19·44′, and the corresponding $\angle$ at C is 360°−(36° 35·86′−7° 9·72′) = 360° −29° 26·14′ = 330° 33·86′, and so on; the complete list of tangential angles being as follows:

Chord No.	Theodolite at A		Theodolite at C		
	From Tangent A B		From Tangent C B		Reading on Theodolite
1	$\angle$ B A 1	7° 9·72′	$\angle$ B C 1	36° 35·86′	323° 24·14′
2	,, B A 2	14° 19·44′	,, B C 2	29° 26·14′	330° 33·86′
3	,, B A 3	21° 29·16′	,, B C 3	22° 16·42′	337° 43·58′
4	,, B A 4	28° 38·87′	,, B C 4	15° 6·71′	344° 53·29′
5	,, B A 5	35° 48·59′	,, B C 5	7° 56·99′	352° 3·01′
6	,, B A 6	42° 58·31′	,, B C 6	47·27′	359° 12·73′
7	,, B A C	43° 45′			

The $\angle$ B A C, if calculated according to the tangential $\angle$ for a 2-chain chord, would be 43° 45·58′, or nearly 35 seconds in excess of the $\angle$ of deflection, owing to the difference between the true length of the curve and the sum of 6·11 chords of 2 chains each. A difference of this nature always exists in the case of a curve set out by chords; but in all ordinary cases the difference is so small as to be immaterial. When, however, the radius of the curve is small relatively to the length of the chords, the difference becomes so great that, in order to avoid confusion by suggestion of error in the work, the final tangential $\angle$ should be so modified as to make up the total $\angle$ of deflection; as is done in the foregoing example.

Curves of different radii – It may happen that whilst for good reasons it may be desirable to traverse a certain portion of the ground by a curve of say 60 chains radius, yet an obstruction may occur which involves either a change in the radius of the curve, or (what is frequently done) the stoppage of the original curve at some point, and after a short length of straight line the adoption of a curve of different radius in order to avoid the obstruction. Thus in Fig. 295 we see that after setting out a certain distance from A to *b* with a radius of 50 chains, that from this latter point it is necessary to reduce the radius to 40 chains. Now, assuming that we have set out 8 chords from A, then the tangential angle B A *b* will be 4° 35′. Remove the

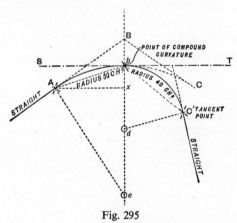

Fig. 295

theodolite from A to *b* and set the vernier at 335° 25′ (being 360°−4° 35′, as we are now working the upper plate from right to left), clamp the two plates, direct the telescope on to A, clamp the lower and unclamp the upper plate, fix the latter at zero, and we obtain a tangent-line s *b* T common to the two curves, and from *b*, which is termed *the point of compound curvature*, we may now proceed to set out the tangential angles for the curve whether of greater or smaller radius than the first one.

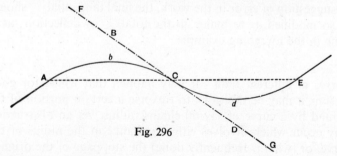

Fig. 296

Curves of contraflexure – "Reverse" curves or curves of contraflexure, as Fig. 296, are set out by establishing a common tangent-line F G by the same process as just described, and

setting out tangential angles from right to left from C, in which
case each angle for one chord must be consecutively deducted
from 360 deg.

It should here be stated that a length of straight line, usually
two chains, should always intervene between any curves,
whether similar or reversed, as it is under very exceptional
circumstances – at least as far as English practice is concerned –
that one curve proceeds directly from another.

Setting out curves by offsets – I shall very briefly consider these
methods, experience having proved that they can be used in
cases only where accuracy is not of much importance.

The most usual system is by means of an offset from the
tangent-line, at the first point on the curve; and from the chord
produced, for each subsequent point (Figs. 297, 298).

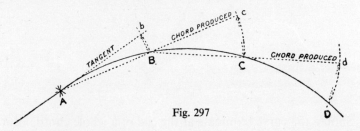

Fig. 297

L = length of chords expressed in the same units as the radius
    of the curve.

O = offset.

R = radius of curve.

Then $O = \dfrac{L^2}{R}$.

The first offset from the tangent produced is equal to $\dfrac{O}{2}$ and
the length measured along the tangent, A b, is equal to the base
of a right-angled triangle of which the hypoteneuse is the length
of the chord and the perpendicular the length of the half offset.

Thus, if L = 1 chain and R = 20 chains,

$$O = \frac{1^2}{20} = \frac{1}{20} \text{ chains} = \frac{66}{20} \text{ feet} = 3\cdot3 \text{ ft.}$$

$$\tfrac{1}{2}O = 1\cdot65 \text{ ft.}$$

The half offset is set out at right angles to the tangent in practice, at such a distance along the same that the extreme end of the offset gives exactly a one-chain chord from A to B. The full offsets *c* C, *d* D, etc., form the bases of isosceles triangles the sides of which are equal in length to the chords.

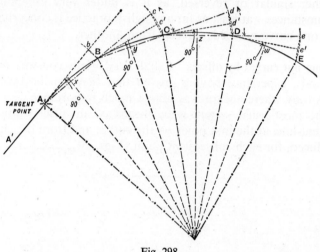

Fig. 298

Should the curve terminate at the end of a whole chord, as at D (Fig. 298), the offset must be the same as that for the first point, viz. *b* B, and should exactly reach to the straight line D *e'* beyond the curve. If the curve terminates on a broken chord, the length of the offset must bear the same proportion to the first one as the fractional length of the chord does to the length measured along the first tangent.

To set out a curve by this or the next following method requires the very greatest care. Any error, even if slight, has a

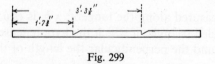

Fig. 299

tendency to accumulate throughout the work. I have always used an offset-staff (Fig. 299), made of a lath of good hard wood a little longer than the longest offset, having on one edge, at the exact length of the tangential and the chord offsets, two notches to admit the arrow by which the point of the curve is to be marked. The length A *b* having been measured along the tangent, and the end of the offset-staff set at the arrow there fixed, the chain is laid from A to B and held at the first notch, and an arrow there put in. The chord-line A B is then produced to *c* and measured, becoming the line from which the second offset is to be measured. Here the same operation is repeated, but the chain is now laid from B to the second notch, and an arrow put in; and so on.

Setting out curves from same tangent – Another method of setting out a curve by offsets is from the same tangent (Fig. 300), the offsets being all at right angles thereto. In this system the first offset is found by the same rule as in the preceding method;

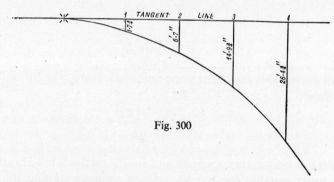

Fig. 300

and the subsequent offsets are this result multiplied by the square of the number of points. Thus for a 20-chain curve:

		Inches		Ft.	In.
1st offset	. .	19·81	=	1	$7\frac{3}{4}$
2nd ,,	. .	19·81 × 4 =		6	7
3rd ,,	. .	19·81 × 9 =		14	$9\frac{3}{4}$
4th ,,	. .	19·81 × 16 =		26	$4\frac{3}{4}$
5th ,,	. .	19·81 × 25 =		41	3

etc., etc., etc.

Owing to the great length of the offsets and the variation in the distances along the tangent, this method is less desirable for use than even the one last described.

Setting out curves by ordinates – This consists in setting up ordinates at right angles to a chord-line of the intended curve, their position on the chord, and their length, determining the several points of the curve. In Fig. 301 the reference of the letters is thus:

C = Chord
v = Versed sine
R = Radius of curve
x = Distance of ordinate from centre of chord
o = Length of ordinate.

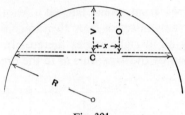

Fig. 301

All dimensions are in the same unit of measure. The formulae are these:

$$v = R - \sqrt{R^2 - (\tfrac{1}{2}C)^2}$$
$$o = \sqrt{R^2 - x^2} - (R - v).$$

It is not only a very accurate and simple method, but also the one most suitable for use in a forest country or one much obstructed with bush and coppice-wood, the clearing required being but slight. The calculation of the ordinates involves a certain amount of time and trouble rendering it cumbersome for use in the field if they have to be made on the spot. But with a set of simple tables it is easy and extremely expeditious.

Finally, as regards curves in general, it is to be borne in mind that the permanent chain-stumping of the curve should always be set out by careful measurement after the setting-out (by whatever method performed) is completed.

Degree curve system – It will be remembered that in the example given on page 323 the angle subtended at the centre of a 30 chain curve by a one chain chord is twice the tangential angle,

57·296 minutes. In the example given on page 324, since the tangent point does not fall at an even chain, the most usual condition, a proportion of the tangential angle has to be taken for the first setting of the instrument, and a very awkward angle has to be added for each following chord round the curve. Finally, another proportion sum has to be worked out for the last chord up to the further tangent point.

These proportional sums can hardly ever be avoided, but they would be simplified, and so also is the constant addition for whole chords, by the adoption of such a radius for the curve that the angle subtended at the centre by one chain shall be one, or a multiple of one degree. The constant addition to tangential angle will then be one half, or a multiple of one half, degree. The radius will not differ to an important extent from 30 chains, and the labour of setting out will be much diminished. This system is extensively used in the British Empire, and other countries.

An arc of a circle equal in length to the radius subtends at the centre an angle of 57·2958 degrees. An arc, 100 feet long, will subtend an angle of one degree at the centre of a curve with a radius of 5729·58 degrees. Whatever be the length of the standard chain in use, 100 or 66 feet, 20 or 30 metres, an arc of that length will subtend one degree on a curve of a radius of the standard length multiplied by 57·2958. By adopting a curve of radius 1891 feet, the constant addition to tangential angle in the example given will be one degree instead of 57·296 minutes, and the proportional calculations at both ends will be simplified.

A further advantage is that the volume of tables is much smaller. A set of tables for a one degree curve is adaptable to curves of other radii by a simple division. This applies to every function of a curve in which the denominator is R, the radius, converted into 5730/D, the degree of the curve.

Examination Questions

1. A straight B C deflects 26° right from a straight A B. They are to be joined by two cubic parabola transition curves such that the rate of change of acceleration is 1 ft./sec.²/sec. and the design speed 30 m.p.h.

Tabulate the data for setting out one of the curves.

(University of London B.Sc. (Eng.) 1956)

2. A gradient of 1 in 40 uphill is followed by one of 1 in 80 downhill. Their point of intersection is at chainage 18 50 and reduced level 231·20. These gradients are to be connected by a vertical curve 350 ft. long, pegs being driven at 50 ft. intervals from the starting point of the curve.

Recording your calculations in tabular form, determine the levels of successive pegs.

(*University of London B.Sc. Estate Management*, 1957)

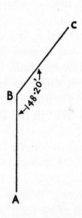

3. The centre-line of a circular railway curve is to be set out in the field and is to connect two straights A B and B C. The radius of the curve is to be 2,500 ft. and pegs are to be driven at each chord length of 100 ft. The deflection angle is 148° 20′ as shown on Fig. 1.

Calculate the information necessary to set out the curve.

(*Royal Institution of Chartered Surveyors*, 1957)

4. A circular curve is to be set out with pegs at every even 50 ft. chainage between two straights intersecting at chainage 3625·0 ft. with a deflection angle of 27°. The radius of the curve is to be such that the minimum distance of the curve from the inter-section point of the straights is 50 ft. Calculate the following:

(1) The radius of the curve.
(2) The chainage of the initial and final tangent points.
(3) The chord lengths for the setting out of the pegs.

(*Royal Institution of Chartered Surveyors*, 1955)

5. It is required to set out a simple curve which will be tangential to three straights, two of which X Y and Y Z intersect at Y and the third runs from A on X Y to B on Y Z. The following angles are known: A Y B = 104° 36'; B A X = 148° 54'; Z B A = 135° 42'. The chainage at A is 127+76 and at Y is 142+96. What will be the chainage of the tangent point T on the straight X Y and the through chainage of the point P where the curve touches the straight A B?

(*The Institution of Civil Engineers, October* 1957)

6. The whole circle bearings of two consecutive straights in a layout are 64° 30' and 90° 10'. A circular arc is to be inserted tangential to the two straights and the arc must pass through a fixed point which is located at an offset distance of 15 ft. measured from a point 25·47 ft. back from the intersection point on one of the tangents.

Calculate the tangent lengths of the arc and thence determine the radius.

(*Institution of Municipal Engineers*, 1950)

7. From the following data, prepare a table of angles and measurements to enable pegs at every 100 ft. chainage to be set out on a circular curve, using for the purpose a chain and theodolite.

Intersection angle of straights: 15° 38' 00"
Radius of curve: 3,500 ft.
Chainage at point of intersection of straights: 28800+34 ft.

(*Institution of Municipal Engineers*, 1957)

Chapter 12

GEODESY AND SPECIALIST SURVEYING

GEODESY is the higher form of surveying and requires specialized
study. There exists a number of excellent thesis devoted solely
to the subject to which the student is referred. In an elementary
work such as *Practical Surveying* detailed consideration would
be out of place, even if space permitted, but a description of
some of the more important subjects are included in this
chapter as an introduction to more detailed study which will be
found elsewhere.

Triangulation survey – The determination of various points in a
survey, to be afterwards filled-in by detailed chain or other
surveys, is performed by triangulation founded upon observations starting from a measured base-line. For all triangulation
work, the measurement of this needs, as already mentioned,
special care. In great undertakings such as the Ordnance and
other official surveys, in which the largest base yet measured is
short in comparison with the sides of triangles thereon built
up – some of these upwards of eighty and even a hundred miles
in length – the matter is one of national importance. To ensure
its utmost accuracy, extraordinary pains have been bestowed
upon it; particulars whereof, too lengthy to be adequately
described here, are to be found detailed in several works dealing
with the subject. From the measured base, triangles are successively deduced, the length of their sides being increased as

338

rapidly as possible; and upon these, secondary and tertiary systems of triangulation are in turn continued. In the setting-out of all these, attention has to be paid to their being "well-conditioned," *i.e.* that their angles are neither too obtuse nor too acute. The limits recommended as the maximum and minimum of those for great surveys, 120° and 30°, cannot, however, always be adhered to in minor work nor in observations for calculation of heights and distances.

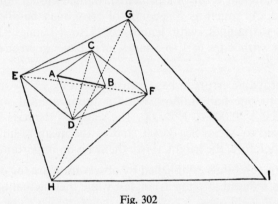

Fig. 302

A B (Fig. 302) is supposed to be the measured base, of two or three miles, or as long as can conveniently be obtained; and c and D the nearest trigonometrical points. All the angles being observed, the distances of c and D from the extremities of the base are very carefully calculated. Then in each of the triangles, D A C and D B C, we have two sides and the contained angles, to find D C; one calculation acting as a check upon the other. This line, D C, is again made the base from which the distances of the stations E and F are computed from D and C; and the length of E F is afterwards obtained in the two triangles E D F and E C F. In like manner the relative positions of the points H, G, I, etc. are obtained; and some such system should be pursued until the stations arrive at the required distance apart. . . . The length of the sides of the smallest triangles must depend upon the intended method of filling in the interior. If the contents of parishes, estates, etc., are to be computed, the distances between the points must be diminished to one or two miles, for an en-closed country; and to two or three perhaps, for one more open.

If no contents are required, and the object of the triangulation is solely to ensure the accuracy of a topographical survey, the distances may be augmented according to the degree of minuteness required. The average length of side of the primary triangles of the Ordnance survey of the United Kingdom was from 40 to 60 miles; of the secondary ones about 10 to 12 miles; and of the tertiary ones 1 mile to 3 miles.

The triangular error of a principal triangle should not exceed 1 second. As much as 5 seconds of error may be allowed in secondary triangles, with lengths of 5 to 10 miles. Tertiary triangles, with sides of 1 to 5 miles, may have an error of 15 to 20 seconds.

The probable errors in base measurement may be from 1 in a quarter to one half million, but for topographical work the standard is 1/10,000 to 1/50,000. The length of the base-line will be reduced to Mean Sea Level, and to the mean radius of the earth. Therefore, the height above the sea is an important factor.

The triangles thus established by observation are for practical purposes reduced to plane triangles, while their actual nature is that of spherical ones. A correction, therefore, has to be applied for spherical excess. In the case of small triangles this correction is unnecessary by reason of the minuteness of the difference, which is sufficient, however, to occasion in extensive ones a measurable variation from absolute correctness. In a spherical triangle the sum of the three angles exceeds 180°, the amount of this excess in any given case being proportional to the area of the triangle. Let E represent the spherical excess in seconds, A the area of the triangle calculated as a plane one, and R the mean radius of the earth (these two being expressed in terms of the same unit of measurement), and π circumference in terms of diameter; then

$$E = \frac{A \times 648000}{R^2 \pi}.$$

Another rule is: From the log of the area of the triangle in square feet subtract the number 9·3267737, and the remainder will be the log of the spherical excess in seconds.

A simple method of determining the spherical excess, when very great accuracy is not required, is by dividing the area of the triangle in square miles by 76, the result being the spherical excess in seconds.

For the practical application of the correction, the simplest of three possible methods is that of Legendre, viz.: "In any spherical triangle, the sides of which are very small compared with the radius of the sphere, if each of the angles be diminished by one-third of the true spherical excess, the sines of these angles will be proportional to the lengths of the opposite sides, and the triangle may therefore be calculated as if it were plane." The area of the triangle having been calculated as a plane one from the *observed* data, and the spherical excess E obtained by the formula, the sum of the observed angles should $= 180° + $E. The difference (if any) is due to error of observation; and, if an error of excess, one-third of it is to be deducted from, and if of defect to be added to, each of the angles. From each of them is then to be deducted one-third of the spherical excess; and from the thus corrected angles and a given side the other sides are calculated as those of a plane triangle.

Measurement of base-line – The correctness of any triangulation survey depends upon the accuracy with which the base-line A B (Fig. 302) has been measured, since the whole complex system is built up on this measured base. The principles and equipment are very similar for both measurement of base-line and precise traverse surveying so that both headings will be dealt with under the following.

Precise traverse surveying – The degree of precision in measurement of length and in observation of angles in a primary traverse must be very high and in a secondary traverse considerably higher than in many classes of surveying. Such precise work is usually carried out in tropical countries, where highly skilled surveyors command a high remuneration. It is important to frame an organisation such that the surveyor does not waste time or energy, the preliminary work being entrusted to reliable but less highly paid assistants. The equipment also must be carefully organised. If account has to be taken of differences of height of instrument, this slows up the work considerably, and so does the setting up of the tripod at successive instrument

z

stations, if only one tripod is in use. It is essential that the tripods and tribrachs shall be interchangeable. They should accommodate the theodolite, the supplementary instrument for laying out the traverse, the targets, and the measuring heads. The fiducial points of the targets should be at the same height above the tribrach as the horizontal axis of the theodolite. A typical organisation may be briefly described.

A first assistant is charged with the fixing of traverse stations, with legs as nearly as possible in exact multiples of 100 feet, but preferably of 300 feet, the length of the tape. He erects a tripod over each station, using the optical plummet shown in Fig. 303 to centre the tribrach over the peg. This tripod he leaves in

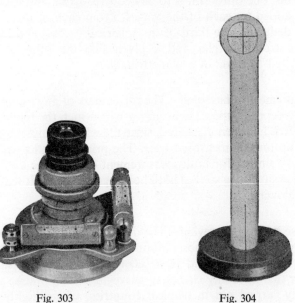

Fig. 303   Fig. 304

position, replacing the plummet on the tribrach by a sighting vane, Fig. 304, the mark on which is at the same height above the tribrach as the optical axis of the theodolite. He also places pegs, on every leg longer than 300 feet, at a distance of 300 feet from the near station. Assuming that he keeps three stations ahead of the surveyor, he will require four tripods, three in position and one being carried forward when finished with as a back sight by the surveyor.

A second assistant is in charge of a fifth tripod, to place over the intermediate theodolite stations, the theodolite being set up

Fig. 305

every 600 feet, if the leg exceeds that distance. After optical plumbing, this assistant places a target, Fig. 305, on the tribrach, turning the target parallel to the leg so that measurement may be made to the centre. For base-line measurement and primary traverse work a measuring head is used on the tribrach. This head is countersunk to allow for tape thickness, and bevelled to allow for the catenary curve of the tape.

The steel tape is 100 to 300 feet long and $\frac{1}{8}$ inch wide. It is supported at every 100 feet on ball-bearing supports, adjustable on a pole, Fig. 306. A detachable target facilitates alignment of the poles, which thus are just off the line of sight of the theodolite. The tape is stretched to a tension of 20 lb. on a spring balance, or a form of straining trestle with a 20 lb. weight is used, as shown in Fig. 307. The tape is graduated to feet and hundredths, if not throughout, at least at both ends, in which case the length of the traverse legs must be in multiples of 300 feet.

Fig. 306   Fig. 307

In the outfit described a Cook, Troughton and Simms optical micrometer theodolite is used, and this fits the tribrachs, in interchange with the targets, etc. The theodolite is carried from station to station on a sixth tripod. Should the leg be longer than 600 feet, the fifth tripod being in use at 300 feet, this tripod is set up at 600 feet. In principle, an accurate measuring point must be provided at both ends of every tape length. Targets also must be employed to determine the difference in slope between the ends of the tape for reduction to the horizontal, with or without a necessary allowance for temperature. As a back sight the surveyor uses a target of the form shown in Fig. 305, the centre of which can be illuminated for night work.

Corrections must be made for the following:

1. Slope of the ground.
2. Temperature.
3. Sag.
4. Pull.
5. Height above sea level.

1. The correction for *slope* of ground has been explained in Chapter 4 and the table on page 162 will be found of value in determining the correction necessary under this heading.

2. *Temperature* correction which must be *added* is made from the formula

$$a(t_1 - t_2)l$$

where a = coefficient of expansion of the metal tape

t_1 = temperature at the time of measurement

t_2 = temperature at which tape has been standardized

l = length of tape in use.

3. *Sag.* The formula for the correction of sag in the tape which is to be *deducted* is

$$\frac{w^2 l}{24 p^2}$$

where w = total weight of tape

l = length of tape

p = pull applied to tape.

4. *Pull.* The correction for pull is to be *added* and is found by the formula

$$\frac{l(P_1 - P_2)}{A\,E}$$

where l = length of tape

P_1 = pull applied in the field

P_2 = pull applied at standardization

A = Cross section area of tape

E = Young's Modulus for tape ($28\frac{1}{2}$ million lbs/sq. in. for steel and about 22 million lbs/sq. in. for invar).

If the field pull is less than the standardization pull, the correction is to be *deducted* and not added.

5. *Height above sea level* is *added* for base lines below mean sea level and *deducted* for those above mean sea level.

The correction is

$$\frac{l\,h}{R+h}$$

where l = length of base-line
  h = height above mean sea level
  R = radius of earth (say 3,958 miles).

The Geodimeter – The development of electronics during the past decades led designers to consider how they could adapt microwave band techniques to assist the surveyor in the accurate measurement of distance. The geodimeter was the first precise instrument for distance measurement. This instrument, based on electronic optics and using the fundamental constant, the velocity of light, enabled considerable accuracy to be obtained in the field. The distance was determined by measuring the time interval from the wave front of a light beam to travel from the geodimeter to a distant mirror and back. Since the velocity of light is known, the distance can be easily computed. It is claimed that the probable error for the geodimeter is from 1/500,000 to 1/4,000,000.

Tellurometer system of distance measurement – Following on the geodimeter, research has produced the tellurometer an electronic distance measuring system which operates in the 10 cm wavelength region and measures the travel time of radio waves over the length to be determined with an accuracy of a fraction of a millimicro second.

The great advantage claimed for this instrument is that it can be used by day or by night and visibility is immaterial but, in general, optical line of sight is required, although isolated obstructions in mid-path are of little account. An accuracy consistant with the requirements of first order triangulations is claimed, the probable error being 3/1,000,000±2 inches on line of sight up to 35 miles. The primary purpose of the instrument was intended as a means of replacing existing methods of taping a geodetic base and on this a great measure of success has been achieved. It is possible to set up the instrument, measure the distance and dismantle and re-pack within the space of less than half an hour.

The tellurometer is shown in Fig. 308. The apparatus consists of a master station and remote station, both instruments being similar but are not interchangeable. Allowances have to be

Fig. 308

made in the measurement for temperature and altitude and difficulties are sometimes experienced by what is known as "ground swing" when taking measurements. These ground swings are due to indirect paths taken by some radio waves caused by phenomena not yet fully understood which results in increasing the time of travel of the wave and thus affecting the error in measurement. Despite these initial troubles the telluro-meter is an immense step forward from the orthodox and protracted method of measuring a base-line by tape. The tellurometer is manufactured in Cape Town, Union of South Africa and distributed in Great Britain by Messrs Cook, Troughton & Simms of London. The following table shows the accuracy claimed by the makers:

Distance	Probable Error in Inches
10 miles	2 ins. approx.
20 ,,	4 ,, ,,
30 ,,	6 ,, ,,
40 ,,	8 ,, ,,

Celestial observation – In all work connected with map projection, triangulation and traverse surveys of geodetic importance a knowledge of celestial co-ordinates is essential.

Astronomy – Practical surveying is largely concerned with the making of plans or maps for various purposes, and especially cadastral plans for the land register, or maps, such as that on the scale of 25 inches to the mile, prepared and continually revised by the Ordnance Survey. There are also topographical plans and maps. When, however, it is desired to combine the work into small scale maps of the earth, or geodetic surveying, purely local topographic features must be collated into a harmonious whole. It then becomes necessary to refer the work to co-ordinates of latitude and longitude, and to draw meridians on the map. This involves astronomical work, which cannot be neglected by the student, although here only an outline can be given. The work demands a considerable amount of study and practice, but the elements should be mastered for examination purposes and for later application.

First of all, it is necessary to become familiar with the constellations, the star groups into which the heavens have been divided up for ages. Those forming one belt, Aries, Taurus, Gemini, etc., the Ram, the Bull, the Twins, etc., are fairly well known. There are many others which can be studied with the aid of star maps, such as are published by some newspapers, or are collected into books. The study of the constellations, in the open and by night, is facilitated by using a photographic red lamp to illuminate the book, otherwise time is lost in accustoming the eyes to the faint specks of light seen in the telescope. If a theodolite is used to read angles, then the crosswires on the diaphragm must be faintly illuminated by a lamp, which will not throw its light into the observer's eye.

Nautical almanac – It is possible to take observations of larger sources of light, such as the sun, or of reflected light, such as the moon, or the planets, or the satellites of certain planets, such as Jupiter and Saturn. It will be necessary to learn to distinguish these planets and their satellites from the "fixed" stars among which they have an apparent motion. Not until such knowledge has been attained will it be of much service to study the "Nautical Almanac and Astronomical Ephemeris," which gives the positions of these bodies as referred to certain co-ordinates. A certain amount of information will be found in "Whitaker's Almanac," to which the student is likely to have easier access. There have been important alterations to the Nautical Almanac recently, and therefore the latest edition should be studied in preference to an earlier one.

Co-ordinates – There are several systems of co-ordinates, all of which are involved in calculations from astronomical observations. The principal object is to establish the Latitude and Longitude of a station, and the Azimuth of one ray in a trigonometrical series. The same operation at another station will provide a check on the work and a basis for correction. In aerial surveying much more frequent observation will be necessary to provide a ground control on the necessarily uncertain factors which give a scale to the map, and even tend to distort that scale, as will be seen elsewhere.

The first system of co-ordinates applies to the observer's position. A truly levelled and adjusted theodolite will give him a true vertical above his head and a horizontal plane, tangent to a radius of the earth, provided always that there is no eccentricity of attraction of the plumb-bob, a factor which can be observed in the plain of the Ganges River under the influence of the Himalaya Mountains. These co-ordinates are the Horizontal plane and planes passing through the Zenith, true North and South, and true East and West. Both of these must, however, be determined by calculation. The first will be the plane of the meridian, the second that of the prime vertical.

There will, however, be two things which can be measured. One is the altitude of the sun, or planet or star, above the horizon. The Co-altitude, or Zenith Distance, can then be calculated. The other measurement will be the horizontal angle between the body and any other object, such as a trigonometrical station, giving the difference in Azimuth. The true Azimuth, referred to the North Pole, can only be determined by reference to other co-ordinates, with a common origin, the position of the Royal Observatory at Greenwich.

Terrestrial co-ordinates – We must now consider the earth, assumed to have the true shape of a sphere, with North and South Poles, on an axis between which the sphere revolves. If a line be drawn from the centre of the earth to the centre of the sun, the axis of the earth is inclined to this line by about 24 deg. As the earth moves in its orbit round the sun, the axis being continually inclined, the sun in northern latitudes appears to mount high in summer and to decline in height in winter. At the equator the sun swings either way about 24 deg., so that the Tropics are about 47 deg. wide. On no two successive days will the sun appear at the same height above the horizon at mid-day or noon. Nor will the same constellation appear in the same position from day to day or be visible at night all the year round.

A circle is a plane figure generated by the rotation of the radius through 360 deg. A sphere is a solid figure, generated by the rotation through 360 deg. of a circle, with radius equal to that of the sphere. The mean radius of the earth is just under 4,000 miles, but it is not an exact sphere. The generating circle may rotate in any direction, so that there are infinite Great Circles, cutting one another at any observer's station. The shortest distance from point to point on the earth's surface lies along a Great Circle, passing through the centre and the two points. Hence the practice of "Great Circle Sailing". The Great Circle at any station passing through the poles and the station is called the Meridian. There is an infinite number of points on one Meridian, and by measurement of an arc of the Meridian, or of the Equator reduced to mean sea-level, it is possible to arrive at the diameters of the earth.

In map making every Meridian is not shown, but if they are

spaced at 15 deg., they correspond to one hour of time, since the earth revolves through 360 deg. in 24 hours, the length of an hour being a convention, founded on a mean, as will be seen. Hence arises the necessity for interpolating a day every four years, except the century years. Map Meridians run 180 deg. east and 180 deg. west of Greenwich. To avoid great confusion groups of countries, or one large country such as India, keep a Local Standard Time, based on a mean. Thus, at 12 o'clock in Great Britain, it is 1 o'clock in Berlin or Poland, 2 o'clock in Russia, 5.30 in India, and so on, with correspondingly earlier Local Times kept in countries West of Greenwich.

Meridians are described in degrees, minutes, and seconds of Longitude, east or west of Greenwich. The surface of the earth is divided also into degrees and parts of degrees of Latitude with the same inclination of the plumb-bob to the plane of the Equator. Latitude circles, however, are not Great Circles, but parallel to the Equator. A degree measured along a circle of Latitude has not the same length in miles as a degree measured along the Equator, which is a Great Circle midway between the Poles, at right angles to the earth's axis. The modern use of calculating machines has produced a tendency to describing parts of degrees as decimals, instead of in minutes and seconds. Otherwise, an arc of Longitude can be converted into Time at the rate of 4 minutes per degree, 4 seconds per minute, and four-thirds of a second per second of arc. Latitude has no effect on Time. Co-latitude is the angular measurement from the zenith of the observer to the Pole, that is, 90 deg. minus Latitude, measured along the Meridian.

Celestial co-ordinates – We can now imagine the Meridians, supposedly marked out on the earth's surface, extended to infinite radius, and projected on the heavens. If a very powerful light were established at the centre of the earth, and a slit cut along the Meridian of Greenwich, the circle of light would sweep along the sky as the earth revolved. The slight gyratory movement of the earth will not permit this circle always to describe the same path, and it is the business of astronomers to determine the variation from year to year. It is therefore necessary to produce a yearly edition of the Nautical Almanac. Celestial Meridians can thus be determined, and the Celestial

Equator described in the same manner. From these two co-ordinates the position of any celestial body at any moment can be described, but in different terms.

Some point must be taken as the noon of this great clock. This is called the "First Point of Aries," although the passage of the ages, and slight variations, have brought this point into the constellation of Pisces, the preceding constellation. This "zero hour" is determined by the moment of the mean equinox, and is the point then marked in the heavens by a line from the centre of the earth produced through the centre of the sun. When the Meridian of Greenwich cuts that point it is "zero hour" at Greenwich, in Sidereal Time, for the purpose of the Nautical Almanac. Almanacs can, of course, be framed for any or every Meridian, and when the Meridian of an observer's station cuts this point it is zero hour in Sidereal Time for his station. This will happen twice a day, but when it occurs at the moment of possible observation that is the moment of Upper Culmination. At Lower Culmination the earth would prevent observation. A star visible one night at Upper Culmination will be at Lower Culmination six months later and invisible.

The co-ordinates of a star, or other heavenly body, instead of being described as its Longitude and Latitude, are called Right Ascension and Declination, given for every day at Upper Transit of Greenwich. Right Ascension is measured eastwards along the Celestial Equator and is the arc intercepted between the First Point of Aries and the Meridian, or Declination Circle, through the star. It is reckoned in hours and parts of hours instead of degrees and parts of degrees. Thus the Right Ascension of the sun at the vernal equinox is 0 hours, in July will be over 6 hours, in October over 12 hours, and in January nearly 19 hours. Declination is measured in degrees and parts of degrees, and is the arc of a Great Circle, through the Celestial Poles and the star, intercepted between the plane of the Celestial Equator and the star. It is described as Plus or Minus, according as it is above or below the plane of the Equator. In 1931 the Declination of the sun was about +4 deg. on April 1st, +23, −2, −23 deg., on the first of July, October, and January respectively. Polar distance or co-declination is 90 deg. minus the declination.

Formerly a certain correction had to be made because Sidereal Time used to be given from noon of Civil Mean Time at Greenwich, but since 1931 this has been eliminated, and Sidereal Time is given from midnight. The Sidereal Time of the sun on April 1st is about 12 hr. 33 min.

Sun observation – It is a comparatively simple matter to observe the Altitude of a star, and to take from the Nautical Almanac the Right Ascension and Declination, the latter varying very little throughout the year with the slight gyratory motion of the earth. It is not possible here to give the various operations for determination of Latitude, Longitude or Meridian, Time, and Azimuth, or the calculations following on the observations and data. Such work is done nowadays by the use of a prismatic Astrolabe, for the study of which the student is referred to the works of Ball and Knox-Shaw.

The sun presents a difficulty in observation, and many more data are required, although there is an advantage in being able to observe in daylight. Dark glass diaphragms must be inserted inside or over the eyepiece, or the image can be projected on a sheet of paper held in the right position. It is impossible to judge correctly the exact centre of the sun, and it is necessary to take two double observations. First, the crosswires of the diaphragm must be brought into alignment with the edge of the sun's circle, the sun being, let us say, in the lower left-hand quadrant of the diaphragm. When contact is made with the vertical and horizontal wires the time must be noted and both circles of the theodolite read. Then the telescope is transited, the upper plate revolved through 180 deg., and a second observation taken in the same quadrant. By bringing the sun into the upper right-hand quadrant there is an important elimination of the sun's semi-diameter, but instrumental errors are not eliminated. It must be remembered that the apparent top of the sun is really the bottom of the sun's disc, owing to inversion in the telescope. The double observation is repeated in the afternoon, time and angles being recorded.

Data about the sun fill many pages of the Nautical Almanac, and include variations per hour. The reasons are numerous. The earth, in accordance with laws discovered by Kepler, does not move round the sun at an even speed, and the sun is situated at one focus of an elliptical orbit of the earth. Consequently, the apparent motion of the sun and its diameter vary, besides its Declination, as mentioned above. The semi-diameter of the sun is about 16 minutes, more or less, in appearance. It would be quite impracticable to alter the watch continually to compensate for the varying speed of the earth, so that a Mean Time is worked out for clocks. One hour of Mean Time = 1 hr. 0 min. 10 sec. nearly in Sidereal Time. The difference between this Mean Time and Apparent Sun Time is called the Equation of Time, and is given on right-hand pages in the Nautical Almanac. It is to be noted that the month by month arrangement of the sun and moon ephemerides has been abandoned, while the ephemeris for Physical observations of the sun is now given for every day instead of for every fifth day. The sun's Longitude, Latitude, and rectangular co-ordinates are now referred to the mean Equinox at the beginning of the year and not to the true Equinox of the date. The true Equinox is given for twenty-four-hour intervals instead of twelve-hour, but first and second differences are given.

Photographic surveying – The employment of photographic views as data upon which to construct a topographical survey, was originally suggested by Colonel Laussedat a French officer, some time Professor in the École Polytechnique and Director of the École Centrale des Arts et Metiers, whose exposition of the theory and procedure still forms the foundation of its application in practice. Various points and features of the ground surveyed are shown in views photographed from various stations, and are located by intersection of the sight-lines from two or more such stations; the position of the several stations being fixed by a trigonometrical survey. The general principle is the same as that of plane-table surveying; but whereas the plotting of the work in the case of the latter is, practically speaking, done on the ground, that of a photographic survey is performed at leisure in the office. The process of this plotting is one of considerable complexity, and the business altogether requires no small acquaintance with the theory and practice of photography. To teach a learner the work of such a survey by a brief description is impossible: a course of instruction possessing any real value would form a

treatise in itself, and even this would be of little use unless
supplemented by illustrative teaching and practical example.
The student is referred to textbooks which go fully into the
subject, and carry the learner as far as is possible in print,
beyond which nothing but actual experience in practice can
qualify him in knowledge.

Photography has been extensively employed in Government
surveys in Canada and elsewhere and is advantageous for a
general topographical survey of mountainous and rough
country, as a basis for subsequent detailed surveys by the
ordinary methods. A Hilger & Watts Photo-Theodolite is
illustrated in Fig. 109 Chapter 2.

Aerial surveying – The rapidity in which air surveying has
advanced in recent years is due to the precision which it is now
possible to obtain by this method of photoplanimetry and the
speed in which the work can be completed. Such surveys are
invaluable in terrain difficult or impossible to conduct ground
surveys.

Precise work of aerial surveying depends on a certain amount
of ground control since it is essential that the aerial photographs
should be tied up to the control points of the ground in order
to correct any error that might otherwise arise due to distortion,
camera lens defects, tilt, sequences of height, etc. Most of
these defects are automatically rectified by the use of modern
cartographic method but it is doubtful whether aerial surveying
can be satisfactorily accomplished on its own account without
the close liaison of ground control in cases where extreme
accuracy is required.

In aerial surveying vertical photographs are taken by cameras
fixed in an aircraft and directed vertically downwards, but
oblique photographs are also taken at an angle to the vertical
which provides valuable information of a more general
character. These oblique photographs can be used either for
direct plotting or to assist in the interpolation of vertical
photographs.

The scale of the negative depends upon the accuracy which
is required and this decides the altitude and type of lens used.
It is possible to cover from one to eighty square miles by a
single exposure and to prepare maps up to large scales such as

1/500. The area surveyed is covered by overlapping photographs, each part of the ground being photographed at least twice with an overlap of up to 60%. Fig. 309 shows the method diagrammatically.

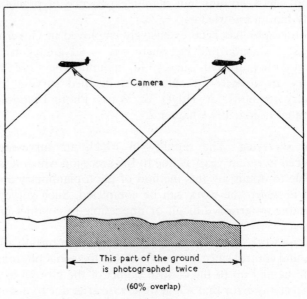

This part of the ground is photographed twice

(60% overlap)

Fig. 309
By courtesy of Hunting Aerosurveys Ltd.

The position of the aircraft at the point of each camera exposure is known as the "air station" and each pair of photographs taken overlapping each other is known as a "stereo pair." This is so called because the negative, when printed and enlarged, will be placed under a stereoscope to give a three-dimensional picture. The film negatives are prepared on glass to prevent distortion and the "stereo pair" (or a number of stereo pairs forming a mosaic in the large, complex projectors used for precise map and contour plotting) will be arranged in such a position that when viewed through the stereoscope the picture will present exactly the same conditions as when viewed by the aircraft camera. Thus the stereoscopic effect provides a scale relief which is optically read and by means of complex plotting devices of the projector apparatus the stereoscopic

model can be altered in size and measurements can be taken
from it. The operator can adjust the scale to any desired ratio
and in this way he can plot a true plan. He can also measure
relative heights to scale of any resected points within the model,
by means of the plotting table which carries underneath a
drawing pencil which is immediately below a reference mark on
the table top; by adjusting the height position of the plotting
table so that one of the resections occurs exactly on the
reference mark, the operator can plot the true position (to
scale) on the main table below. Fig. 310(A) shows in diagram

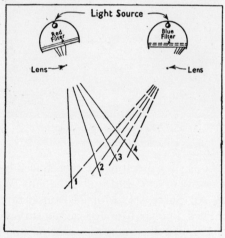

Fig. 310(a)

By courtesy of Hunting Aerosurveys Ltd.

form the principle of the projectors which take the place of the
camera and are set at exactly the same angle of tilt so that
points 1, 2, 3 and 4 occur in the same relative position in space
as they did in nature but to a smaller scale.

Fig. 310(B) shows the apparatus when in use.

Fig. 311 is an illustration of the Watts Radial Line Plotter for
use in plotting planimetric details from air photos.

Contour mapping with stereo-plotting instruments can be
obtained to an accuracy of ± half a contour interval and
planimetric accuracy is claimed to be well within the accepted

AA

tolerance of 1/50 inch at the scale of the map. Furthermore, the speed of aerial mapping may be anything up to ten times as rapid as ground surveys.

Fig. 310(b) – Multiplex model.
By courtesy of Hunting Aerosurveys Ltd.

The illustrations shown before are reproduced by courtesy of the Hunting Aerosurveys Ltd. of Boreham Wood, Herts. Messrs Fairey Air Surveys Ltd. of 24 Bruton Street, London, W.1, another well known firm for aerial surveys, undertake similar work. Fig. 312 illustrates the value of map revision and the aerial photograph in Fig. 313 shows clearly the undulations

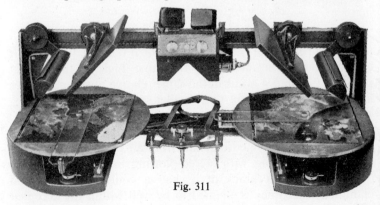

Fig. 311

of the terrain below from which contour mapping by means of sterio-plotting instruments is obtained; both illustrations are reproduced by courtesy of Messrs Fairey Air Surveys Ltd.

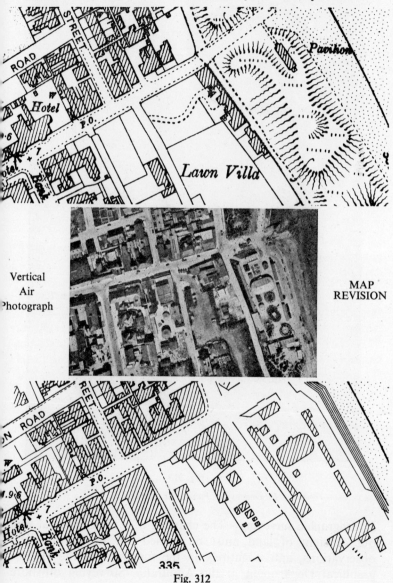

Vertical
Air
Photograph

MAP
REVISION

Fig. 312

By courtesy of Fairey Air Survey Ltd.

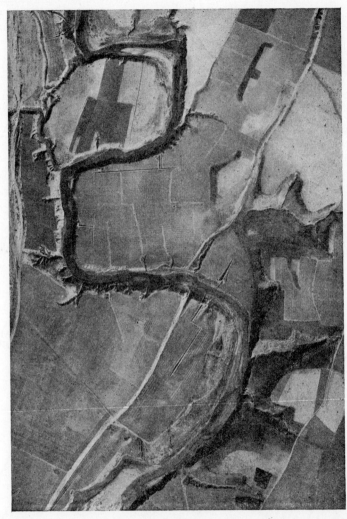

Fig. 313

By courtesy of Fairey Air Survey Ltd.

Hydrographic surveying – The charting of a rock or shoal well out of sight of land must be carried out by astronomical observations, and is entirely in the functions of the Hydrographical Department of the Admiralty. Surveying off-shore is directed to the contouring of the bed of the sea or of a harbour.

In certain rivers it is necessary to survey shifting bars continually for the safety of navigation. It may be necessary to obtain cross-sections of a river-bed, and to measure the velocity of the current, so as to arrive at an estimate of the volume of the water in times of high flood, and thus to design a bridge to pass that volume.

It is not necessary to detail each one of these operations, but in every case there must be set up beacons, appropriately differentiated in aspect, to which observations may be taken to determine positions at which soundings are taken. The placing of these beacons must be such, and their number must be adequate, to give good intersections at every position of the sounding boat. At most positions a double observation to three beacons is necessary, and no reading on the sextant should be less than 30 deg. The work will be plotted by a station pointer,

Fig. 314

shown in Fig. 314, one arm being fixed, and the two movable arms being set to graduations on either side, the verniers reading to one minute. The method is the same as resection of a plane table from three points, as described in Chapter 2, but actual angles are read instead of rays being drawn on transparent paper.

The sounding is usually made by line and lead, from a well in the boat, instead of over the side, or rods 15 to 25 feet in length may be used. The lead may weigh up to 20 lb. in a current or 8 to 10 lb. in a harbour. The observer and his leadsmen, the navigating and mooring crew, must have plenty of room without mutual interference.

All soundings must eventually be referred to a datum, as in every levelling operation. Water surface continually changes under the action of the tides, floods, evaporation, and so on. When surveying in tidal waters or estuaries a Tide and Time base-line must be prepared by observation or enquiry. Moreover, the wind and atmospheric pressure affect tides as well as the sun and moon, whose pulls may be calculable for tide prediction in Tide Tables. Corrections, therefore, must be applied to results, and only continuous observation of a tide gauge can produce a correct base-line. The intervals between high and low tides are not equal, as may be observed at any seaside resort. A prime means a shorter interval, a lag means a longer interval, than the normal.

For river surveying a current meter (Fig. 315) may be required.

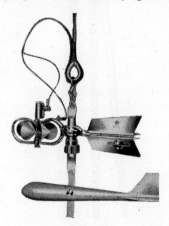

Fig. 315

Sextant – The essential difference between the sextant and the box sextant is that the former is used for vertical and the latter for horizontal angular measurement. The sextant is used on board ship for astronomical observations, since a steady platform for a theodolite is not obtainable. It is also used for marine surveying off-shore, principally because the surveyors are better acquainted with the instrument than with the box sextant, although the angles to be observed are horizontal. It suffers from the same disadvantage, if the celestial bodies or shore targets observed differ much in altitude.

Fig. 316

The instrument is shown in Fig. 316. It consists of a frame, approximating to a segment of a circle, with graduations on the arc, and a handle. Pivoted at the centre of the segment is an arm, carrying a telescope socket and a mirror, and also a vernier. On one of the sides of the segment is a half silvered mirror, so that the object can be viewed direct and by reflection, and brought into coincidence. The arc is divided to 140 or 150 deg. and the vernier reads to 10 seconds. Dark glass shades are provided for use when taking a sight to the sun. For astronomical observations a mercury artificial horizon (Fig. 317) is often used, in which case the observed angle is twice the true altitude.

Fig. 317

Not much space need be devoted to the adjustments. Briefly, the wholly silvered, or index, mirror, and the half silvered, or horizon, mirror, must be adjusted at right angles to the plane of the arc. If, then, the object, viewed both direct and by reflection, is brought to coincidence, the reading on the vernier should be zero, otherwise an index error should be recorded and applied. The line of sight of the telescope may then be checked to see that it is at right angles to the plane of the arc.

Echo sounding – The rapid advance that has been made in the field of electronics in recent years has brought its advantages to the surveyor. An important development in hydrographic surveying is the use of electronics in echo sounding apparatus. The system has been fully developed by Messrs Kelvin Hughes Ltd. of 99 Fenchurch Street, London, E.C.3 who not only provide the necessary equipment but are organized to carry out complete land and water surveys if desired.

The use of the echo sounder requires some preliminary knowledge and the principles must be fully understood before its use is attempted, otherwise errors are certain to occur. Used intelligently and with due regard to its limitations the echo sounder is claimed to be unsurpassed in accuracy. The limitations referred to concern errors that may occur in reading "beam" angles, separation, lack of sounding caused by aeration and in readings taken in a rough or heavy swell. These can be overcome by practice and experience and should afford little difficulty once the principles have been mastered.

The echo sounder is an instrument which sends out a short supersonic pulse of sound, measures the time required for the resulting echo to return from the sea or river bed, and records the measurement as a depth. It may be used in harbour, river or in open sea and is of the utmost value in civil engineering. The instruments have a basic scale of 0-45 feet on fast speed or 0-90 feet on slow speed, extending over a chord length of 5 inches. The range can be extended by continuous multiple phasing of 30 ft. on the fast speed and 60 on the slow speed to 270 ft. or 540 ft. respectively.

The sounding will be recorded on paper to such accuracy that, in still water, the final plotted figures can be produced to within 3 inches.

Fig. 318

The sounding rate is 533 per minute, one sounding every ninth second approx. With the survey craft moving at 6 knots a sounding is thus recorded at every 1·14 foot advance.

Fig. 318 shows the Kelvin Hughes Type MS.26 A & F with recording chart in action.

Like all hydrographical survey work echo sounding is dependent upon a complete and accurate shore framework. Any error in the land survey would affect the accuracy of the whole hydrographic survey. It is therefore essential that a reliable shore control and framework is built up. This framework relies on the position of objects, either natural or artificial, to be accurately determined onto which angles can be taken from the survey craft so as to fix its position. These objects are used as targets for the whole of the survey. Fig. 319 will make the principle clear.

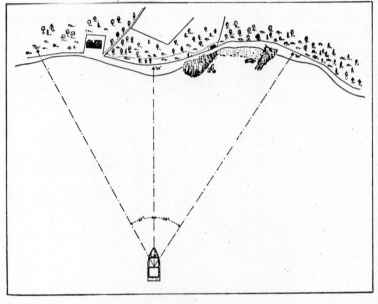

Fig. 319

By courtesy of Messrs. Kelvin and Hughes

When the shore framework is established the area to be surveyed can be sounded, the soundings being reduced to a tidal or definite datum. "Chart Datum" has been established at most places throughout the world related to the land levelling ordnance datum system and for civil engineering construction it is convenient to adopt this method. When the survey is required for navigational purposes, a tidal datum is used.

Chart datum is a normally accepted zero, a level below which the tide seldom falls (see Fig. 320). Its value for the relative position under observation can be obtained from Admiralty Charts and Tide Tables.

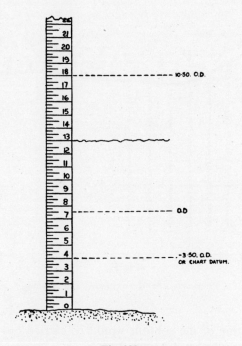

Fig. 320

By courtesy of Messrs. Kelvin and Hughes

In taking the soundings it is essential that the survey craft is kept in the desired track and that its position is fixed as often as possible. The procedure of keeping the vessel in the correct lines or transits (referred to as conning) is done by first plotting the area to be surveyed on a sounding sheet, and deciding the general direction of the transits and how far apart they should be. Where the transits are run at right angles to the shore they can be marked out on the shore by two targets, one as a front and one as a back mark and if the Coxswain keeps the two targets in line while running the transit he will be on a correct course.

The sounding lines with contours afterwards plotted would appear as in Fig. 321.

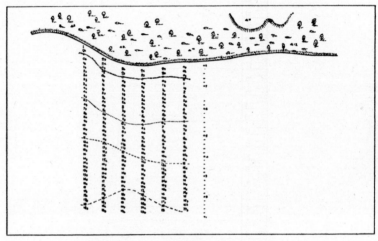

Fig. 321

By courtesy of Messrs. Kelvin and Hughes

The plotting of the contour would be carried out by similar methods described in Chapter 9.

When the whole survey has been completed a final plan can be drawn up from the information obtained from the transit charts.

Soundings may be taken and booked with the use of small depth indicators which work on a similar principle to echo sounding. Such an instrument is shown in Fig. 322, from which it will be noted that the range varies from 0-120 feet. The instrument is remarkably efficient for its size and cost and has a number of uses to civil engineers and surveyors in ascertaining depths of water. It is produced by the Submarine Signal Co. (London) Ltd. of Watford, Hertfordshire. The same firm also

Fig. 322

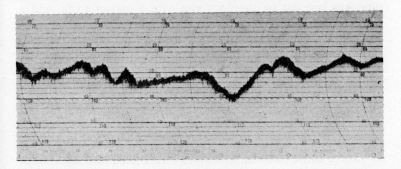

Fig. 323

manufactures a Graph Recorder similar to the Kelvin Hughes Echo Sounder. It will be seen from the transit chart (Fig. 323) that the contours are clearly indicated in section form.

Echo sounding demands a high degree of efficiency on the part of the surveyor and the use of optical measuring instruments, such as theodolite and sextant for measuring angles and azimuths; plotting instruments, such as the station pointer; current meters, to ascertain the velocity and direction of sea and river currents, and silt and bottom sampling apparatus; besides the electronic echo sounder and a knowledge of navigation. The principles involved require careful study and the student is referred to works devoted solely to this interesting and rewarding subject.

Examination Questions

1. A loading quay is to be constructed on a fairly level foreshore. Describe:
   (a) how you would take and locate soundings for an area extending 1,000 ft. from low water mark and 2,000 ft. along the shore;
   (b) how you would relate the soundings to Ordnance datum;
   (c) how you would obtain the volume of material to be dredged to allow ships access to the quay.
   (*University of London B.Sc.(Eng.*) 1956)

2. Two brass plates with finely marked lines have been set into the floor of a building and have been used as a "100-foot standard" for some time. In remeasuring this distance a steel tape was laid flat on the floor and with a pull of 15 lb. and a temperature of 70°F. the recorded distance between the marks was 99·942 ft. The tape had previously been standardised in catenary and measured 100 ft. at 45°F under a pull of 25 lb. What was the true length between the marks on the floor to the nearest 0·001 ft.? Weight of tape = 3·49 lb.; sectional area = 0·0103 sq. in.; coefficient of expansion = 0·0000065 per °F; E = 30×10⁶lb. per sq. in.
   (*The Institution of Civil Engineers, October* 1957)

3. Three shore stations, A, B and C, were fixed near high water level. The whole circle bearings of lines A B and B C were 110° 40′ and 85° 20′ respectively, and the lengths of A B and B C were 4,120 ft. and 2,500 ft.
   Horizontal angles were observed simultaneously with two sextants in a boat at X and were found to be A X B = 45° 30′ and

B X C = 30° 20′. Determine the distances of the boat from each of the shore stations A, B and C.

(Institution of Municipal Engineers, 1949)

4. Today, air survey methods are regularly and confidently used in map making from scales of 1/100,000 with 50 ft. contour intervals to scales of 1/500 with a contour interval of 2 feet. Twenty years ago air survey methods were considered suitable only for making approximate maps of inaccessible areas. What are the major developments that have led to this change of practice?

(The Institution of Civil Engineers, April 1957)

5. The figures tabulated refer to a baseline measured by suspending a steel band on successive nominal 100 ft. lengths, on undulating ground and at varying temperature, at a mean elevation of 4,000 ft. above sea level:

Spans	Rise	Temperature	Tension
ft.	ft.	°F.	lb.
100·170	+1·25	82	30
100·186	+2·20	82	30
100·010	+0·15	83	30
100·135	−4·78	84	30
100·024	+3·35	84	30

The steel band used weighed 0.015 lbs. per lineal foot, had a cross-sectional area of 0·0045 sq. in., and was certified 100 ft. when under 20 lbs. tension at 62°F. Calculate the corrected length of base to the nearest $\frac{1}{1000}$th of 1 foot and reduce to sea level.

The earth's radius may be taken as 20,890,000 ft., coefficient of thermal expansion of steel 0·00000625 per 1°F. and Young's modulus 30,000,000 lbs. per sq. inch.

(Institution of Municipal Engineers, 1948)

APPENDIX I

TRIGONOMETRY REQUIRED IN SURVEYING

Plane surface—Plane angle—Plane rectilineal angle—Perpendicular—Obtuse angle—Acute angle—Circle—Centre of circle—Diameter of circle—Semi-circle—Segment of circle—Rectilineal figures—Trilateral figures—Quadrilateral figures—Multilateral figures—Equilateral triangle—Isosceles triangle—Scalene triangle—Right-angled triangle—Obtuse-angled triangle—Acute-angled triangle—Theorems—Trigonometrical ratios or functions—Cotangent of greater or less angles—Sin A in terms of Cos A—Tan A in terms of Sin A—Tan A in terms of Cos A—Cos A in terms of Tan A—Sin A in terms of Tan A—Sin A in terms of Sec A—Cos A in terms of Cosec A—Cot A in terms of Sec A—To express Cosec A in terms of Sec A—To express Sin A in terms of Tan A—Complemental Angles—Supplemental angles—Use of the + and — signs—Relations of lines to functions of the angle of reference—Radius unity—Basis of formulae for tables of Sines, etc.—Sines, etc., for 45 degrees—Sines, etc., for 60 degrees—Sines, etc., for 30 degrees—Sines, etc., for 60 and 30 degrees—Sines, etc., for 18 degrees—Sines, etc., for 120 degrees—Sines, etc., for 225 degrees—Ratio of radius—Solution of right-angled triangles—Trigonometrical ratios of two angles—Sum and difference of Sines and Cosines—The Sine and Cosine of twice an angle, in terms of the Sine and Cosine of the angle—The Sine and Cosine of an angle in terms of half the angle—Sine, Cosine and Tangent of the sum of three angles—The Sine, Cosine and Tangent of three time an angle—Oblique-angled triangles—Sines and Cosines of angles in terms of sides—Sines and Cosines of semi-angles—Logarithms—Multiplication by Logarithms—Division by Logarithms—Proportion by Logarithms—Involution by Logarithms—Evolution by Logarithms—Natural and Logarithmic Sines, Cosines, etc.—Solution of triangles by arithmetical computation—Right-angled triangles—Oblique-angled triangles.

TRIGONOMETRY has for its object the solution of triangles, and its application to surveying is the "art of measuring and computing the sides of plane triangles, or of such whose sides are straight lines." Triangles consist of six parts, viz. three sides and three angles; and in every case in trigonometry three parts must be given in order to find the other three; and of those three given parts one must be a side, because with the same angles the sides may be greater or less in proportion.

We will commence with a few of the principal definitions of Euclid's geometry which bear upon trigonometry.

1. Plane surface - A plane surface, or plane, is a surface in which if any two points be taken, the straight line between them lies wholly in that surface.

2. Plane angle – A plane angle is the inclination of two lines to each other in a plane, which meet together, but are not in the same direction.

Note – This definition includes angles formed by two curved lines, or by a curve and a straight line, as well as angles formed by two straight lines.

3. Plane rectilineal angle – A plane rectilineal angle is the inclination of two straight lines to one another, which meet together, but are not in the same straight line.

Note – When an angle is simply spoken of, a plane rectilineal angle is always meant.

4. Perpendicular – When a straight line standing on another straight line makes the adjacent angles equal to one another,

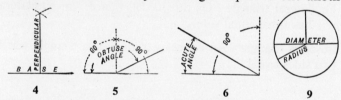

each of these angles is called a right angle, and the straight lines are said to be perpendicular to each other.

5. Obtuse angle – An obtuse angle is greater than a right angle.

6. Acute angle – An acute angle is less than a right angle.

7. Circle – A circle is a plane figure contained by one line, which is called the circumference, and is such that all lines drawn from a certain point within the figure to the circumference are equal to one another.

8. Centre of circle – And this point is called the centre of the circle.

9. Diameter of circle – The diameter of a circle is a straight line drawn through the centre, and terminated both ways by the circumference.

Note – The radius of a circle is a straight line drawn from the centre to the circumference.

10. Semi-circle – A semi-circle is a figure contained by a diameter and by the part of the circumference cut off by the diameter.

11. Segment of circle – A segment of a circle is a figure contained by any straight line and a part of the circumference which it cuts off.

12. Rectilineal figures – Rectilineal figures are those which are contained by straight lines.

13. Trilateral figures – Trilateral figures or triangles by three straight lines.

14. Quadrilateral figures – Quadrilateral figures by four straight lines.

15. Multilateral figures – Multilateral figures, or polygons, by more than four straight lines.

16. Equilateral triangle – Of three-sided figures, an equilateral triangle has three equal sides.

17. Isosceles triangle – An isosceles triangle is a triangle which has two sides equal.

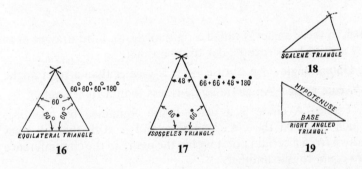

18. Scalene triangle – A scalene triangle has three unequal sides.

19. Right-angled triangle – A right-angled triangle is a triangle which has a right angle.

Note – The side which subtends, that is, is opposite to the right angle, is called the hypotenuse.

20. Obtuse-angled triangle – An obtuse-angled triangle is a triangle which has an obtuse angle, which by Def. 5 is greater than a right angle.

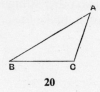

20

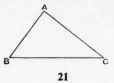

21

21. Acute-angled triangle – An acute-angled triangle is a triangle which has three acute angles.

Theorems – 1. If two triangles have two sides of the one equal to two sides of the other, each to each, and have likewise the angle contained by those sides equal to one another, they shall likewise have their bases or third sides equal, and the two triangles shall be equal, and their angles shall be equal each to each, namely those to which the equal sides are opposite.

2. The angles at the base of an isosceles triangle, A B C and A C B, are equal to one another; and if the equal sides be produced the angles on the other side of the base, D B C and B C E, shall be equal to one another.

3. If two triangles have two sides of the one equal to two sides of the other, each to each, and have likewise their bases equal;

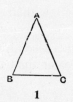

1

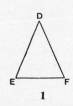

1

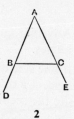

2

the angle which is contained by the two sides of the one shall be equal to the angle which is contained by the two sides equal to them of the other.

4. The angles which one straight line makes with another straight line on one side of it either are two right angles or are together equal to two right angles.

5. If at a point in a straight line, A B, two other straight lines, C B and B D, upon the opposite sides of it, make the adjacent

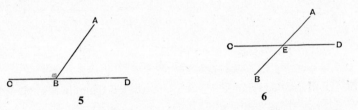

angles together equal to two right angles, these two straight lines, C B and B D, shall be in one and the same line.

6. If two straight lines cut one another, the vertically opposite angles shall be equal.

7. If one side of a triangle, B C, be produced to D, the exterior angle, A C D, is greater than either of the interior opposite angles, C A B and A B C.

8. Any two angles of a triangle are together less than two right angles.

9. If one side of a triangle, A C, be greater than a second, A B, the angle, A B C, opposite the first must be greater than that opposite the second, A C B.

10. If one angle of a triangle be greater than a second, the side opposite the first must be greater than that opposite the second.

11. Any two sides of a triangle are together greater than the third side.

12. If, from the ends of the side of a triangle, C and B, there be drawn two straight lines, B E and C D, to a point D, within the

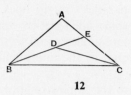

12

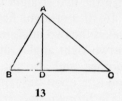

13

triangle, then B D and C D will be together less than the other sides, B A and A C, of the triangle, but will contain a greater angle, B D C.

13. Every straight line, A D, drawn from the vertex of a triangle to a point D within the base, is less than the greater of the two sides, A C, or than either, if they be equal.

Theory of Parallel Lines – Hamblin Smith has very properly detached the propositions, in which Euclid treats of parallel lines, from those which precede and follow them in the first book, in order that the student may have a clearer notion of the difficulties attending this division of the subject. It is necessary here to explain some of the technical terms used.

14. If the straight line E F cut two other straight lines A B, C D, it makes with those lines eight angles, to which particular names

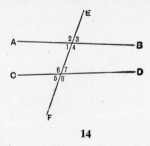

14

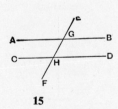

15

are given. Thus the angles numbered 1, 4, 6, 7 are called the *interior* angles; and 2, 3, 5, 8 are called the *exterior* angles; 1 and 7, and 4 and 6, are called *alternate* angles; and the pairs of angles, 1 and 5, 2 and 6, 4 and 8, 3 and 7 are called the *corresponding* angles.

The angles 1, 4, 6, and 7 are equal to four right angles.

15. If a straight line, E F, falling upon two other straight lines, A B and C D, make the alternate angles equal to one another, then the two straight lines must be parallel.

16. If a straight line fall upon two parallel straight lines, it makes the two interior angles upon the same side together equal to two right angles, and also the alternate angles equal to one another, and also the exterior angle equal to the interior and opposite upon the same side.

17. Straight lines which are parallel to the same straight line are parallel to one another.

18. If a side of any triangle B C be produced to D, the exterior angle is equal to the two interior and opposite angles, and the three interior angles of every triangle are together equal to two right angles.

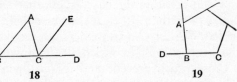

18   19

19. The exterior angles of any convex rectilinear figure, made by producing each of its sides in succession, are together equal to four right angles.

Now one of the most essential things to be understood with regard to angular measurement is the circle and its various divisions. A circle is divided into 360 equal parts or degrees, each

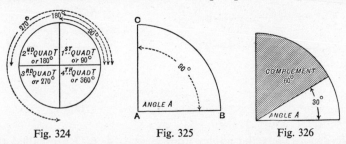

Fig. 324   Fig. 325   Fig. 326

degree into 60 minutes, and each minute into 60 seconds. The following symbols are used to denote these divisions and sub-divisions: degrees (°), minutes ('), and seconds ("), so that 85 degrees, 27 minutes, and 13 seconds would be shown thus: 85° 27′ 13″.

The circle (Fig. 324) is divided into four quadrants of 90 degrees each, and by Definition 4 (p. 376) each of these is a right angle.

In trigonometry it is usual to consider the radius of a quadrant as unity; and, as a line identical with the horizontal arm of the quadrant moves in an upward direction towards the vertical arm A C, Fig. 325, so the angle formed by this line produces certain functions which, for simplicity, are considered in the

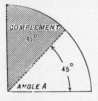

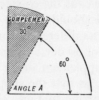

Fig. 327   Fig. 328

terms of the angle so formed, usually called the angle A. Thus Fig. 326 shows the angle A equal to 30 deg.; Fig. 327, the angle A equal to 45 deg.; Fig. 328, the angle A equal 60 deg.; and so a diagram may be constructed to represent an angle which is any fractional part of 90 deg.

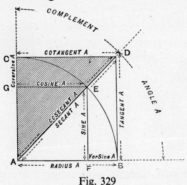

Fig. 329

It may be well here to introduce and explain the trigonometrical canon or diagram (Fig. 329), which shows the different trigonometrical functions in terms of the angle A to the radius = 1.

Now here, for simple illustration, I have taken the angle A as 45 deg.

The trigonometrical functions of the angle A are as follows: The SINE, CO-SINE, TANGENT, CO-TANGENT, SECANT, and CO-SECANT, with the VERSINE and CO-VERSINE, but the two latter do not enter largely into the consideration of the solution of triangles.

Now Fig. 330, illustrating the functions of an angle of 30 deg., shows by the strong lines certain positive functions of that angle, such as the sine, secant, and tangent; whilst the extended dotted lines, and dotted lines, show the complementary functions of the same angle, as the co-sine, co-secant, and co-tangent.

Here I should explain that the complement* of an angle is equal to its difference from 90 deg., so that 60 deg. is the complement of 30 deg.

The supplement of an angle is equal to its difference from 180 deg., so that the supplement of 30 deg. is 150 deg.

By referring to Figs. 330 and 331 it will be seen that in the former case the sine, secant, and tangent are much less than the co-sine, co-secant, and co-tangent (which are shown by dotted lines) by reason of the angle being small; whilst in Fig. 331 it will

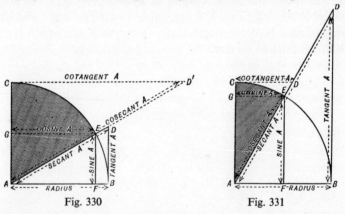

Fig. 330   Fig. 331

be seen that the sine, secant, and tangent are greater than are the co-sine, co-secant, and co-tangent; and going back to Fig. 329, we have the sine equal to the co-sine, the tangent equal to the co-tangent, and the secant equal to the co-secant, of an angle of 45°.

NOTE – It is beneficial to a beginner to draw the trigonometrical canon to scale, taking unity as the radius.

* The difference between an acute angle and a right angle is called its complement (*i.e.* the angle lacking to complete or fill up the right angle).

From the foregoing it will be seen that:

Trigonometrical ratios or functions – 1. *Sine* – The sine of an arc is a perpendicular let fall from the extremity of one radius to the other, as E F (Figs. 329, 330, and 331).

2. *Tangent* – The tangent is a perpendicular line drawn from the extremity of the radius to meet the other produced, as B D (B D′ in Fig. 331).

3. *Secant* – The secant is that radius which forms the angle, produced until it meets the tangent, as A D (A D′ in Fig. 331).

4. *Cosine* – The cosine is a line parallel and equal to that part of the radius which lies between the foot of the sine and the centre, as G E.

5. *Cotangent* – The cotangent is a horizontal line, commencing at the termination of the quadrant, and terminating on the radius A E produced, in D (Fig. 329), D′ (Fig. 330), and D (Fig. 331).

6. *Cosecant* – The cosecant is one of the radii produced until it intersects the cotangent in D (Fig. 329), and D′ (Figs. 330 and 331).

7. *Versed sine* – The versed sine is the portion of the radius between the foot of the sine and the arc, as F B.

8. *Coversed sine* – The coversed sine is the portion of the perpendicular between the cosine and the arc, as G C.

9. *Chord* – The chord of an arc is a line joining the extremities of the arc.

I should like here to explain what may appear to be an anomaly, viz. why the lines G E (cos A), C D′ (cot A), and A D′ (cosec A) (Fig. 330), should be complementary to the functions of the angle A. But I hope the following will elucidate the matter. We have found that the complement of an angle is the angle lacking to complete or fill up the right angle; and by reference to Fig. 330 it will be seen that the line G E bears the same relation to the angle E A C as E F does to the angle A or E A B, consequently G E must be the sine of the angle E A C. Thus what is the sine of an angle (less than 90 deg.) is the cosine of the remaining angle or complement, and *vice versa*. The line C D′ bears the same relation to the angle E A C as D B bears to the angle E A B, therefore what is the cotangent of the angle

E A B is the tangent of the angle E A C; and the same equally applies to the secant and cosecant.

These trigonometrical functions are abbreviated as follows:

Sin A	= The sine of the angle A.	
Cos A	= The cosine	do.
Tan A	= The tangent	do.
Cot A	= The cotangent	do.
Sec A	= The secant	do.
Cosec A	= The cosecant	do.
Vers A	= The versed sine	do.
Covers A	= The coversed sine	do.
Cho A	= The chord	do.

Relation of hypotenuse to the other sides of right angled triangle – Perhaps it may be better to refer to the 47th proposition of Euclid, which states the theorem: "In any right-angled triangle, the square which is described on the side subtending the right angle is equal to the sum of the squares described on the sides which contain the right angle" (Fig. 332).

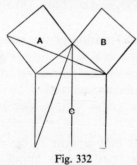

Fig. 332

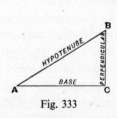

Fig. 333

By this proposition the sum of the squares on the sides A and B is equal to that on the side C; in other words, taking another form of a right-angled triangle, as Fig. 333:

Let A B = Hypotenuse.

A C = Base.

B C = Perpendicular.

Then

$$\text{Hypotenuse} = \sqrt{\text{Base}^2 + \text{Perp.}^2}$$
$$\text{Base} = \sqrt{\text{Hyp.}^2 - \text{Perp.}^2}$$
$$\text{Perp.} = \sqrt{\text{Hyp.}^2 - \text{Base}^2}$$

Now in the preceding descriptions of the various trigono-metrical functions, I have shown that they all have reference to the angle A of the triangle B A C, a portion of the first quadrant (see Fig. 334), which is placed in the centre of the circle called the circle of reference.

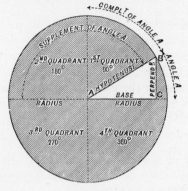

Fig. 334

Fig. 335

We will now consider the functions of the angle A (B A C) in terms of the sides of the triangle A C B. We have seen (Figs. 330, 331) that the functions are the ratios borne by certain lines to the radius; and as a ratio or proportion may always be expressed in the form of a fraction, the functions may be obtained by dividing these lines by the radius. Now, so long as the angles of a triangle remain unchanged, the ratios of the sides of that triangle remain unchanged; hence, comparing Fig. 335 with Fig. 330, or Fig. 331, we are able to express the functions of the angles A in terms of the sides A B, B C, C A.

Thus

$$\text{Sin A} = \frac{\text{PERP}}{\text{HYP}} = \frac{\text{B C}}{\text{A B}}. \qquad \text{Cos A} = \frac{\text{BASE}}{\text{HYP}} = \frac{\text{A C}}{\text{A B}}.$$

$$\text{Tan A} = \frac{\text{PERP}}{\text{BASE}} = \frac{\text{B C}}{\text{A C}}. \qquad \text{Cot A} = \frac{\text{BASE}}{\text{PERP}} = \frac{\text{A C}}{\text{B C}}.$$

$$\text{Sec A} = \frac{\text{HYP}}{\text{BASE}} = \frac{\text{A B}}{\text{A C}}. \qquad \text{Cosec A} = \frac{\text{HYP}}{\text{PERP}} = \frac{\text{A B}}{\text{B C}}.$$

$$\text{Vers A} = \frac{\text{HYP} - \text{BASE}}{\text{HYP}} = \frac{\text{A B} - \text{A C}}{\text{A B}}.$$

$$\text{Covers A} = \frac{\text{HYP} - \text{PERP}}{\text{HYP}} = \frac{\text{A B} - \text{B C}}{\text{A B}}.$$

$$\text{B C} = \text{A B cos B}; \text{ A C} = \text{A B sine B}; \text{ A B} = \text{B C sec B}.$$

$$\text{B} = \text{complement of A} = 90 - \text{A}.$$

$$\text{A} + \text{B} + \text{C} = 180°.$$

I may explain, by reference to Fig. 329, that the tangent, co-tangent, secant, and cosecant appear therein much longer than the lines E F, A F, and E A, which correspond with the lines B C, A C, and A B in Figs. 334 and 335; and my reason for referring to it is to show that, as these lines are simply ratios to the radius, so what in Fig. 329 is the tangent of A, viz. $\frac{\text{B D}}{\text{A B}}$ is exactly the same ratio as $\frac{\text{B C}}{\text{A C}}$ in Figs. 334, and 335, or as follows:

	Fig. 329		Figs. 334 and 335
Sin A	$= \dfrac{\text{E F}}{\text{A E}}$	$=$	$\dfrac{\text{B C}}{\text{A B}}.$
Cos A	$= \dfrac{\text{G E}}{\text{A E}} = \dfrac{\text{A F}}{\text{A E}}$	$=$	$\dfrac{\text{A C}}{\text{A B}}.$
Tan A	$= \dfrac{\text{B D}}{\text{A B}}$	$=$	$\dfrac{\text{B C}}{\text{A C}}.$
Cot A	$= \dfrac{\text{C D}}{\text{A C}}$	$=$	$\dfrac{\text{A C}}{\text{B C}}.$
Sec A	$= \dfrac{\text{A D}}{\text{A B}}$	$=$	$\dfrac{\text{A B}}{\text{A C}}.$
Cosec A	$= \dfrac{\text{A D}}{\text{A C}}$	$=$	$\dfrac{\text{A B}}{\text{B C}}.$

A little reflection will serve to impress upon the mind the equality of these ratios under the two circumstances I have illustrated.

Cotangent of greater or less angles – Here the cotangent and cosecant in Fig. 330 appear extravagantly out of proportion with the condition of those in Figs. 334, and 335, but seeing that we are dealing with ratios of lines one towards another, and not the actual lengths of the lines themselves, there will I think be no difficulty in comprehending this fact.

I have thus in some detail endeavoured to clear up a difficulty that appears to have presented itself to many students with regard to the relations of these functions, and having done so, I now proceed to consider the practical application of these ratios to the solution of triangles, for which purpose I shall abandon the more complicated reference letters, and, as illustrated in Fig. 336, shall refer to each side as *a*, *b*, or *c*, and the angles as A, B, or C. C being the right angle, *c* is the hypotenuse, and *b* is the side adjacent to the angle considered.

Fig. 336

The angle B is the complement of A, since two acute angles in a right-angled triangle must be always equal to one right angle (for all the angles of *every* triangle equal *two* right angles).

Hence, with the altered lettering, we have a new list of functions:

$$\text{Sin A} = \frac{a}{c}. \qquad \text{Cos A} = \frac{b}{c}.$$

$$\text{Tan A} = \frac{a}{b}. \qquad \text{Cot A} = \frac{b}{a}.$$

$$\text{Sec A} = \frac{c}{b}. \qquad \text{Cosec A} = \frac{c}{a}.$$

If we know the numerical value of any one of these ratios we can find A. In other words, if the ratio between any two sides of a right-angled triangle is given we can define all the angles.

Now the relations of trigonometrical ratios to one another (since the square of the hypotenuse of a right-angled triangle is equal to the sum of the squares of the two sides) are as follows:

Since $a^2+b^2 = c^2$,

dividing by c^2, $\dfrac{a^2}{c^2}+\dfrac{b^2}{c^2} = \dfrac{c^2}{c^2} = 1$;

or $\sin^2 A+\cos^2 A = 1.$ . . . . . . (1)

Dividing the first equation by b^2, we get $\left(\dfrac{a}{b}\right)^2+1 = \left(\dfrac{c}{b}\right)^2$; or reversing the order, $\sec^2 A = 1+\tan^2 A.$ . . . . (2)

Dividing the same by a^2, we get $1+\left(\dfrac{b}{a}\right)^2 = \left(\dfrac{c}{a}\right)^2$; or reversing the order as before, $\operatorname{cosec}^2 A = 1+\cot^2 A.$ . . . . (3)

Since $\dfrac{a}{b}\times\dfrac{b}{a} = 1$, $\tan A \cot A = 1.$ . . . . . (4)

Again $\tan A = \dfrac{a}{b} = \dfrac{\frac{a}{c}}{\frac{b}{c}}$, $\therefore \tan A = \dfrac{\sin A}{\cos A}$ . . (6)

Again $\cot A = \dfrac{b}{a} = \dfrac{\frac{1}{a}}{\frac{1}{b}}$, $\therefore \cot A = \dfrac{1}{\tan A}$ . . (7)

Again $\cot A = \dfrac{b}{a} = \dfrac{\frac{b}{c}}{\frac{a}{c}}$, $\therefore \cot A = \dfrac{\cos A}{\sin A}$ . . (8)

Again $\sec A = \dfrac{c}{b} = \dfrac{1}{\frac{b}{c}}$, $\therefore \sec A = \dfrac{1}{\cos A}$ . . (9)

Again $\operatorname{cosec} A = \dfrac{c}{a} = \dfrac{1}{\frac{a}{c}}$, $\therefore \operatorname{cosec} A = \dfrac{1}{\sin A}$ . . (10)

Vers $A = 1-\cos A$, and covers $A = 1-\sin A$ . . (11)

The foregoing equations enable us to find the value of any function in terms of any other functions, thus:

Sin A in terms of cos A – Let it be required to express sin A in terms of cos A and *vice versa*. By equation (1) we have seen that

$$\text{Sin}^2 \text{A} + \cos^2 \text{A} = 1. \text{ Consequently}$$

$$\text{Sin A} = \sqrt{1 - \cos^2 \text{A}} \quad . \quad . \quad . \quad (12)$$

$$\text{Cos A} = \sqrt{1 - \sin^2 \text{A}} \quad . \quad . \quad . \quad (13)$$

Tan A in terms of sin A – Let it be required to express tan A in terms of sin A.

Tan $\text{A} = \dfrac{\sin \text{A}}{\cos \text{A}}$ (6), and in (13) we have seen cos A $= \sqrt{1 - \sin^2 \text{A}}$,

$$\therefore \text{Tan A} = \frac{\sin \text{A}}{\sqrt{1 - \sin^2 \text{A}}} \quad . \quad . \quad . \quad (14)$$

Tan A in terms of cos A – Let it be required to express tan A in terms of cos A. Since by (6), tan $\text{A} = \dfrac{\sin \text{A}}{\cos \text{A}}$; and, by (12), sin A $= \sqrt{1 - \cos^2 \text{A}}$,

$$\therefore \text{Tan A} = \frac{\sqrt{1 - \cos^2 \text{A}}}{\cos \text{A}} \quad . \quad . \quad . \quad (15)$$

Cos A in terms of tan A – Let it be required to express cos A in terms of tan A.

By equation (9) cos $\text{A} = \dfrac{1}{\sec \text{A}}$ . . . (15*)

But by equation (2) sec^2 A $= 1 + \tan^2$ A,

$$\therefore \sec \text{A} = \sqrt{1 + \tan^2 \text{A}},$$

and therefore cos $\text{A} = \dfrac{1}{\sqrt{1 + \tan^2 \text{A}}}$ . . (16)

Sin A in terms of tan A – Let it be required to express sin A in terms of tan A. Now $\sin A = \cos A \times \tan A$, therefore by preceding article

$$\mathrm{Sin}\ A = \frac{\tan A}{\sqrt{1+\tan^2 A}} \quad \cdots \quad (17)$$

Sin A in terms of sec A – Let it be required to express sin A in terms of sec A.

Since $\sin^2 A = 1 - \cos^2 A$; substituting (by (15*)) for cos A, $\sin^2 A = 1 - \dfrac{1}{\sec^2 A}$; $\therefore$ reducing to a common denominator and

taking the square root we have $\sin A = \dfrac{\sqrt{\sec^2 A - 1}}{\sec A}$. . (18)

Cos A in terms of cosec A – To express cos A in terms of cosec A.

By (8) $\cot A = \dfrac{\cos A}{\sin A}$; $\therefore \cos A = \cot A \sin A$,

and $\therefore \cos A = \dfrac{\sqrt{\mathrm{cosec}^2 A - 1}}{\mathrm{cosec}\ A}$ . . (19). See (10) and (3)

Cot A in terms of sec A – To express cot A in terms of sec A.

$$\mathrm{Cot}\ A = \frac{1}{\tan A} = \frac{1}{\sqrt{\sec^2 A - 1}} \quad \cdots \cdots \quad (20)$$

To express cosec A in terms of sec A.

$$\mathrm{Cosec}\ A = \frac{1}{\sin A}\ (\text{see }(10)) = \frac{1}{\sqrt{1 - \cos^2 A}}\ (\text{see }(12))$$

$$= \frac{1}{\sqrt{1 - \dfrac{1}{\sec^2 A}}} = \frac{1}{\sqrt{\dfrac{\sec^2 A - 1}{\sec^2 A}}} = \frac{1}{\dfrac{\sqrt{\sec^2 A - 1}}{\sec A}},$$

and therefore $\mathrm{cosec}\ A = \dfrac{\sec A}{\sqrt{\sec^2 A - 1}}$ . . . . . (21)

To express sin A in terms of tan A – Since $\sin A = \tan A$,

$$\cos A = \tan A \frac{1}{\sqrt{1+\tan^2 A}}; \therefore \sin A = \frac{\tan A}{\sqrt{1+\tan^2 A}}. \quad (22)$$

Following on, we arrive at these results:

Tan A $= \sqrt{\sec^2 A - 1}$ . . . (23). See (2)

Sec A $= \sqrt{1+\tan^2 A}$ . . . (24)

Cot A $= \sqrt{\csc^2 A - 1}$ . . . (25). See (3)

Cosec A $= \sqrt{1+\cot^2 A}$ . . . (26)

It is very desirable to learn to express every function in terms of every other function, as by means of working these out in detail the mind is impressed, and the relations of one function to another will become familiar.

Complemental angles – It has been shown that the complement of an angle (*i.e.* of an acute angle) is the difference between it and a right angle, or commonly called its "defect." Thus if the angle A be 30 deg. the complement will be 90 deg. −30 deg. = 60 deg. Again, if the angle A = 56 deg. 16 min. then its complement will be 90 deg. −56 deg. 16 min. = 33 deg. 44 min.

Now, I have endeavoured to explain by the trigonometrical canon the various functions, which are as follows: To the lines which are the trigonometrical functions of the arc correspond certain ratios which are the trigonometrical functions of the angles which the arc subtends.

In Fig. 337 I have shown the angle A = 30 deg., the sine of

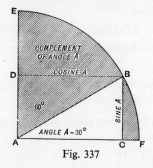

Fig. 337

this angle is B C, whilst the cosine is B D, and the angle B A E is its complement. Now the sine is that line lying within the arc
cc

which is perpendicular to the base, which in the angle B A C is B C. But if B D is perpendicular to E A, and since A D is the cosine of the angle B A E, and A D = B C, therefore the cosine of the angle B A E or the complement of A equals the sine of A.

Thus we may deduce the following facts:

The cosine of an angle is equal to the sine of its complement.

The cotangent of an angle is equal to the tangent of its complement.

The cosecant of an angle is equal to the secant of its complement, etc.

So far so good, referring to the diagram in Fig. 337; but I want to impress on the student that in trigonometry we have in practice to do without the canon and consider only the triangle.

Now, as a simple illustration, we will take the case of a right-angled triangle as Fig. 337, the angle B A C of which is 30 deg. We know B C A to be 90 deg., thereupon the angle A B C will be 90 deg. −30 deg. = 60 deg., which is the complement.

If, as we have seen, sin A (Fig. 333) is $\dfrac{\text{PERP}}{\text{HYP}}$ or $\dfrac{\text{B C}}{\text{A B}}$, and cos A is $\dfrac{\text{BASE}}{\text{HYP}}$ or $\dfrac{\text{A C}}{\text{A B}}$; from the foregoing it will not be difficult to realise that in a triangle the functions of the angle and its complement are in the inverse ratio. To better illustrate this, somewhat anticipating the practical application of the foregoing, I may say that the value of the

Nat sin 30 deg. = 0·50000.   Nat sin 60 deg. = 0·86603.
Nat cos 30 deg. = 0·86603.   Nat cos 60 deg. = 0·50000.

Supplemental angles – *The supplement of an angle is the difference between it and two right angles.*

Thus two right angles are equal to 180 deg., consequently if the angle A = 30° the supplement will be 180° −30° = 150°; or, if the angle A is 29° 16′, then the supplement will be 180° −29° 16′ = 150° 44′.

The sine of an angle is equal to the sine of its supplement.

In Fig. 338, c' A B' is the supplement of the angle F A B', and is equal to F A B, and also C B is equal to c' B', and therefore $\dfrac{c'\,B'}{A\,B'} = \dfrac{C\,B}{A\,B}$, but $\dfrac{C\,B}{A\,B}$ is the sine of the angle A, and $\dfrac{c'\,B'}{A\,B'}$ is the sine of the supplement, therefore they are equal.

The cosine of an angle is equal to the cosine of its supplement, but of opposite sign.

Use of the + and − signs – Before proceeding to reason this out it is necessary to speak of the conventional signs, plus and minus, used in trigonometry. As in Fig. 339, we may divide a circle into four quadrants, commencing with the first right-hand one above the horizontal or datum line F' A F. With A as centre or origin, if a line revolving from the initial line A F forms any

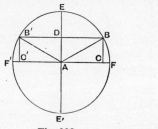

Fig. 338

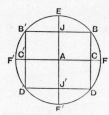

Fig. 339

angle less than 90 deg., it is treated, as has been explained, as the angle A proper; but if this revolving line has passed through 90 deg. and makes therefore an angle greater than 90 deg. with the initial line, the supplement of this angle is less than 90 deg., and is the angle to be considered.

The definitions of trigonometrical functions are perfectly general, and therefore applicable to arcs of any magnitude. If an arc be greater than a quadrant some of the lines which have been defined as the trigonometrical functions lie to the left of the vertical diameter E A E', and some below the horizontal diameter F' A F. In order to take account of these variations of position, mathematicians have been led to adopt the following conventional signs as to the plus and minus, which enable us at the same time to represent the position as well as the magnitude of the line in question. Referring to Fig. 339, the lines F' F and E E' represent the horizontal and vertical diameter working around the centre or origin A. Now all horizontal lines, provided they are to the right of E E′, are positive or +, and those to the left are negative or −. Similarly, every vertical line, if it lie above F′ A F is positive, and negative if below that line. Thus A C is +, because it lies to the right of E E′; B C is + because it lies above A; and upon the same principle A C′ and C′ D′ are both −; B′ C′ is + and C D is −.

Referring to Fig. 340, if we trace the value of the sine in its progress round the circle from right to left, in direction of the arrow, we shall find that as the revolving line progresses through

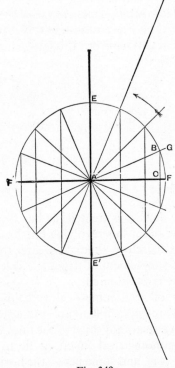

Fig. 340

the four quadrants, in the first and second the sine is positive, whilst in the third and fourth it is negative. Now it has been established that:

1st. Any line drawn parallel to F′ A F to the right of E E′ is

to be positive, and consequently any line drawn parallel to
F A F' to the left of E E' is to be negative.

2nd. Any line drawn parallel to E' A F above F' F is positive,
and consequently any line drawn parallel to E E' below F' F is
negative.

3rd. The revolving line A B (Figs. 341, 342, 343, 344) is
always positive.

We have previously seen that the following are some of the
ratios.

$$\sin \text{B A C} = \frac{\text{C B}}{\text{A B}}; \quad \cos \text{B A C} = \frac{\text{A C}}{\text{A B}}; \quad \tan \text{B A C} = \frac{\text{B C}}{\text{A C}}.$$

Therefore, keeping in mind that in the first quadrant C B is
positive, being above G D; A C is positive because it is drawn to
the right of E F, and A B is always positive.

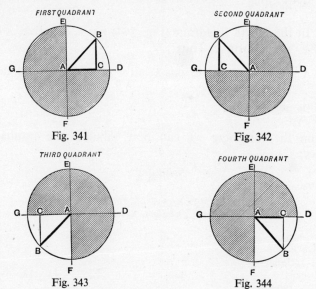

Fig. 341   Fig. 342

Fig. 343   Fig. 344

(1) Thus if the angle A be anywhere within the first quadrant
(Fig. 341)

$\text{Sin A} = \dfrac{\text{C B}}{\text{A B}}$ is positive; $\cos \text{A} = \dfrac{\text{A C}}{\text{A B}}$ is positive; and $\tan \text{A}$
$= \dfrac{\text{B C}}{\text{A C}}$ is positive.

When the angle A lies in the second quadrant (Fig. 342) C B is positive, because above G D; A C is negative, because to the left of E F, and A B is positive.

(2) Thus for second quadrant

$$\text{Sin A} = \frac{C\,B}{A\,B} \text{ is positive; } \cos A = \frac{A\,C}{A\,B} \text{ is negative; and tan A}$$

$$= \frac{C\,B}{A\,C} \text{ is negative.}$$

(3) In the third quadrant (Fig. 343) C B is negative, A C is negative, and A B is positive, consequently

$$\text{Sin A} = \frac{B\,C}{A\,B} \text{ is negative; } \cos A = \frac{A\,C}{A\,B} \text{ is negative; and tan A}$$

$$= \frac{B\,C}{A\,C} \text{ is positive.}$$

(4) In the fourth quadrant (Fig. 344) B C is negative, A C is positive, A B is positive. Thus:

$$\text{Sin A} = \frac{B\,C}{A\,B} \text{ is negative; } \cos A = \frac{A\,C}{A\,B} \text{ is positive; and tan A}$$

$$= \frac{B\,C}{A\,C} \text{ is negative.}$$

From the foregoing we can now tabulate the results as follows:

TABLE 1

	First Quadrant	Second Quadrant	Third Quadrant	Fourth Quadrant
Sine ..	+	+	—	—
Cosine ..	+	—	—	+
Tangent ..	+	—	+	—

NOTE – The secant, cosecant, and cotangent of the angle A have the same sign as the sine, cosine, and tangent of the angle A.

Now to prove that "the cosine of an angle is equal to the cosine of its supplement, but of opposite sign." Referring to Fig. 338, the lines A C and A C' are equal, but being in different quadrants, A C lies in a different direction to A C′, and thus they have different signs.

Therefore, having regard to sign, $\dfrac{A\,C}{A\,B} = -\dfrac{A\,C'}{A\,B'}$;

Now $\dfrac{A\,C}{A\,B} = \cos A$, and $\dfrac{A\,C'}{A\,B'} = \cos$ of the supplement of A (viz. C A B′)

$$\text{Cos } A = -\cos(180° - A) \quad . \quad . \quad . \quad (27)$$

Relations of lines to functions of the angle of reference – Before proceeding any further in the practical application of the foregoing formulae, I will speak of the relation the lines (or functions of the arc) bear to certain ratios, which are the trigonometrical functions of the angles which the arc subtends. They are as follows:

Definition – The sine, cosine, tangent, etc., of an angle at the centre of a circle is equal to the ratio of the sine, cosine, tangent, etc., of the corresponding arc to the radius of the circle.

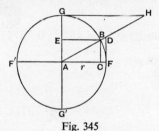

Fig. 345

The radius A F (Fig. 345) is denoted by r, and the angle H A F is denoted by A.

Then

$$\text{Sin } A = \frac{B\,C}{r}; \cos A = \frac{A\,C}{r}; \tan A = \frac{D\,F}{r}; \sec A = \frac{A\,D}{r};$$

$$\cot A = \frac{G\,H}{r}; \operatorname{cosec} A = \frac{A\,H}{r}; \text{vers } A = \frac{C\,F}{r}; \text{and covers } A = \frac{E\,G}{r}.$$

Radius unity – In trigonometrical tables the radius is commonly taken as representing unity, and for practical purposes, if the radius is divided into the length of any one of the lines representing functions, it will give the value of that function.

Basis of formulae for tables of sines, etc. – It is necessary now to briefly consider how the foregoing equations may be worked out, so as to be of practical value. This has been done by many eminent mathematicians in the form of tables of natural sines, cosines, etc. With such available, it would be a waste of time to undertake calculations for ourselves, and a set of such tables sufficient for the purpose of this work will be found in the Appendix II. To illustrate the basis upon which such tables are prepared, I will select a few examples, as follows, for angles of 18 deg., 30 deg., 45 deg., and 60 deg. I will take that of 45 deg. first.

By the equation (1), $\sin^2 A + \cos^2 A = 1.$

$$\therefore \sin^2 45° + \cos^2 45 = 1.$$

But since the complement of 45° is 90° − 45° = 45°

$$\therefore \sin 45° = \cos 45°, \text{ and } \sin^2 45° = \cos^2 45°.$$

$$\therefore 2 \sin^2 45° = 1; \text{ and } 2 \cos^2 45° = 1.$$

$$\therefore \sin^2 45° = \tfrac{1}{2}, \text{ and } \sin 45° = \frac{1}{\sqrt{2}} = 0.70711;$$

Similarly, $\cos 45° = 0.70711.$

Again, by (6), $\tan A = \dfrac{\sin A}{\cos A},$

$$\therefore \tan 45° = \frac{\sin 45°}{\cos 45°} = \frac{0.70711}{0.70711} = 1.$$

Then by (7), $\cot A = \dfrac{1}{\tan A},$

$$\therefore \cot 45° = \frac{1}{\tan 45°} = 1.$$

Similarly, by (9), $\sec A = \dfrac{1}{\cos A},$

$$\therefore \sec 45° = \frac{1}{\cos 45°} = \frac{1}{0.70711} = 1.41421.$$

And finally, by (10), $\operatorname{cosec} A = \dfrac{\sin A}{1},$

$$\therefore \operatorname{cosec} 45° = \frac{1}{\sin 45°} = \frac{1}{0.70711} = 1.41421.$$

Sines, etc., for 45 degrees – The following is the result of the preceding investigations:

$$\text{Sin } 45° = 0·70711.$$
$$\text{Cos } 45° = 0·70711.$$
$$\text{Tan } 45° = 1·00000.$$
$$\text{Cot } 45° = 1·00000.$$
$$\text{Sec } 45° = 1·41421.$$
$$\text{Cosec } 45° = 1·41421.$$

In the case of the angle of 60 deg., the revolving line forms a portion of an equilateral triangle, whereof A B, A F, and F B (Fig. 346), are equal sides, consequently the line B C, or sine,

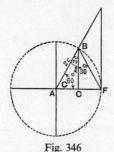

Fig. 346

bisects the triangle; now the angle B A C = 60 deg. and the angle A B C = 30 deg., therefore as the length of the base A F is equal to that of the two other sides, then A C is half A F.

Sines, etc., for 60 degrees – Let B C be represented by x, A C by c, A B by $2c$.

Then $x^2 = (2c)^2 - c^2 = 4c^2 - c^2 = 3c^2$
$$\therefore x = \sqrt{3} \times c$$

And since $\sin 60° = \sin \text{B A C} = \dfrac{\text{B C}}{\text{A B}} = \dfrac{\sqrt{3} \times c}{2c} = \dfrac{\sqrt{3}}{2} = 0·86603$

Again, $\cos 60° = \dfrac{\text{A C}}{\text{A B}} = \dfrac{c}{2c} = \quad\quad \tfrac{1}{2} = 0·50000$

And $\tan 60° = \tan \text{B A C} = \dfrac{\text{B C}}{\text{A C}} = \dfrac{\sqrt{3} \times c}{c} = \dfrac{\sqrt{3}}{1} = \sqrt{3} = 1·7321$

$\cot 60° = \cot \text{B A C} = \dfrac{1}{\tan 60°} = \dfrac{1}{\sqrt{3}} \quad\quad = 0·57735$

$$\text{Sec } 60° = \text{sec B A C} = \frac{1}{\cos 60°} = \frac{1}{\frac{1}{2}} = 2 \qquad = 2\cdot0000$$

$$\text{Cosec } 60° = \text{cosec B A C} = \frac{1}{\sin 60°} = \frac{2}{\sqrt{3}} \qquad = 1\cdot15470$$

Again, take the angle of 30 deg., when, because A C is half A F (Fig. 346), and the angle A B F, which is 60 deg., is bisected by B C, then A B C = F B C = $\frac{1}{2}$ the angle A B F = 30 deg.

Thus:

$$\text{Sin } 30° = \sin \text{A B C} = \frac{\text{C A}}{\text{B A}} = \frac{c}{2\,c} = \frac{1}{2} \qquad = 0\cdot50000$$

Sines, etc., for 30 degrees

$$\text{Cos } 30° = \cos \text{A B C} = \frac{\text{B C}}{\text{B A}} = \frac{\sqrt{3}\times c}{2\,c} = \frac{\sqrt{3}}{2} \qquad = 0\cdot86603$$

$$\text{Tan } 30° = \tan \text{A B C} = \frac{\text{C A}}{\text{C B}} = \frac{c}{c\sqrt{3}\times c} = \frac{1}{\sqrt{3}} = 0\cdot57735$$

$$\text{Cot } 30° = \cot \text{A B C} = \frac{\text{B C}}{\text{C A}} = \frac{c\sqrt{3}\times c}{c} = \sqrt{3} = 1\cdot7321$$

$$\text{Sec } 30° = \sec \text{A B C} = \frac{\text{B A}}{\text{B C}} = \frac{2\,c}{c\sqrt{3}\times c} = \frac{2}{\sqrt{3}} = 1\cdot15470$$

$$\text{Cosec } 30° = \text{cosec A B C} = \frac{\text{B A}}{\text{A C}} = \frac{2\,c}{c} = 2 \qquad = 2\cdot0000$$

Sines, etc., for 60 and 30 degrees – From the foregoing results we may tabulate the natural sines, etc., of the angles 60 and 30 degrees respectively, viz.:

Sine	of 60° = 0·86603.		Sine	30° = 0·50000.
Cos	of 60° = 0·50000.		Cos	30° = 0·86603.
Tan	of 60° = 1·73210.		Tan	30° = 0·57735.
Cotan	of 60° = 0·57735.		Cotan	30° = 1·73210.
Sec	of 60° = 2·00000.		Sec	30° = 1·15470.
Cosec	of 60° = 1·15470.		Cosec	30° = 2·00000.

Thus it will be seen that the value of the sine of 60 deg. = cos 30 deg.; tan 60 deg. = cot 30 deg.; and sec 60 deg. = cosec 30 deg., and *vice versa*.

Now, take the angle 18 deg. as another example, of which it is required to find the sine, cosine, and tangent, etc.

Sines, etc., for 18 degrees – Let the angle B A C (Fig. 347) = 18 deg., drop the perpendicular B C, which produce to meet the circumference in B′, then it is evident that the angle B A B′ is twice the angle B A C, or 36 deg. B B′ is therefore one side of a

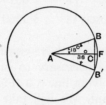

Fig. 347

decagon, inscribed in the circle; and therefore B B′ is equal to the greater segment of the radius cut in extreme and mean ratio (Euclid IV. 11, and II. 11), and therefore

$$B B'^2 = A F (A F - B B')$$

Solving this as an ordinary quadratic equation we get

$$B B' = A F \times \frac{\sqrt{5} - 1}{2}$$

But B C = $\frac{1}{2}$ B B′, therefore

$$\text{Sin } 18° = \frac{B B'}{2 A F} = \frac{\sqrt{5} - 1}{4} \qquad = 0.30902$$

$$\text{Cos } 18° = \sqrt{1 - \sin^2 18°} = \sqrt{1 - \cdot 30902^2} = 0.95106$$

By (6)

$$\text{Tan } 18° = \frac{\sin 18°}{\cos 18°} = \frac{\cdot 30902}{\cdot 95106} \qquad = 0.32492$$

and by (7)

$$\text{Cot } 18° = \frac{1}{\tan 18°} = \frac{1}{\cdot 32492} \qquad = 3.07768$$

and by (9)

$$\text{Sec } 18° = \frac{1}{\cos 18°} = \frac{1}{\cdot 95106} \qquad = 1.05146$$

and by (10)

$$\text{Cosec } 18° = \frac{1}{\sin 18°} = \frac{1}{\cdot 30902} \qquad = 3.23607$$

From the foregoing we can now tabulate the following:

$$\text{Sin} \quad 18° = 0\!\cdot\!30902$$
$$\text{Cos} \quad 18° = 0\!\cdot\!95106$$
$$\text{Tan} \quad 18° = 0\!\cdot\!32492$$
$$\text{Cot} \quad 18° = 3\!\cdot\!07768$$
$$\text{Sec} \quad 18° = 1\!\cdot\!05146$$
$$\text{Cosec} \; 18° = 3\!\cdot\!23607$$

As far as we have gone we have considered only angles less than 90 deg., but it is necessary to briefly investigate what happens when the revolving line A B (Figs. 341, 342, 343, 344) passes the first quadrant. We will take 120 deg., or 90 deg. +30 deg. as the angle B A D. Now we are dealing with two right angles, consequently the angle B A D if deducted from 180 deg. will give us the value of B A G or 180 deg. — 120 deg. = 60 deg. = B A G.

Sines, etc., for 120 degrees – Therefore, sine 120 deg. $= \dfrac{\text{B C}}{\text{A B}}$ which is equal to the sine of 60 deg., its supplement.

Therefore, sin 120 deg. = sin 60 deg., and being in the second quadrant as we have seen in Table I, it is positive, whilst the cosine and tangent are negative.

Thus

$$\text{Sin} \; 120° = \frac{\sqrt{3}}{2}$$
$$\text{Cos} \; 120° = -\tfrac{1}{2}$$
$$\text{Tan} \; 120° = -\sqrt{3}.$$

Sines, etc., for 225 degrees – Passing into the third quadrant, suppose it be required to find the sine, cosine, tangent, etc., of 225 deg.

Then 225 deg. — 180 deg. = 45 deg. = B A G (Fig. 343), and in the third quadrant from the Table I we have seen that the sine and cosine are negative whilst the tangent is positive.

Consequently

$$\text{Sin } 225° = -\frac{1}{\sqrt{2}}$$

$$\text{Cos } 225° = -\frac{1}{\sqrt{2}}$$

$$\text{Tan } 225° = 1$$

From the foregoing remarks we have seen the various functions of right-angled triangles, and have been able to deduce certain formulae which enable us to arrive at the numerical value of each. These values are what are termed natural sines, cosines, etc., and they are based upon the understanding that the radius is always unity, in other words they are relatively circumstanced to unity. Thus sin 45 deg. = 0·70711, but the tan 45 deg. and the cotan 45 deg. = 1 = radius. To illustrate my meaning:

Ratio of radius – Suppose the radius of a circle to be 40 ft., and a right-angled triangle formed by the base, perpendicular and hypotenuse of an angle of 45 deg. as in Fig. 348. A F = A B = 40 ft., and it is required to know the length of B C; referring to the trigonometrical canon (Fig. 329), we find E F (which is the same as B C in Fig. 348) is the sine.

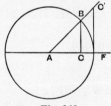

Fig. 348

Therefore as we have seen that sin 45 deg. = 0·70711, then if we multiply 0·70711 by 40 we shall get the length B C = 28·28440 ft., so that 28·28440 represents the ratio of B C to the radius 40 ft. just exactly as 0·70711 is its ratio to the radius of unity.

Again, if we want the length A C′ we know by our canon that A C′ is the secant (and also the cosecant of 45 deg.). Now our tables tell us that sec 45 deg. = 1·41421, therefore this multiplied by the radius of 40 ft. gives us

1·41421 × 40 ft. = 56·56840 ft. = the length A C'.

Now B A C = 45°, ∴ A C = B C = 28·28440 ft.

At the risk of being considered irregular, if not too elementary, I have elected to illustrate the foregoing examples in a somewhat rule-of-thumb style, for this work does not profess to do more than seek, by as graphic a manner as possible, to bridge over many of the difficulties which the student has to encounter.

Solution of right-angled triangles – All triangles consist of six parts, viz., three sides and three angles; and it is possible with three of these, one part at least being a side, to find the others. Referring back to Fig. 336, if we take the sides as represented by a, b, and c, and the angles by A, B, and C, with the following approximate lengths of each, $a = 21·838$ feet, $b = 60$ feet, and $c = 63·851$ feet, we have the following results.

We have seen that $\dfrac{a}{b} = \tan$ A, then $\tan$ A $= \dfrac{a}{b} = \dfrac{21·838}{60·00}$ = 0·36397, which by reference to a table of natural tangents indicates that the angle A = 20°. And since C is 90°, then B = 90° − 20° = 70°.

Take $b = 60$ and $c = 63·851$. Then as $\dfrac{b}{c}$ is cos A,

∴ cos A $= \dfrac{60}{63·851} = 0·93969.$

Take $a = 21·838$ and B = 70°, $c = \dfrac{a}{\cos B} = \dfrac{21·838}{·34202}$ = 63·851 ft.

Take $c = 63·851$ and A = 20°. Then $a = c \sin$ A = 63·851 × 0·34202 = 21·838 feet, and $b = c \cos$ A = 63·851 × 0·93969 = 60 ft.

Trigonometrical ratios of two angles – It has been clearly established that the relations between the sine, cosine, tangent, etc., of the sum or difference of two or more angles, and the sines, cosines, etc., of the angles themselves, are based on the following fundamental propositions:

$$\text{Sin } (A+B) = \sin A \cos B + \cos A \sin B \ . \quad . \quad (28)$$
$$\text{Cos } (A+B) = \cos A \cos B - \sin A \sin B \ . \quad . \quad (29)$$
$$\text{Sin } (A-B) = \sin A \cos B - \cos A \sin B \ . \quad . \quad (30)$$
$$\text{Cos } (A-B) = \cos A \cos B + \sin A \sin B \ . \quad . \quad (31)$$

In this case (Fig. 349) A and B are the angles. Sin $(A+B)$ is a fraction, but sin A + sin B is the sum of two fractions, and care should be taken to avoid any misunderstanding.

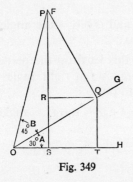

Fig. 349

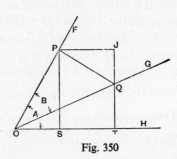

Fig. 350

Then let us take H O G = angle A and G O F = the angle B. Then H O F = angle $(A+B)$. In the line O F which bounds the angle $(A+B)$ take any point P, and let drop the perpendicular P Q on O G, and P S on O H. Draw the perpendiculars Q R and Q T to the lines P S and O H.

Then

$$Q P R = 90° - R Q P = R Q O = H O G = A$$

Now

$$\text{Sin } (A+B) = \sin H O F = \frac{P S}{O P} = \frac{S R + R P}{O P} = \frac{Q T}{O P} + \frac{R P}{O P}$$

$$= \frac{Q T}{O Q} \times \frac{O Q}{O P} + \frac{P R}{P Q} \times \frac{P Q}{O P}$$

$$= \sin H O G \cos G O F + \cos R P Q \sin G O F$$

$$= \sin A \cos B + \cos A \sin B$$

Again

$$\text{Cos (A+B)} = \cos \text{H O F} = \frac{\text{O S}}{\text{O P}} = \frac{\text{O T} - \text{S T}}{\text{O P}} = \frac{\text{O T}}{\text{O P}} - \frac{\text{R Q}}{\text{O P}}$$

$$= \frac{\text{O T}}{\text{O Q}} \times \frac{\text{O Q}}{\text{O P}} - \frac{\text{R Q}}{\text{Q P}} \times \frac{\text{Q P}}{\text{O P}}$$

$$= \cos \text{H O G} \cos \text{G O P} - \sin \text{R P Q} \sin \text{G O P}$$

$$= \cos \text{A} \cos \text{B} - \sin \text{A} \sin \text{B}.$$

To prove that

Sin $(A-B) = \sin A \cos B - \cos A \sin B$, and cos $(A-B)$ $= \cos A \cos B + \sin A \sin B$.

Let H O F (Fig. 350) = the angle A and G O F = the angle B. Consequently H O G is the angle $(A-B)$.

In O G take any point Q, and from this let drop the perpendiculars Q T, Q P, on O H, O F. Then draw P J at right angles to Q T produced, and P S at right angles to O H.

Then the angle P Q J $= 90° - $ J P Q $=$ J P F $=$ H O F $=$ angle A.

Thus

$$\text{Sin (A}-\text{B)} = \sin \text{H O G} = \frac{\text{T Q}}{\text{O Q}} = \frac{\text{T J} - \text{Q J}}{\text{O Q}} = \frac{\text{S P}}{\text{O Q}} - \frac{\text{Q J}}{\text{O Q}}$$

$$= \frac{\text{S P} \times \text{O P}}{\text{O P} \times \text{O Q}} - \frac{\text{Q J} \times \text{P Q}}{\text{P Q} \times \text{O Q}} = \frac{\text{S P}}{\text{O P}} \times \frac{\text{O P}}{\text{O Q}} - \frac{\text{Q J}}{\text{P Q}} \times \frac{\text{P Q}}{\text{O Q}}$$

$$= \sin \text{H O F} \cos \text{G O F} - \cos \text{J Q P} \sin \text{G O F}$$

$$= \sin \text{A} \cos \text{B} - \cos \text{A} \sin \text{B}.$$

Similarly

$$\text{Cos (A}-\text{B)} = \cos \text{H O G} = \frac{\text{O T}}{\text{O Q}} = \frac{\text{O S} + \text{S T}}{\text{O Q}} = \frac{\text{O S}}{\text{O Q}} + \frac{\text{P J}}{\text{O Q}}$$

$$= \frac{\text{O S} \times \text{O P}}{\text{O P} \times \text{O Q}} + \frac{\text{P J} \times \text{P Q}}{\text{P Q} \times \text{O Q}} = \frac{\text{O S}}{\text{O P}} \times \frac{\text{O P}}{\text{O Q}} + \frac{\text{P J}}{\text{P Q}} \times \frac{\text{P Q}}{\text{O Q}}$$

$$= \cos \text{H O F} \cos \text{G O F} + \sin \text{J Q P} \sin \text{G O F}$$

$$= \cos \text{A} \cos \text{B} + \sin \text{A} \sin \text{B}.$$

To illustrate the foregoing formulae we will find the value of sin 75°.

By the preceding

Sin 75° = sin $(45° + 30°)$ = sin 45° cos 30° + cos 45° sin 30°.

And we have seen that

$$\sin 45° = \frac{1}{\sqrt{2}}; \cos 45° = \frac{1}{\sqrt{2}}; \sin 30° = \frac{1}{2}; \cos 30° = \frac{\sqrt{3}}{2}.$$

Therefore

Sin 75° = sin 45° cos 30° + cos 45° sin 30°

$$= \frac{1}{\sqrt{2}} \times \frac{\sqrt{3}}{2} + \frac{1}{\sqrt{2}} \times \frac{1}{2}$$

$$= \frac{\sqrt{3}+1}{2\sqrt{2}} = \frac{\sqrt{2}(\sqrt{3}+1)}{4}$$

$$= \frac{1\cdot41421(1\cdot73204+1)}{4} = \frac{3\cdot8636924305}{4} = 0\cdot96592.$$

Again

Cos 75° = cos 45° × cos 30° − sin 45° × sin 30°

$$= \frac{1}{\sqrt{2}} \times \frac{\sqrt{3}}{2} - \frac{1}{\sqrt{2}} \times \frac{1}{2}$$

$$= \frac{\sqrt{3}-1}{2\sqrt{2}} = 0\cdot25882.$$

From the foregoing remarks we have seen that:

1st. The sine of the sum of two angles is equal to the sine of the first into the cosine of the second, together with the cosine of the first into the sine of the second.

2nd. The cosine of the sum of two angles is equal to the product of the cosines of the angles less the product of their sines.

3rd. The sine of the difference of two angles is equal to the sine of the first angle into the cosine of the second less the cosine of the first into the sine of the second.

4th. The cosine of the difference of the two angles is equal to the product of the cosines of the angles, together with the product of their sines.

Again

The tangent of the sum of two angles is equal to the sum of their tangents, divided by unity less the product of their tangents.

Take the angles A and B as before. Then

$$\text{Tan } (A+B) = \frac{\tan A + \tan B}{1 - \tan A \tan B}$$

DD

And in proof of this, if we use the foregoing formulae, we have as follows:

$$\text{Tan} \ (A+B) = \frac{\sin \ (A+B)}{\cos \ (A+B)} = \frac{\sin A \cos B + \cos A \sin B}{\cos A \cos B - \sin A \sin B}$$

And dividing the numerator and denominator by cos A cos B, we have

$$\text{Tan} \ (A+B) = \frac{\sin \ (A+B)}{\cos \ (A+B)} = 1 - \frac{\dfrac{\sin A}{\cos A} + \dfrac{\sin B}{\cos B}}{\dfrac{\sin A}{\cos A} \times \dfrac{\sin B}{\cos B}}$$

Therefore

$$\text{Tan} \ (A+B) = \frac{\tan A + \tan B}{1 - \tan A \tan B} \quad . \quad . \quad . \quad (32)$$

And similarly

$$\text{Tan} \ (A-B) = \frac{\tan A - \tan B}{1 + \tan A \tan B} \quad . \quad . \quad . \quad (33)$$

We have seen by the fundamental formulae that

Sin $(A+B) = \sin A \cos B + \cos A \sin B$
Sin $(A-B) = \sin A \cos B - \cos A \sin B$
Cos $(A+B) = \cos A \cos B - \sin A \sin B$
Cos $(A-B) = \cos A \cos B + \sin A \sin B$

And from these, by addition and subtraction, we get

Sum and difference of sines and cosines –

Sin $(A+B) + \sin (A-B) = 2 \sin A \cos B$
Sin $(A+B) - \sin (A-B) = 2 \cos A \sin B$
Cos $(A+B) + \cos (A-B) = 2 \cos A \cos B$
Cos $(A-B) - \cos (A+B) = 2 \sin A \sin B$

The sum of the sines of any two angles is to the difference of their sines in the same ratio as the tangent of half their sum is to the tangent of half their difference,

Or,

Sin $A + \sin B$: sin $A - \sin B$: : tan $\frac{1}{2} (A+B)$: tan $\frac{1}{2} (A-B)$.

For, from the preceding formulae,

$$\frac{\text{Sin} A + \sin B}{\text{Sin} A - \sin B} = \frac{2 \sin \frac{1}{2} (A+B) \cos \frac{1}{2} (A-B)}{2 \sin \frac{1}{2} (A-B) \cos \frac{1}{2} (A+B)}$$

$$= \text{Tan} \ \tfrac{1}{2} (A+B) \cot \tfrac{1}{2} (A-B).$$

Or in the form of proportion,

Sin A $+$ sin B : sin A $-$ sin B : : tan $\frac{1}{2}$ (A $+$ B) : tan $\frac{1}{2}$ (A $-$ B).

The sine and cosine of twice an angle, in terms of the sine and cosine of the angle – By putting A $=$ B in eq. (28) we get sin 2 A $=$ 2 sin A cos A. In eq. (29) we get cos 2 A $=$ cos^2 A $-$ sin^2 A; and it was shown by eq. (1) that 1 $=$ cos^2 A $+$ sin^2 A; whence by addition and subtraction we obtain

$$1 + \cos 2 A = 2 \cos^2 A \quad \ldots \quad (a)$$
$$\text{and } 1 - \cos 2 A = 2 \sin^2 A \quad \ldots \quad (b)$$

By transposition the following expressions for the cosine of twice the angle are obtained:

$$\text{Cos } 2 A = 1 - 2 \sin^2 A \quad \ldots \quad (c)$$
$$\text{Cos } 2 A = 2 \cos^2 A - 1 \quad \ldots \quad (d)$$

The sine and cosine of an angle in terms of half the angle – Putting A for 2 A on the left, and $\frac{1}{2}$ A for A on the right-hand side of the above equations

$$\text{Sin } A = 2 \sin \tfrac{1}{2} A \cos \tfrac{1}{2} A \quad \ldots \quad (e)$$
$$1 + \cos A = 2 \cos^2 \tfrac{1}{2} A. \quad \ldots \quad (f)$$
$$1 - \cos A = 2 \sin^2 \tfrac{1}{2} A \quad \ldots \quad (g)$$
$$\text{Cos } A = 2 \cos^2 \tfrac{1}{2} A - 1 \quad \ldots \quad (h)$$
$$\text{Cos } A = 1 - 2 \sin^2 \tfrac{1}{2} A \quad \ldots \quad (i)$$

Sine, cosine, and tangent of the sum of three angles –

Sin (A $+$ B $+$ C) $=$ sin (A $+$ B) cos C $+$ cos (A $+$ B) sin C
$=$ sin A cos B cos C $+$ sin B cos C cos A
$+$ sin C cos A cos B $-$ sin A sin B sin C . . . (k)

Cos (A $+$ B $+$ C) $=$ cos (A $+$ B) cos C $-$ sin (A $+$ B) sin C
$=$ cos A cos B cos C $-$ cos A sin B sin C
$-$ cos B sin A sin C $-$ cos C sin A sin B . . . (l)

Tan (A $+$ B $+$ C) $= \dfrac{\sin \ (A+B+C)}{\cos \ (A+B+C)} =$

$$\frac{\sin A \cos B \cos C + \sin B \cos C \cos A + \sin C \cos A \cos B - \sin A \sin B \sin C}{\cos A \cos B \cos C - \cos A \sin B \sin C - \cos B \sin A \sin C - \cos C \sin A \sin B}.$$

Dividing both numerator and denominator of the last expression by cos A cos B cos C, we obtain the tangent of the sum of three angles in terms of the tangents of the angles themselves:

$$\text{Tan} (A+B+C) = \frac{\tan A+\tan B+\tan C-\tan A \tan B \tan C}{1-\tan A \tan B-\tan B \tan C-\tan C \tan A}.(m)$$

The sine, cosine, and tangent of three times an angle – In the above equations (k) (l) and (m), put A = B = C, then

$$\text{Sin } 3A = 3 \sin A - 4 \sin^3 A \quad . \quad . \quad . \quad (n)$$

$$\text{Cos } 3A = 4 \cos^3 A - 3 \cos A \quad . \quad . \quad . \quad (o)$$

$$\text{Tan } 3A = \frac{3 \tan A - \tan^3 A}{1 - 3 \tan^2 A} \quad . \quad . \quad . \quad (p)$$

As another proof the latter

$$\text{Tan } 3A = \tan (2A+A) = \frac{\tan 2A+\tan A}{1-\tan 2A \tan A}$$

$$= \frac{\dfrac{2 \tan A}{1-\tan^2 A}+\tan A}{1-\dfrac{2 \tan A}{1-\tan^2 A} \tan A} = \frac{2 \tan A+\tan A-\tan^3 A}{1-\tan^2 A-2 \tan^2 A}$$

$$= 3 \frac{\tan A-\tan^3 A}{1-3 \tan^2 A}$$

Oblique-angled triangles – I now pass on to the consideration of oblique-angled triangles, which, in the limited space at my command, I can discuss only in brief terms. I will commence by submitting the following propositions:

A. Any two sides of a plane triangle are in the same ratio as the sines of the opposite angles.

B. In a plane triangle, the sum of their sides is to their difference, as the tangent of half the sum of the angles at the base is to the tangent of half their difference.

C. In a plane triangle, the sum of the sides is to the base as the cosine of half the difference of the base angles is to the cosine of half their sum; and the difference of the sides is to the base as the sine of half the difference of the base angles is to the sine of half their sum.

D. The square on a side of a plane triangle, which is opposite an acute or obtuse angle, is equal to the sum of the squares on the sides which contain the angle, less twice the rectangle contained by them, into the cosine of the angle.

The foregoing propositions form the basis of the consideration of the formulae for the solution of oblique angles, and we will briefly consider them *seriatim:*

Proposition A. Take the triangle A B C (Figs. 351 and 352),

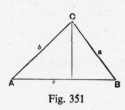

Fig. 351

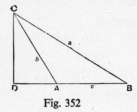

Fig. 352

and from C drop the perpendicular C D on to A B in Fig. 351 of A B produced in Fig. 352. Then

$$\frac{a}{b} = \frac{\sin A}{\sin B}; \text{ for } \sin A = \frac{C D}{b} \text{ and } \sin B = \frac{C D}{a}$$

Therefore

$$\frac{\sin A}{\sin B} = \frac{\dfrac{C D}{b}}{\dfrac{C D}{a}} = \frac{a}{b}$$

Similarly

$$\frac{a}{c} = \frac{\sin A}{\sin C}; \frac{b}{c} = \frac{\sin B}{\sin C}.$$

It should be noted that if the angle A or B be a right angle, there is no necessity to drop the perpendicular C D. From this proposition we may state the ratio between the sides and the sines of opposite angles. Thus

$$\frac{\sin A}{a} = \frac{\sin B}{b} = \frac{\sin C}{c} \quad \cdot \quad \cdot \quad \cdot \quad (q)$$

Proposition B. From the preceding we have

$$\frac{a}{b} = \frac{\sin A}{\sin B}$$

Then by rule of proportion

$$\frac{a+b}{a-b} = \frac{\sin A + \sin B}{\sin A - \sin B}$$

Whence

$$\frac{a+b}{a-b} = \frac{\tan \frac{1}{2}(A+B)}{\tan \frac{1}{2}(A-B)}$$

which may be treated thus:

Since $\frac{1}{2}(A+B) = \frac{1}{2}(180° - C)$;

Therefore

$$\tan \frac{1}{2}(A+B) = \tan(90° - \frac{1}{2}C) = \cot \frac{1}{2}C;$$

$$\therefore \frac{a+b}{a-b} = \frac{\cot \frac{1}{2}C}{\tan \frac{1}{2}(A-B)} = \cot \frac{1}{2}(A-B) \cot \frac{1}{2}C$$

Whence

$$\frac{a-b}{a+b} = \tan \frac{1}{2}(A-B) \tan \frac{1}{2}C$$

Proposition C.

$$A+B = 180° - C, \therefore \sin(A+B) = \sin C$$

$$\therefore \frac{a}{c} = \frac{\sin A}{\sin(A+B)}, \text{ and } \frac{b}{c} = \frac{\sin C}{\sin(A+B)}.$$

And by equations (k) *et seqq.* we get

$$\frac{a+b}{c} = \frac{\sin A + \sin B}{\sin(A+B)} = \frac{2 \sin \frac{1}{2}(A+B) \cos \frac{1}{2}(A-B)}{2 \sin \frac{1}{2}(A+B) \cos \frac{1}{2}(A+B)}$$

Consequently $\dfrac{a+b}{c} = \dfrac{\cos \frac{1}{2}(A-B)}{\cos \frac{1}{2}(A+B)}.$

And similarly by subtracting the second from the first equation instead of adding,

$$\frac{a-b}{c} = \frac{\sin \frac{1}{2}(A-B)}{\sin \frac{1}{2}(A+B)}.$$

Proposition D. In the case of an acute angle, Fig. 351,

$$B C^2 = A C^2 + A B^2 - 2 A B \times A D \text{ (Euclid, ii. 13)}.$$

But $\cos A = \dfrac{A D}{A C}, \therefore A D = A C \cos A$

and $\therefore B C^2 = A C^2 + A B^2 - 2 A B \times A C \cos A.$

In the case of an obtuse angle, Fig. 352,

$$B C^2 = A C^2 + A B^2 + 2 A B \times A D$$

But $\qquad A D = A C \cos (180° - A) = -A C \cos A$

and $\qquad \therefore B C^2 = A C^2 + A B^2 - 2 A B \times A C \times \cos A$

Therefore $\qquad a^2 = b^2 + c^2 - 2 b c \cos A$

Similarly $\qquad b^2 = c^2 + a^2 - 2 c a \cos B$

and $\qquad c^2 = a^2 + b^2 - 2 a b \cos C.$

Sines and cosines of angles in terms of sides – From the foregoing we get by transposition:

$$\text{Cos A} = \frac{b^2 + c^2 - a^2}{2 b c} \qquad \cdots \qquad (r)$$

$$\text{Cos B} = \frac{c^2 + a^2 - b^2}{2 c a}$$

$$\text{Cos C} = \frac{a^2 + b^2 - c^2}{2 a b}$$

Now $\qquad \text{Sin}^2 A = 1 - \cos^2 A$

$$= (1 + \cos A)(1 - \cos A)$$

$$= \frac{1 - (b^2 + c^2 - a^2)^2}{4 b^2 c^2} = \frac{2 b^2 c^2 + 2 c^2 a^2 + 2 a^2 b^2 - a^4 - b^4 - c^4}{4 b^2 c^2},$$

therefore $\quad \sin A = \frac{\sqrt{2 b^2 c^2 + 2 c^2 a^2 + 2 a^2 b^2 - a^4 - b^4 - c^4}}{2 b c}.$

If, however, we substitute s for $\dfrac{a+b+c}{2}$ (or, as it is sometimes designated, the *semiperimeter* of the triangle) so that $(a + b + c) = 2 s$, and

$$2 (s-a) = b+c-a,$$
$$2 (s-b) = a+c-b,$$
$$2 (s-c) = a+b-c;$$

then by extracting the root we get

$$\text{Sin A} = \frac{2\sqrt{s (s-a)(s-b)(s-c)}}{b c},$$

$$\text{Sin B} = \frac{2\sqrt{s (s-a)(s-b)(s-c)}}{c a},$$

$$\text{Sin C} = \frac{2\sqrt{s(s-a)(s-b)(s-c)}}{ab}.$$

Sines and cosines of semi-angles – We have (g) seen that

$$\text{Sin}^2 \tfrac{1}{2} \text{A} = \tfrac{1}{2}(1-\cos \text{A}) = \tfrac{1}{2}\left(1 - \frac{b^2+c^2-a^2}{2bc}\right)$$

$$= \frac{a^2-(b-c)^2}{4bc} = \frac{(a-b+c)(a+b-c)}{4bc} = \frac{(s-b)(s-c)}{bc}$$

and extracting the square root we get

$$\text{Sin } \tfrac{1}{2}\text{A} = \sqrt{\frac{(s-b)(s-c)}{bc}}$$

and similarly

$$\text{Sin } \tfrac{1}{2}\text{B} = \sqrt{\frac{(s-c)(s-a)}{ca}},$$

and

$$\text{Sin } \tfrac{1}{2}\text{C} = \sqrt{\frac{(s-a)(s-b)}{ab}}.$$

Again, by (f) and (r)

$$\text{Cos } \tfrac{1}{2}\text{A} = \sqrt{\frac{s(s-a)}{bc}},$$

$$\text{Cos } \tfrac{1}{2}\text{B} = \sqrt{\frac{s(s-b)}{ca}},$$

$$\text{Cos } \tfrac{1}{2}\text{C} = \sqrt{\frac{s(s-c)}{ab}}.$$

Consequently, since $\tan \text{A} = \dfrac{\sin \text{A}}{\cos \text{A}}$

$$\therefore \text{Tan } \tfrac{1}{2}\text{A} = \frac{\sin \tfrac{1}{2}\text{A}}{\cos \tfrac{1}{2}\text{A}} = \sqrt{\frac{(s-b)(s-c)}{s(s-a)}},$$

and $\qquad$ $\operatorname{Tan} \tfrac{1}{2} \text{B} = \sqrt{\dfrac{(s-c)\,(s-a)}{s\,(s-b)}}$,

and $\qquad$ $\operatorname{Tan} \tfrac{1}{2} \text{C} = \sqrt{\dfrac{(s-a)\,(s-b)}{s\,(s-c)}}$.

Logarithms – It is necessary at this stage to say a few words regarding logarithms, or the ratio of numbers, without which it is impossible to consider the question of the solution of triangles. The principle is, that a fixed number called the base, raised to the proper power, may be made to represent any required number.

I must refer the student, who has yet to master the theory of logarithms, to the many suitable works upon the subject. In this present work space will only admit of an explanation of the use of tables of logarithms.

We propose to use the *common system* of logarithms, in which the base is 10. In calculations, they are usually designated by the abbreviated term "log."

Logarithms of numbers consist of two parts, viz. the *index or characteristic* and the *mantissa*. The *index* or *characteristic* is a numeral expressing the number of digits in the integral part of the number which the logarithm represents. It is one *less* than the number of those digits, and is placed immediately before the decimal part of the logarithm; thus, if there are seven integral figures, the characteristic is 6, if six figures 5, if five 4, and so on. If there are no integral figures, the characteristic is negative (the negative sign being placed over it), and is one *more* than the number of ciphers (if any) immediately following the decimal point. If there is no such cipher, the characteristic is $\bar{1}$; if there is a single cipher, the characteristic is $\bar{2}$; if two such ciphers, $\bar{3}$; and so on.

The *mantissa* is the decimal part of the logarithm, and is found, in the columns of mathematical tables, on a line with the number which the logarithm represents. It is the same whether that number is integral or not. Thus, ·6614151 is the mantissa of the log. of 45858, 4585·8, 458·58, and so on, the only difference being in the characteristic, as will be seen in the following example:

Number	Logarithm
45858·	4·6614151
4585·8	3·6614151
458·58	2·6614151
45·858	1·6614151
4·5858	0·6614151
·45858	$\bar{1}$·6614151
·045858	$\bar{2}$·6614151
·0045858	$\bar{3}$·6614151
·00045858	$\bar{4}$·6614151

The mantissa alone appears in the tables, and it is always positive. The characteristic has to be supplied by the calculator.

Here let me explain that most tables of logarithms have numbers only to 9999, and by reference thereto they appear thus:

No.	0	1	2	3	4	5	6	7	8	9	D
7695	8862086	2143	2199	2256	2312	2368	2425	2481	2538	2594	57

so that in reality we only get the logarithm of the first four of the five figures, viz. log. of 7695 = ·8862086; but we want the log. of 76952, to get which we must look in the column marked 2, and for the last four decimals, viz. 2086, substitute the four in column 2, viz. 2199, so that our log. of 76952 is ·8862199; equally if we wanted the logarithm of 76959 we should take 2594 in column 9 instead of the four last decimals opposite 7695, so that the logarithm of 76959 = ·8862594. Now in the last column, headed D, will be noticed one set of figures, viz. 57; this means that it is the difference between the logarithm of the number and that of the following unit.

Thus   log. 7695 = ·8862086.   Add 57.
                                        57
                                    ───────
Then   log. 76951 = ·8862143.   Add 57.
                                        57
                                    ───────
                    log. 76952 = ·8862200.* Add 57.
                                        57
                                    ───────
                    ·8862257, and so on.

Multiplication by logarithms – *Rule* – Find the logarithms of the numbers to be multiplied, and add them together. The sum will be the logarithm of the product. Thus:

Multiply 621 by 412.

$$\text{log. } 621 = 2 \cdot 7930916$$
$$\text{log. } 412 = 2 \cdot 6148972$$
───────
$$\text{log. of product} = 5 \cdot 4079888 = \text{log. } 255852$$
$$\therefore \text{product} = 255852.$$

Division by logarithms – *Rule* – Subtract the logarithm of the divisor from that of the dividend, and the remainder will be the logarithm of the quotient.

Example

Divide 3882·2 by 4·7.

$$\text{log. } 3882 \cdot 2 = 3 \cdot 5890779$$
$$4 \cdot 7 = 0 \cdot 6720979$$
───────
$$\text{log. of quotient} = 2 \cdot 9169800 = \text{log. } 826$$
$$\therefore \text{quotient} = 826.$$

* Tables of logarithms are worked out to more decimals than are printed; and, the last printed figure being here and there increased because of the following figure (omitted in printing) exceeding 5, the difference between two successive logarithms occasionally varies from that given in the "difference" column. Thus, the difference between log. 76951 and log. 76952 is 56, between this and log. 76953 it is 57; between this and log. 76954 it is 56; but the printed difference can in general be used without material error resulting from this variation.

Proportion by logarithms – *Rule* – The logarithms of the two middle terms are to be added together, and from their sum the logarithm of the first must be subtracted, and the remainder will be the logarithm of the quantity required;

Or, instead of subtracting the logarithm of the first term from the sum of the second and third, add its *arithmetical complement* (*ar. comp.*), and from this sum deduct 10 from the characteristic.

Note – The *arithmetical complement* of a logarithm is found by deducting it from 10. Thus, if the logarithm of 885 = 2·9469433, its *ar. comp.* = 10·0000000−2·9469433 = 7·0530567.

The following example will serve to illustrate the two methods of performing proportion:

If the wages of a servant be £25 per annum, what amount should he receive for 87 days' service?

Then:

$$\text{As } 365 : 87 : : £25 : ?$$

By logarithms	By arithmetical complement
As log. 87 = 1·9395193	1·9395193
log. £25 = 1·3979400	1·3979400
log. 365 = 2·5622929	*ar. comp.* 7·4377071*
0·7751664	0·7751664

Answer, £5 19s. 2$\frac{1}{7}$d.

Involution by logarithms – *Rule* – Multiply the logarithm of the given number by the exponent of the power, and the product will be the logarithm of the required power.

Find the square of 75.

$$\log. 75 = 1·8750613$$
$$2$$

∴ log. product = 3·7501226 = log. 5625
∴ $75^2 = 5625$.

Similarly find the cube of 62.

$$\log. 62 = 1·7923917$$
$$3$$

∴ log. product = 5·3771751 = log. 238328
∴ $62^3 = 238328$.

* 10·0000000—2·5622929=7·4377071

Again, find the fifth power of 18.

$$\text{log. } 18 = 1 \cdot 2552725$$
$$5$$
$$\overline{}$$

$\therefore$ log. product $= 6 \cdot 2763625 =$ log. 1889568

$\therefore 18^5 = 1889568.$

Evolution by logarithms – *Rule* – Divide the logarithm of the given number by the exponent of the root, and the quotient will be the logarithm of the required root.

Examples

Find the square root of 256.

$$\text{log. } \sqrt{256} = \tfrac{1}{2} \text{ log. } 256 = \tfrac{1}{2} \times 2 \cdot 4082400$$
$$= 1 \cdot 2041200$$
$$= \text{log. } 16.$$
$$\text{And } \therefore \sqrt{256} = 16.$$

Again, find cube root of 256

$$\text{log. } \sqrt{256} = \tfrac{1}{3} \times 2 \cdot 4082400$$
$$= 0 \cdot 8027466$$
$$= \text{log. } 6 \cdot 3496$$
$$\therefore \sqrt[3]{256} = 6 \cdot 3496.$$

And so evolution to any extent may be performed, simply by dividing the logarithm of the given number by the exponent of the root.

Natural and logarithmic sines, cosines, etc. – We have seen that the ratio of the perpendicular to the hypotenuse, of that of the base to the hypotenuse, etc., give the natural sine, cosine, etc. As in the case of the angle of 45 deg., we found that

$$\begin{aligned}
\text{Sin} \quad &45^\circ = 0 \cdot 70711 \\
\text{Cos} \quad &45^\circ = 0 \cdot 70711 \\
\text{Tan} \quad &45^\circ = 1 \cdot 00000 \\
\text{Cotan} \;&45^\circ = 1 \cdot 00000 \\
\text{Sec} \quad &45^\circ = 1 \cdot 41421 \\
\text{Cosec} \;&45^\circ = 1 \cdot 41421
\end{aligned}$$

And similarly

$$
\begin{array}{ll}
\text{Sin} & 60° = 0·86603 \\
\text{Cos} & 60° = 0·50000 \\
\text{Tan} & 60° = 1·73210 \\
\text{Cot} & 60° = 0·57735 \\
\text{Sec} & 60° = 2·00000 \\
\text{Cosec } 60° = 1·15470 \text{ and so on.}
\end{array}
$$

We have further seen that these values express the lengths of the sines and cosines of arcs of a circle whose radius = 1.

Thus the natural sine of 37° = 0·60182, whilst the logarithmic sine of 37° = L 9·77946. In tables of logarithmic sines, cosines, etc., the logarithms are those representing the natural sines, cosines, etc., 10 being added to their characteristics in order to avoid the occurrence of negative ones in the tables: these logarithms are then termed *tabular logarithms*, and in calculations are denoted by the letter L instead of the term "log."

The natural sines, cosines, tangents, etc., may be found from the logarithmic sines, cosines, tangents, etc., by subtracting 10 from the indices of the latter, and then the number corresponding to this logarithm is the natural sine, cosine, tangent, etc., required.

Example – The logarithmic sine of 37 deg. = 9·77946, from which it is required to find the natural sine.

$$
\begin{array}{ll}
L \text{ sin. } 37° & = 9·77946 \\
\text{Subtract} & 10· \\
\hline
\text{log. nat. sin.} & = \overline{1}·77946 \\
\text{Hence natural sin.} & = ·60182.
\end{array}
$$

It may be well here to state some of the peculiar properties of the lines in and about a circle as follows:

1. The square of the diameter is equal to the sum of the squares of the chord of an arc, and of the chord of its supplement to a semicircle.

2. The square of the radius is equal to the sum of the squares of the sine and cosine.

3. The sum of the cosine and versed sine is equal to the radius.

4. Radius is to the sine as twice the cosine is to the sine of twice the arc, or as the secant is to the tangent.

5. As the cosine is to the sine, so is the radius to the tangent.

6. Radius is the mean proportional between the tangent and the cotangent, and also between secant and cosine.

Solution of triangles by arithmetical computation – The terms of proportion must be stated according to rule, these terms consisting partly of the numbers which express the given lengths of sides, and partly of the sines etc., of the given angles.

Add together the logarithms of the second and third terms, and from their sum subtract the logarithm of the first term.

Or,—

To the sum of the logarithms of the second and third terms, add the arithmetical complement of that of the first term, and from the characteristic of the sum subtract 10.

The logarithm resulting from either of the above operations represents the natural number which is the fourth term of the proportion.

When the three angles of any triangle are given, but no side, the actual length of the sides cannot be determined, but only their ratio to one another.

I. Right-angled triangles.

The solution of right-angled triangles has four cases, viz:

1. When the hypotenuse and a side are given.
2. When the two sides are given.
3. When the hypotenuse and an acute angle are given.
4. When a side and an acute angle are given.

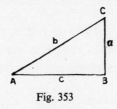

Fig. 353

Let A B C (Fig. 353) be a right-angled triangle, B being the right angle and b the hypotenuse.

CASE 1 – Given hypotenuse $b = 500$ links
  side $a = 286 \cdot 788$ links.

  Required angles A and C, and side c.

By logarithms:

$$\sin A = \frac{a}{b} = \log. \ a - \log. \ b$$

$$10 + \log. \ a = 12 \cdot 4575613$$
$$\log. \ b = \ \ 2 \cdot 6989700$$

$$9 \cdot 7585913 = L \sin A = 35°.$$

$$C = 90° - 35° = 55°;$$
$$c = \sqrt{b^2 - a^2} = 409 \cdot 576 \text{ links.}$$

By natural sines, etc.:

Data as before. Required angles A and C, and side c.

$$\cos C = \frac{a}{b} = \frac{286 \cdot 788}{500} = 0 \cdot 7585913 = \text{nat. cos. } 55°.$$

CASE 2 – Given side $a = 286 \cdot 788$
  ,, $c = 409 \cdot 576$

  Required angle A.

$$\tan A = \frac{a}{c}, \text{ and } L \tan A = 10 + \log. \ a - \log. \ c$$
$$= 12 \cdot 4575613 - 2 \cdot 6123345 = 9 \cdot 8452268$$
$$= L \tan 35°.$$

CASE 3 – Given hypotenuse $b = 500$
  angle A $= 35°$

  Required C, a, and c.

$$C = 90° - A = 55°$$

$$\frac{a}{b} = \sin A, \ \therefore \ a = b \sin A$$

$$\log. \ b, \ 500 = 2 \cdot 6989700$$
$$L \sin A - 10 = 1 \cdot 7585913$$

$$2 \cdot 4575613 = \log. \ 286 \cdot 788 = a.$$

For base c:

$$\frac{c}{b} = \sin 55°, \therefore c = b \sin \text{C} = \log. b + L \sin \text{C} - 10$$

$$\log. b = 2 \cdot 6989700$$
$$L \sin \text{C} - 10 = \bar{1} \cdot 9133645$$

$$2 \cdot 6123345 = \log. 409 \cdot 576 = c.$$

CASE 4 – Given side $a = 286 \cdot 788$
    angle A $= 35°$
Required C, b, and c.

C $= 90° - \text{A} = 55°$

$$\frac{a}{b} = \sin \text{A}, \therefore b = \frac{a}{\sin \text{A}}, \text{ and } \log. b = \log. a - (L \sin \text{A} + 10)$$

$$\log. a = 2 \cdot 4575613$$
$$L \sin \text{A} - 10 = 1 \cdot 7585913$$

$$2 \cdot 6989700 = \log. 500 = b.$$

For base c:

$$\frac{a}{c} = \tan \text{A}, \therefore c = \frac{a}{\tan \text{A}}$$
$$\log. c = \log. a - (L \tan \text{A} + 10)$$
$$\log. a = 2 \cdot 4575613$$
$$L \tan \text{A} - 10 = \bar{1} \cdot 8452268$$

$$2 \cdot 6123345 = \log. 409 \cdot 576 = c.$$

II. Oblique-angled triangles.

The solution of oblique-angled triangles has four cases, viz.:

1. When two angles and a side opposite to one of them are given.

2. When two sides and the included angle are given.

3. When two sides and an angle opposite to one of them are given.

4. When three sides are given.

EE

Case 1 – *Rule* – The sines of the angles are in the same ratio as their opposite sides.

In the triangle A B C (Fig. 354); given

$$\text{side } c = 610$$
$$\text{angle B} = 115°$$
$$\text{,,} \quad \text{C} = 42° \; 30'$$

To find the side *b*:

sin C : *c* : : sin B (suppl. = 65°) : *b*

$$L \sin 42° \; 30' \; ar. \; comp. = 0·1703167$$
$$\log. \; 610 = 2·7853298$$
$$L \sin 65° = 9·9572757$$

$$2·9129222 = \log. \; 818·32 = b.$$

To find the side *a*:

$$L \sin 42° \; 30' \; ar. \; comp. = 0·1703167$$
$$\log. \; 610 = 2·7853298$$
$$L \sin \text{A}, 180° - (115° + 42°30') = 22°30' = 9·5828397$$

$$2·5384862 = \log. \; 345·53 = a.$$

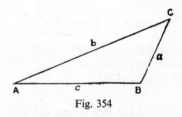

Fig. 354

Case 2 – *Rule* – As the sum of the two given sides is to the difference of those sides, so is the tangent of half the sum of their opposite angles to the tangent of half their difference.

This half difference added to the half sum will give the greater angle, and taken from the half sum will give the less angle.

In the triangle A B C (Fig. 355); given

$$\text{side } a = 1272$$
$$\text{,,} \quad c = 1636$$
$$\text{angle B} = 97° \; 30'$$

To find angles A and C:

log. $c+a$, (2908) *ar. comp.* = 6·5364056
log. $c-a$, (364) = 2·5611014

$$L \tan\left(\frac{A+C}{2}\right) = \left(\frac{180°-B}{2}\right) = 9·9429879 = L \tan 41° 15'$$

$$L \tan\left(\frac{A-C}{2}\right) = \begin{Bmatrix} \textit{(sum of these)} \\ \textit{logs} -10) \end{Bmatrix} = 9·0404949 = L \tan \ \ 6° 15' 52''$$

their sum 47° 30' 52'' = C
their diff. 34° 59' 8'' = A

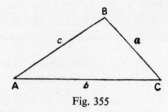

Fig. 355

To find the side b:

$L \sin$ A *ar. comp.* = 0·2415645
log. a = 3·1044872
$L \sin$ suppl. B, 82° 30' = 9·9962686

3·3423203 = log. 2199·48 = b.

CASE 3 – *Rule* – Same as in Case 1. Formula:

$$\frac{a}{\sin A} = \frac{b}{\sin B} = \frac{c}{\sin C}$$

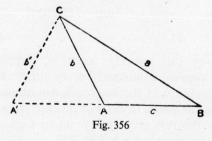

Fig. 356

In the triangle A B C (Fig. 356); given side $a = 923·6$, side $b = 530$ and angle B $= 29° 26'$: required angles A and C and side c.

Log. a = log. 923·6:   2·9654839
Log. b = log. 530 = 2·7242759, ar. compl.:   7·2757241
Log. sin B = log. sin 29° 26′:   9·6914445

Log. sin A: sum   9·9326525

(The angle is given by its sine and to a given sine correspond two angles smaller than 180°, namely, the value given in the Tables and the value obtained by subtracting this from 180°. There are, therefore, two different triangles corresponding to the given data, A B C and A′ B C (shown by the dotted lines in Fig. 356) with $b' = b$ and the third side being either A B or A′ B. For this reason, this case is called *the ambiguous case*).

		Triangle A′ B C	Triangle A B C
Angle A:		58° 54′ 34″	121° 5′ 26″
Angle B:		29° 26′	29° 26′
A+B:	sum	88° 20′ 34″	150° 31′ 26″
180°:		179° 59′ 60″	179° 59′ 60″
C = 180°−(A+B): difference		91° 39′ 26″	29° 28′ 34″

To find the side c:

		Triangle A′ B C	Triangle A B C
Log. sin C (or 88° 20′ 34″ above)		9·9998183	9·6920186
Log. b		2·7242759	2·7242759
Log. sin B, ar. compl.:		0·3085555	0·3085555
	sum	3·0326497	2·7248500
c:		1078·3	530·7

The ambiguity can scarcely occur in ordinary practice, because in a properly conducted survey other measurements obtained in the course of the work will determine whether the angle A is obtuse or acute. In cases of this sort, it is best to solve the triangle by the rule given below under Case 4, or by the method given for triangle C A B, Fig. 247.

CASE 4 – *Rule* – From the greatest angle let fall a perpendicular to the opposite side (which we will call the base), dividing it into two parts and the whole triangle into two right-angled triangles. Then

As the whole base : the sum of the other two sides : : the difference of those sides : the difference of the parts of the base.

Half the difference of the parts, added to half the base, will give the greater part; and subtracted from half the base will give the less part.

Fig. 357

In the triangle A B C (Fig. 357); given

$$a = 1272 \ (\text{log.} = 3 \cdot 1044871)$$
$$b = 1636 \ (\text{log.} = 3 \cdot 2137833)$$
$$c = 2200$$

Required the parts A D and D B and the angles.

As 2200 : 2908 : : 364 : $\overline{481}$ diff. of parts A D and D B.

Half diff. of parts = $\overline{240 \cdot 5}$

adding to and subtracting from half the base

$$1100 + 240 \cdot 5 = 1340 \cdot 5 = \text{A D} \ (\text{log.} = 3 \cdot 1272668)$$
$$1100 - 240 \cdot 5 = \ \ 859 \cdot 5 = \text{D B} \ (\text{log.} = 2 \cdot 9342459)$$

For angle A:

$$\cos A = \frac{\text{rad} \times \text{A D}}{b} = 10 + 3 \cdot 1272668 - 3 \cdot 2137833$$
$$= 9 \cdot 9134835 = L \cos 34° \ 58' \ 39''.$$

For angle B:

$$\cos B = \frac{\text{rad} \times \text{D B}}{a} = 10 + 2 \cdot 9342459 - 3 \cdot 1044871$$
$$= 9 \cdot 8297588 = L \cos 47° \ 29' \ 27''$$

and angle C = 180° − (A + B) = 97° 31′ 54″.

If s be put to denote half the sum of the three sides, the case can also be solved by the formula

$$\sin \frac{A}{2} = \sqrt{\frac{(s-b)(s-c)}{bc}}$$

which by due change of letters holds for the other half-angles.

APPENDIX II

TABLES OF NATURAL SINES, TANGENTS, AND SECANTS, WITH THEIR COMPLEMENTS

TABLES of natural sines, cosines, tangents, etc., represent the numerical values of the lengths of the sines, cosines, tangents, etc., of arcs of a circle whose radius $= 1$.

The natural sines etc., also the arcs for any given natural sines etc., are found from the table in the same manner as is used for logarithmic ones.

The natural sines etc., are easily found from logarithmetic ones, by subtracting 10 from the indices of the latter: the number corresponding to this logarithm is the natural sine etc., required.

Given the logarithmic sine of 36° 44', namely 9·7767676, to find the natural sine.

$$L \text{ sine } 36° 44' = 9·7767676$$
$$\text{Subtract} \quad 10·$$

$$L \text{ natural sine} = \bar{1}·7767676$$
$$\text{Hence natural sine} = 0·5980916$$

Conversely, natural sines etc., can be converted into logarithmic ones, by finding the logarithm corresponding to their numerical value and adding 10 to the index.

Given the natural cotangent of 63° 25', namely 0·5003989, to find its logarithmic cotangent.

$$\text{Nat. cot. } 63° 25' = 00·503989$$

$$\log. 0·5003989 = \bar{01}·6993164$$
$$\text{Add} \quad 10·$$

$$L \text{ cotangent } 63° 25' = 9·6993164$$

426

0 Deg.

	Sine	Cosine	
0	0000000	1.0000000	60
1	0002909	1.0000000	59
2	0005818	9999998	58
3	0008727	9999996	57
4	0011636	9999993	56
5	0014544	9999989	55
6	0017453	9999985	54
7	0020362	9999979	53
8	0023271	9999973	52
9	0026180	9999966	51
10	0029089	9999958	50
11	0031998	9999949	49
12	0034907	9999939	48
13	0037815	9999928	47
14	0040724	9999917	46
15	0043633	9999905	45
16	0046542	9999892	44
17	0049451	9999878	43
18	0052360	9999863	42
19	0055268	9999847	41
20	0058177	9999831	40
21	0061086	9999813	39
22	0063995	9999795	38
23	0066904	9999776	37
24	0069813	9999756	36
25	0072721	9999736	35
26	0075630	9999714	34
27	0078539	9999692	33
28	0081448	9999668	32
29	0084357	9999644	31
30	0087265	9999619	30
31	0090174	9999593	29
32	0093083	9999567	28
33	0095992	9999539	27
34	0098900	9999511	26
35	0101809	9999482	25
36	0104718	9999452	24
37	0107627	9999421	23
38	0110535	9999389	22
39	0113444	9999357	21
40	0116353	9999323	20
41	0119261	9999289	19
42	0122170	9999254	18
43	0125079	9999218	17
44	0127987	9999181	16
45	0130896	9999143	15
46	0133805	9999105	14
47	0136713	9999065	13
48	0139622	9999025	12
49	0142530	9998984	11
50	0145430	9998942	10
51	0148348	9998900	9
52	0151256	9998856	8
53	0154165	9998812	7
54	0157073	9998766	6
55	0159982	9998720	5
56	0162890	9998673	4
57	0165799	9998625	3
58	0168707	9998577	2
59	0171616	9998527	1
60	0174524	9998477	0
	Cosine	Sine	

Deg. 89.

1 Deg.

	Sine	Cosine	
0	0174524	9998477	60
1	0177432	9998426	59
2	0180341	9998374	58
3	0183249	9998321	57
4	0186158	9998267	56
5	0189066	9998213	55
6	0191974	9998157	54
7	0194883	9998101	53
8	0197791	9998044	52
9	0200699	9997986	51
10	0203608	9997927	50
11	0206516	9997867	49
12	0209424	9997807	48
13	0212332	9997745	47
14	0215241	9997683	46
15	0218149	9997620	45
16	0221057	9997556	44
17	0223965	9997492	43
18	0226873	9997426	42
19	0229781	9997360	41
20	0232690	9997292	40
21	0235598	9997224	39
22	0238506	9997156	38
23	0241414	9997086	37
24	0244322	9997015	36
25	0247230	9996943	35
26	0250138	9996871	34
27	0253046	9996798	33
28	0255954	9996724	32
29	0258862	9996649	31
30	0261769	9996573	30
31	0264677	9996497	29
32	0267585	9996419	28
33	0270493	9996341	27
34	0273401	9996262	26
35	0276309	9996182	25
36	0279216	9996101	24
37	0282124	9996020	23
38	0285032	9995937	22
39	0287940	9995854	21
40	0290847	9995770	20
41	0293755	9995684	19
42	0296662	9995599	18
43	0299570	9995512	17
44	0302478	9995424	16
45	0305385	9995336	15
46	0308293	9995247	14
47	0311200	9995157	13
48	0314108	9995066	12
49	0317015	9994974	11
50	0319922	9994881	10
51	0322830	9994788	9
52	0325737	9994693	8
53	0328644	9994598	7
54	0331552	9994502	6
55	0334459	9994405	5
56	0337366	9994308	4
57	0340274	9994209	3
58	0343181	9994110	2
59	0346088	9994009	1
60	0348995	9993908	0
	Cosine	Sine	

Deg. 88

2 Deg.

	Sine	Cosine	
0	0348995	9993908	60
1	0351902	9993806	59
2	0354809	9993704	58
3	0357716	9993600	57
4	0360623	9993495	56
5	0363530	9993390	55
6	0366437	9993284	54
7	0369344	9993177	53
8	0372251	9993069	52
9	0375158	9992960	51
10	0378065	9992851	50
11	0380971	9992740	49
12	0383878	9992629	48
13	0386785	9992517	47
14	0389692	9992404	46
15	0392598	9992290	45
16	0395505	9992176	44
17	0398411	9992060	43
18	0401318	9991944	42
19	0404224	9991827	41
20	0407131	9991709	40
21	0410037	9991590	39
22	0412944	9991470	38
23	0415850	9991350	37
24	0418757	9991228	36
25	0421663	9991106	35
26	0424569	9990983	34
27	0427475	9990859	33
28	0430382	9990734	32
29	0433288	9990609	31
30	0436194	9990482	30
31	0439100	9990355	29
32	0442006	9990227	28
33	0444912	9990098	27
34	0447818	9989968	26
35	0450724	9989837	25
36	0453630	9989706	24
37	0456536	9989573	23
38	0459442	9989440	22
39	0462347	9989306	21
40	0465253	9989171	20
41	0468159	9989035	19
42	0471065	9988899	18
43	0473970	9988761	17
44	0476876	9988623	16
45	0479781	9988484	15
46	0482687	9988344	14
47	0485592	9988203	13
48	0488498	9988061	12
49	0491403	9987919	11
50	0494308	9987775	10
51	0497214	9987631	9
52	0500119	9987486	8
53	0503024	9987340	7
54	0505929	9987194	6
55	0508835	9987046	5
56	0511740	9986898	4
57	0514645	9986748	3
58	0517550	9986598	2
59	0520455	9986147	1
60	0523360	9986295	0
	Cosine	Sine	

Deg. 87.

	3 Deg.				4 Deg.				5 Deg.		
	Sine	Cosine			Sine	Cosine			Sine	Cosine	
0	0523360	9986295	60	0	0697565	9975641	60	0	0871557	9961947	60
1	0526264	9986143	59	1	0700467	9975437	59	1	0874455	9961693	59
2	0529169	9985989	58	2	0703368	9975233	58	2	0877353	9961438	58
3	0532074	9985835	57	3	0706270	9975028	57	3	0880251	9961183	57
4	0534979	9985680	56	4	0709171	9974822	56	4	0883148	9960926	56
5	0537883	9985524	55	5	0712073	9974615	55	5	0886046	9960669	55
6	0540788	9985367	54	6	0714974	9974408	54	6	0888943	9960411	54
7	0543693	9985209	53	7	0717876	9974199	53	7	0891840	9960152	53
8	0546597	9985050	52	8	0720777	9973990	52	8	0894738	9959892	52
9	0549502	9984891	51	9	0723678	9973780	51	9	0897635	9959631	51
10	0552406	9984731	50	10	0726580	9973569	50	10	0900532	9959370	50
11	0555311	9984570	49	11	0729481	9973357	49	11	0903429	9959107	49
12	0558215	9984408	48	12	0732382	9973145	48	12	0906326	9958844	48
13	0561119	9984245	47	13	0735283	9972931	47	13	0909223	9958580	47
14	0564024	9984081	46	14	0738184	9972717	46	14	0912119	9958315	46
15	0566928	9983917	45	15	0741085	9972502	45	15	0915016	9958049	45
16	0569832	9983751	44	16	0743986	9972286	44	16	0917913	9957783	44
17	0572736	9983585	43	17	0746887	9972069	43	17	0920809	9957515	43
18	0575640	9983418	42	18	0749787	9971851	42	18	0923706	9957247	42
19	0578544	9983250	41	19	0752688	9971633	41	19	0926602	9956978	41
20	0581448	9983082	40	20	0755589	9971413	40	20	0929499	9956708	40
21	0584352	9982912	39	21	0758489	9971193	39	21	0932395	9956437	39
22	0587256	9982742	38	22	0761390	9970972	38	22	0935291	9956165	38
23	0590160	9982570	37	23	0764290	9970750	37	23	0938187	9955893	37
24	0593064	9982398	36	24	0767190	9970528	36	24	0941083	9955620	36
25	0595967	9982225	35	25	0770091	9970304	35	25	0943979	9955345	35
26	0598871	9982052	34	26	0772991	9970080	34	26	0946875	9955070	34
27	0601775	9981877	33	27	0775891	9969854	33	27	0949771	9954795	33
28	0604678	9981701	32	28	0778791	9969628	32	28	0952666	9954518	32
29	0607582	9981525	31	29	0781691	9969401	31	29	0955562	9954240	31
30	0610485	9981348	30	30	0784591	9969173	30	30	0958458	9953962	30
31	0613389	9981170	29	31	0787491	9968945	29	31	0961353	9953683	29
32	0616292	9980991	28	32	0790391	9968715	28	32	0964248	9953403	28
33	0619196	9980811	27	33	0793290	9968485	27	33	0967144	9953122	27
34	0622099	9980631	26	34	0796190	9968254	26	34	0970039	9952840	26
35	0625002	9980450	25	35	0799090	9968022	25	35	0972934	9952557	25
36	0627905	9980267	24	36	0801989	9967789	24	36	0975829	9952274	24
37	0630808	9980084	23	37	0804889	9967555	23	37	0978724	9951990	23
38	0633711	9979900	22	38	0807788	9967321	22	38	0981619	9951705	22
39	0636614	9979716	21	39	0810687	9967085	21	39	0984514	9951419	21
40	0639517	9979530	20	40	0813587	9966849	20	40	0987408	9951132	20
41	0642420	9979343	19	41	0816486	9966612	19	41	0990303	9950844	19
42	0645323	9979156	18	42	0819385	9966374	18	42	0993197	9950556	18
43	0648226	9978968	17	43	0822284	9966135	17	43	0996092	9950266	17
44	0651129	9978779	16	44	0825183	9965895	16	44	0998986	9949976	16
45	0654031	9978589	15	45	0828082	9965655	15	45	1001881	9949685	15
46	0656934	9978399	14	46	0830981	9965414	14	46	1004775	9949393	14
47	0659836	9978207	13	47	0833880	9965172	13	47	1007669	9949101	13
48	0662739	9978015	12	48	0836778	9964929	12	48	1010563	9948807	12
49	0665641	9977821	11	49	0839677	9964685	11	49	1013457	9948513	11
50	0668544	9977627	10	50	0842576	9964440	10	50	1016351	9948217	10
51	0671446	9977433	9	51	0845474	9964195	9	51	1019245	9947921	9
52	0674349	9977237	8	52	0848373	9963948	8	52	1022138	9917625	8
53	0677251	9977040	7	53	0851271	9963701	7	53	1025032	9947327	7
54	0680153	9976843	6	54	0854169	9963453	6	54	1027925	9947028	6
55	0683055	9976645	5	55	0857067	9963204	5	55	1030819	9946729	5
56	0685957	9976445	4	56	0859966	9962954	4	56	1033712	9946428	4
57	0688859	9976245	3	57	0862864	9962704	3	57	1036605	9946127	3
58	0691761	9976045	2	58	0865762	9962452	2	58	1039499	9945825	2
59	0694663	9975843	1	59	0868660	9962200	1	59	1042392	9945523	1
60	0697565	9975641	0	60	0871557	9961947	0	60	1045285	9945219	0
	Cosine	Sine			Cosine	Sine			Cosine	Sine	

Deg. 86.	Deg. 85.	Deg. 84.

	6 Deg.				7 Deg.				8 Deg.		
	Sine	Cosine			Sine	Cosine			Sine	Cosine	
0	1045285	9945219	60	0	1218693	9925462	60	0	1391731	9902681	60
1	1048178	9944914	59	1	1221581	9925107	59	1	1394612	9902275	59
2	1051070	9944609	58	2	1224468	9924751	58	2	1397492	9901869	58
3	1053963	9944303	57	3	1227355	9924394	57	3	1400372	9901462	57
4	1056856	9943996	56	4	1230241	9924037	56	4	1403252	9901055	56
5	1059748	9943688	55	5	1233128	9923679	55	5	1406132	9900646	55
6	1062641	9943379	54	6	1236015	9923319	54	6	1409012	9900237	54
7	1065533	9943070	53	7	1238901	9922959	53	7	1411892	9899826	53
8	1068425	9942760	52	8	1241788	9922599	52	8	1414772	9899415	52
9	1071318	9942448	51	9	1244674	9922237	51	9	1417651	9899003	51
10	1074210	9942136	50	10	1247560	9921874	50	10	1420531	9898590	50
11	1077102	9941823	49	11	1250446	9921511	49	11	1423410	9898177	49
12	1079994	9941510	48	12	1253332	9921147	48	12	1426289	9897762	48
13	1082885	9941195	47	13	1256218	9920782	47	13	1429168	9897347	47
14	1085777	9940880	46	14	1259104	9920416	46	14	1432047	9896931	46
15	1088669	9940563	45	15	1261990	9920049	45	15	1434926	9896514	45
16	1091560	9940246	44	16	1264875	9919682	44	16	1437805	9896096	44
17	1094452	9939929	43	17	1267761	9919314	43	17	1440684	9895677	43
18	1097343	9939610	42	18	1270646	9918944	42	18	1443562	9895258	42
19	1100234	9939290	41	19	1273531	9918574	41	19	1446440	9894838	41
20	1103126	9938969	40	20	1276416	9918204	40	20	1449319	9894416	40
21	1106017	9938648	39	21	1279302	9917832	39	21	1452197	9893994	39
22	1108908	9938326	38	22	1282186	9917459	38	22	1455075	9893572	38
23	1111799	9938003	37	23	1285071	9917086	37	23	1457953	9893148	37
24	1114689	9937679	36	24	1287956	9916712	36	24	1460830	9892723	36
25	1117580	9937355	35	25	1290841	9916337	35	25	1463708	9892298	35
26	1120471	9937029	34	26	1293725	9915961	34	26	1466585	9891872	34
27	1123361	9936703	33	27	1296609	9915584	33	27	1469463	9891445	33
28	1126252	9936375	32	28	1299494	9915206	32	28	1472340	9891017	32
29	1129142	9936047	31	29	1302378	9914828	31	29	1475217	9890588	31
30	1132032	9935719	30	30	1305262	9914449	30	30	1478094	9890159	30
31	1134922	9935389	29	31	1308146	9914069	29	31	1480971	9889728	29
32	1137812	9935058	28	32	1311030	9913688	28	32	1483848	9889297	28
33	1140702	9934727	27	33	1313913	9913306	27	33	1486724	9888865	27
34	1143592	9934395	26	34	1316797	9912923	26	34	1489601	9888432	26
35	1146482	9934062	25	35	1319681	9912540	25	35	1492477	9887998	25
36	1149372	9933728	24	36	1322564	9912155	24	36	1495353	9887564	24
37	1152261	9933393	23	37	1325447	9911770	23	37	1498230	9887128	23
38	1155151	9933057	22	38	1328330	9911384	22	38	1501106	9886692	22
39	1158040	9932721	21	39	1331213	9910997	21	39	1503981	9886255	21
40	1160929	9932384	20	40	1334096	9910610	20	40	1506857	9885817	20
41	1163818	9932045	19	41	1336979	9910221	19	41	1509733	9885378	19
42	1166707	9931706	18	42	1339862	9909832	18	42	1512608	9884939	18
43	1169596	9931367	17	43	1342744	9909442	17	43	1515484	9884498	17
44	1172485	9931026	16	44	1345627	9909051	16	44	1518359	9884057	16
45	1175374	9930685	15	45	1348509	9908659	15	45	1521234	9883615	15
46	1178263	9930342	14	46	1351392	9908266	14	46	1524109	9883172	14
47	1181151	9929999	13	47	1354274	9907873	13	47	1526984	9882728	13
48	1184040	9929655	12	48	1357156	9907478	12	48	1529858	9882284	12
49	1186928	9929310	11	49	1360038	9907083	11	49	1532733	9881838	11
50	1189816	9928965	10	50	1362919	9906687	10	50	1535607	9881392	10
51	1192704	9928618	9	51	1365801	9906290	9	51	1538482	9880945	9
52	1195593	9928271	8	52	1368683	9905893	8	52	1541356	9880497	8
53	1198481	9927922	7	53	1371564	9905494	7	53	1544230	9880048	7
54	1201368	9927573	6	54	1374445	9905095	6	54	1547104	9879599	6
55	1204256	9927224	5	55	1377327	9904694	5	55	1549978	9879148	5
56	1207144	9926873	4	56	1380208	9904293	4	56	1552851	9878697	4
57	1210031	9926521	3	57	1383089	9903891	3	57	1555725	9878245	3
58	1212919	9926169	2	58	1385970	9903489	2	58	1558598	9877792	2
59	1215806	9925816	1	59	1388850	9903085	1	59	1561472	9877338	1
60	1218693	9925462	0	60	1391731	9902681	0	60	1564345	9876883	0
	Cosine	Sine			Cosine	Sine			Cosine	Sine	

Deg. 83.	Deg. 82.	Deg. 81.

	9 Deg.				10 Deg.				11 Deg.		
	Sine	Cosine			Sine	Cosine			Sine	Cosine	
0	1564345	9876883	60	0	1736482	9848078	60	0	1908090	9816272	60
1	1567218	9876428	59	1	1739346	9847572	59	1	1910945	9815716	59
2	1570091	9875972	58	2	1742211	9847066	58	2	1913801	9815160	58
3	1572963	9875514	57	3	1745075	9846558	57	3	1916656	9814603	57
4	1575836	9875057	56	4	1747939	9846050	56	4	1919510	9814045	56
5	1578708	9874598	55	5	1750803	9845542	55	5	1922365	9813486	55
6	1581581	9874138	54	6	1753667	9845032	54	6	1925220	9812927	54
7	1584453	9873678	53	7	1756531	9844521	53	7	1928074	9812366	53
8	1587325	9873216	52	8	1759395	9844010	52	8	1930928	9811805	52
9	1590197	9872754	51	9	1762258	9843498	51	9	1933782	9811243	51
10	1593069	9872291	50	10	1765121	9842985	50	10	1936636	9810680	50
11	1595940	9871827	49	11	1767984	9842471	49	11	1939490	9810116	49
12	1598812	9871363	48	12	1770847	9841956	48	12	1942344	9809552	48
13	1601683	9870897	47	13	1773710	9841441	47	13	1945197	9808986	47
14	1604555	9870431	46	14	1776573	9840924	46	14	1948050	9808420	46
15	1607426	9869964	45	15	1779435	9840407	45	15	1950903	9807853	45
16	1610297	9869496	44	16	1782298	9839889	44	16	1953756	9807285	44
17	1613167	9869027	43	17	1785160	9839370	43	17	1956609	9806716	43
18	1616038	9868557	42	18	1788022	9838850	42	18	1959461	9806147	42
19	1618909	9868087	41	19	1790884	9838330	41	19	1962314	9805576	41
20	1621779	9867615	40	20	1793746	9837808	40	20	1965166	9805005	40
21	1624650	9867143	39	21	1796607	9837286	39	21	1968018	9804433	39
22	1627520	9866670	38	22	1799469	9836763	38	22	1970870	9803860	38
23	1630390	9866196	37	23	1802330	9836239	37	23	1973722	9803286	37
24	1633260	9865722	36	24	1805191	9835715	36	24	1976573	9802712	36
25	1636129	9865246	35	25	1808052	9835189	35	25	1979425	9802136	35
26	1638999	9864770	34	26	1810913	9834663	34	26	1982276	9801560	34
27	1641868	9864293	33	27	1813774	9834136	33	27	1985127	9800983	33
28	1644738	9863815	32	28	1816635	9833608	32	28	1987978	9800405	32
29	1647607	9863336	31	29	1819495	9833079	31	29	1990829	9799827	31
30	1650476	9862856	30	30	1822355	9832549	30	30	1993679	9799247	30
31	1653345	9862375	29	31	1825215	9832019	29	31	1996530	9798667	29
32	1656214	9861894	28	32	1828075	9831487	28	32	1999380	9798086	28
33	1659082	9861412	27	33	1830935	9830955	27	33	2002230	9797504	27
34	1661951	9860929	26	34	1833795	9830422	26	34	2005080	9796921	26
35	1664819	9860445	25	35	1836654	9829888	25	35	2007930	9796337	25
36	1667687	9859960	24	36	1839514	9829353	24	36	2010779	9795752	24
37	1670556	9859475	23	37	1842373	9828818	23	37	2013629	9795167	23
38	1673423	9858988	22	38	1845232	9828282	22	38	2016478	9794581	22
39	1676291	9858501	21	39	1848091	9827744	21	39	2019327	9793994	21
40	1679159	9858013	20	40	1850949	9827206	20	40	2022176	9793406	20
41	1682026	9857524	19	41	1853808	9826668	19	41	2025024	9792818	19
42	1684894	9857035	18	42	1856666	9826128	18	42	2027873	9792228	18
43	1687761	9856544	17	43	1859524	9825587	17	43	2030721	9791638	17
44	1690628	9856053	16	44	1862382	9825046	16	44	2033569	9791047	16
45	1693495	9855561	15	45	1865240	9824504	15	45	2036418	9790455	15
46	1696362	9855068	14	46	1868098	9823961	14	46	2039265	9789862	14
47	1699228	9854574	13	47	1870956	9823417	13	47	2042113	9789268	13
48	1702095	9854079	12	48	1873813	9822873	12	48	2044961	9788674	12
49	1704961	9853583	11	49	1876670	9822327	11	49	2047808	9788079	11
50	1707828	9853087	10	50	1879528	9821781	10	50	2050655	9787483	10
51	1710694	9852590	9	51	1882385	9821234	9	51	2053502	9786886	9
52	1713560	9852092	8	52	1885241	9820686	8	52	2056349	9786288	8
53	1716425	9851593	7	53	1888098	9820137	7	53	2059195	9785689	7
54	1719291	9851093	6	54	1890954	9819587	6	54	2062042	9785090	6
55	1722156	9850593	5	55	1893811	9819037	5	55	2064888	9784490	5
56	1725022	9850091	4	56	1896667	9818485	4	56	2067734	9783889	4
57	1727887	9849589	3	57	1899523	9817933	3	57	2070580	9783287	3
58	1730752	9849086	2	58	1902379	9817380	2	58	2073426	9782684	2
59	1733617	9848582	1	59	1905234	9816826	1	59	2076272	9782080	1
60	1736482	9848078	0	60	1908090	9816272	0	60	2079117	9781476	0
	Cosine	Sine			Cosine	Sine			Cosine	Sine	

Deg. 80.   Deg. 79.   Deg. 78.

12 Deg.

	Sine	Cosine	
0	2079117	9781476	60
1	2081962	9780871	59
2	2084807	9780265	58
3	2087652	9779658	57
4	2090497	9779050	56
5	2093341	9778442	55
6	2096186	9777832	54
7	2099030	9777222	53
8	2101874	9776611	52
9	2104718	9775999	51
10	2107561	9775387	50
11	2110405	9774773	49
12	2113248	9774159	48
13	2116091	9773544	47
14	2118934	9772928	46
15	2121777	9772311	45
16	2124619	9771693	44
17	2127462	9771075	43
18	2130304	9770456	42
19	2133146	9769836	41
20	2135988	9769215	40
21	2138829	9768593	39
22	2141671	9767970	38
23	2144512	9767347	37
24	2147353	9766723	36
25	2150194	9766008	35
26	2153035	9765472	34
27	2155876	9764845	33
28	2158716	9764218	32
29	2161556	9763589	31
30	2164396	9762960	30
31	2167236	9762330	29
32	2170076	9761699	28
33	2172915	9761068	27
34	2175754	9760435	26
35	2178593	9759802	25
36	2181432	9759168	24
37	2184271	9758533	23
38	2187110	9757897	22
39	2189948	9757260	21
40	2192786	9756623	20
41	2195624	9755985	19
42	2198462	9755345	18
43	2201300	9754706	17
44	2204137	9754065	16
45	2206974	9753423	15
46	2209811	9752781	14
47	2212648	9752138	13
48	2215485	9751494	12
49	2218321	9750849	11
50	2221158	9750203	10
51	2223994	9749556	9
52	2226830	9748909	8
53	2229666	9748261	7
54	2232501	9747612	6
55	2235337	9746962	5
56	2238172	9746311	4
57	2241007	9745660	3
58	2243842	9745008	2
59	2246676	9744355	1
60	2249511	9743701	0
	Cosine	Sine	

Deg. 77.

13 Deg.

	Sine	Cosine	
0	2249511	9743701	60
1	2252345	9743046	59
2	2255179	9742390	58
3	2258013	9741734	57
4	2260846	9741077	56
5	2263680	9740419	55
6	2266513	9739760	54
7	2269346	9739100	53
8	2272179	9738439	52
9	2275012	9737778	51
10	2277844	9737116	50
11	2280677	9736453	49
12	2283509	9735789	48
13	2286341	9735124	47
14	2289172	9734459	46
15	2292004	9733793	45
16	2294835	9733125	44
17	2297666	9732458	43
18	2300497	9731789	42
19	2303328	9731119	41
20	2306159	9730449	40
21	2308989	9729777	39
22	2311819	9729105	38
23	2314649	9728432	37
24	2317479	9727759	36
25	2320309	9727084	35
26	2323138	9726409	34
27	2325967	9725733	33
28	2328796	9725056	32
29	2331625	9724378	31
30	2334454	9723699	30
31	2337282	9723020	29
32	2340110	9722339	28
33	2342938	9721658	27
34	2345766	9720976	26
35	2348594	9720294	25
36	2351421	9719610	24
37	2354248	9718926	23
38	2357075	9718240	22
39	2359902	9717554	21
40	2362729	9716867	20
41	2365555	9716180	19
42	2368381	9715491	18
43	2371207	9714802	17
44	2374033	9714112	16
45	2376859	9713421	15
46	2379684	9712729	14
47	2382510	9712036	13
48	2385335	9711343	12
49	2388159	9710649	11
50	2390984	9709953	10
51	2393808	9709258	9
52	2396633	9708561	8
53	2399457	9707863	7
54	2402280	9707165	6
55	2405104	9706466	5
56	2407927	9705766	4
57	2410751	9705065	3
58	2413574	9704363	2
59	2416396	9703661	1
60	2419219	9702957	0
	Cosine	Sine	

Deg. 76.

14 Deg.

	Sine	Cosine	
0	2419219	9702957	60
1	2422041	9702253	59
2	2424863	9701548	58
3	2427685	9700842	57
4	2430507	9700136	56
5	2433329	9699428	55
6	2436150	9698720	54
7	2438971	9698011	53
8	2441792	9697301	52
9	2444613	9696591	51
10	2447433	9695879	50
11	2450254	9695167	49
12	2453074	9694453	48
13	2455894	9693740	47
14	2458713	9693025	46
15	2461533	9692309	45
16	2464352	9691593	44
17	2467171	9690875	43
18	2469990	9690157	42
19	2472809	9689438	41
20	2475627	9688719	40
21	2478445	9687998	39
22	2481263	9687277	38
23	2484081	9686555	37
24	2486899	9685832	36
25	2489716	9685108	35
26	2492533	9684383	34
27	2495350	9683658	33
28	2498167	9682931	32
29	2500984	9682204	31
30	2503800	9681476	30
31	2506616	9680748	29
32	2509432	9680018	28
33	2512248	9679288	27
34	2515063	9678557	26
35	2517879	9677825	25
36	2520694	9677092	24
37	2523508	9676358	23
38	2526323	9675624	22
39	2529137	9674888	21
40	2531952	9674152	20
41	2534766	9673415	19
42	2537579	9672678	18
43	2540393	9671939	17
44	2543206	9671200	16
45	2546019	9670459	15
46	2548832	9669718	14
47	2551645	9668977	13
48	2554458	9668234	12
49	2557270	9667490	11
50	2560082	9666746	10
51	2562894	9666001	9
52	2565705	9665255	8
53	2568517	9664508	7
54	2571328	9663761	6
55	2574139	9663012	5
56	2576950	9662263	4
57	2579760	9661513	3
58	2582570	9660762	2
59	2585381	9660011	1
60	2588190	9659258	0
	Cosine	Sine	

Deg. 75.

15 Deg.				16 Deg.				17 Deg.			
	Sine	Cosine			Sine	Cosine			Sine	Cosine	
0	2588190	9659258	60	0	2756374	9612617	60	0	2923717	9563048	60
1	2591000	9658505	59	1	2759170	9611815	59	1	2926499	9562197	59
2	2593810	9657751	58	2	2761965	9611012	58	2	2929280	9561345	58
3	2596619	9656996	57	3	2764761	9610208	57	3	2932061	9560492	57
4	2599428	9656240	56	4	2767556	9609403	56	4	2934842	9559639	56
5	2602237	9655484	55	5	2770352	9608598	55	5	2937623	9558785	55
6	2605045	9654726	54	6	2773147	9607792	54	6	2940403	9557930	54
7	2607853	9653968	53	7	2775941	9606984	53	7	2943183	9557074	53
8	2610662	9653209	52	8	2778736	9606177	52	8	2945963	9556218	52
9	2613469	9652449	51	9	2781530	9605368	51	9	2948743	9555361	51
10	2616277	9651689	50	10	2784324	9604558	50	10	2951522	9554502	50
11	2619085	9650927	49	11	2787118	9603748	49	11	2954302	9553643	49
12	2621892	9650165	48	12	2789911	9602937	48	12	2957081	9552784	48
13	2624699	9649402	47	13	2792704	9602125	47	13	2959859	9551923	47
14	2627506	9648638	46	14	2795497	9601312	46	14	2962638	9551062	46
15	2630312	9647873	45	15	2798290	9600499	45	15	2965416	9550199	45
16	2633118	9647108	44	16	2801083	9599684	44	16	2968194	9549336	44
17	2635925	9646341	43	17	2803875	9598869	43	17	2970971	9548473	43
18	2638730	9645574	42	18	2806667	9598053	42	18	2973749	9547608	42
19	2641536	9644806	41	19	2809459	9597236	41	19	2976526	9546743	41
20	2644342	9644037	40	20	2812251	9596418	40	20	2979303	9545876	40
21	2647147	9643268	39	21	2815042	9595600	39	21	2982079	9545009	39
22	2649952	9642497	38	22	2817833	9594781	38	22	2984856	9544141	38
23	2652757	9641726	37	23	2820624	9593961	37	23	2987632	9543273	37
24	2655561	9640954	36	24	2823415	9593140	36	24	2990408	9542403	36
25	2658366	9640181	35	25	2826205	9592318	35	25	2993184	9541533	35
26	2661170	9639407	34	26	2828995	9591496	34	26	2995959	9540662	34
27	2663973	9638633	33	27	2831785	9590672	33	27	2998734	9539790	33
28	2666777	9637858	32	28	2834575	9589848	32	28	3001509	9538917	32
29	2669581	9637081	31	29	2837364	9589023	31	29	3004284	9538044	31
30	2672384	9636305	30	30	2840153	9588197	30	30	3007058	9537170	30
31	2675187	9635527	29	31	2842942	9587371	29	31	3009832	9536294	29
32	2677989	9634748	28	32	2845731	9586543	28	32	3012606	9535418	28
33	2680792	9633969	27	33	2848520	9585715	27	33	3015380	9534542	27
34	2683594	9633189	26	34	2851308	9584886	26	34	3018153	9533664	26
35	2686396	9632408	25	35	2854096	9584056	25	35	3020926	9532786	25
36	2689198	9631626	24	36	2856884	9583226	24	36	3023699	9531907	24
37	2692000	9630843	23	37	2859671	9582394	23	37	3026471	9531027	23
38	2694801	9630060	22	38	2862458	9581562	22	38	3029244	9530146	22
39	2697602	9629275	21	39	2865246	9580729	21	39	3032016	9529264	21
40	2700403	9628490	20	40	2868032	9579895	20	40	3034788	9528382	20
41	2703204	9627074	19	41	2870819	9579060	19	41	3037559	9527499	19
42	2706004	9626917	18	42	2873605	9578225	18	42	3040331	9526615	18
43	2708805	9626130	17	43	2876391	9577389	17	43	3043102	9525730	17
44	2711605	9625342	16	44	2879177	9576552	16	44	3045872	9524844	16
45	2714404	9624552	15	45	2881963	9575714	15	45	3048643	9523958	15
46	2717204	9623762	14	46	2884748	9574875	14	46	3051413	9523071	14
47	2720003	9622972	13	47	2887533	9574035	13	47	3054183	9522183	13
48	2722802	9622180	12	48	2890318	9573195	12	48	3056953	9521294	12
49	2725601	9621387	11	49	2893103	9572354	11	49	3059723	9520404	11
50	2728400	9620594	10	50	2895887	9571512	10	50	3062492	9519514	10
51	2731198	9619800	9	51	2898671	9570669	9	51	3065261	9518623	9
52	2733997	9619005	8	52	2901455	9569825	8	52	3068030	9517731	8
53	2736794	9618210	7	53	2904239	9568981	7	53	3070798	9516838	7
54	2739592	9617413	6	54	2907022	9568136	6	54	3073566	9515944	6
55	2742390	9616616	5	55	2909805	9567290	5	55	3076334	9515050	5
56	2745187	9615818	4	56	2912588	9566443	4	56	3079102	9514154	4
57	2747984	9615019	3	57	2915371	9565595	3	57	3081869	9513258	3
58	2750781	9614219	2	58	2918153	9564747	2	58	3084636	9512361	2
59	2753577	9613418	1	59	2920935	9563898	1	59	3087403	9511464	1
60	2756374	9612617	0	60	2923717	9563048	0	60	3090170	9510565	0
	Cosine	Sine			Cosine	Sine			Cosine	Sine	

Deg. 74.	Deg. 73	Deg. 72.

18 Deg.	Sine	Cosine		19 Deg.	Sine	Cosine		20 Deg.	Sine	Cosine	
0	3090170	9510565	60	0	3255682	9455186	60	0	3420201	9396926	60
1	3092936	9509666	59	1	3258432	9454238	59	1	3422935	9395931	59
2	3095702	9508766	58	2	3261182	9453290	58	2	3425668	9394935	58
3	3098468	9507865	57	3	3263932	9452341	57	3	3428400	9393938	57
4	3101234	9506963	56	4	3266681	9451391	56	4	3431133	9392940	56
5	3103999	9506061	55	5	3269430	9450441	55	5	3433865	9391942	55
6	3106764	9505157	54	6	3272179	9449489	54	6	3436597	9390943	54
7	3109529	9504253	53	7	3274928	9448537	53	7	3439329	9389942	53
8	3112294	9503348	52	8	3277676	9447584	52	8	3442060	9388942	52
9	3115058	9502443	51	9	3280424	9446630	51	9	3444791	9387940	51
10	3117822	9501536	50	10	3283172	9445675	50	10	3447521	9386938	50
11	3120586	9500629	49	11	3285919	9444720	49	11	3450252	9385934	49
12	3123349	9499721	48	12	3288666	9443764	48	12	3452982	9384930	48
13	3126112	9498812	47	13	3291413	9442807	47	13	3455712	9383925	47
14	3128875	9497902	46	14	3294160	9441849	46	14	3458441	9382920	46
15	3131638	9496991	45	15	3296906	9440890	45	15	3461171	9381913	45
16	3134400	9496080	44	16	3299653	9439931	44	16	3463900	9380906	44
17	3137163	9495168	43	17	3302398	9438971	43	17	3466628	9379898	43
18	3139925	9494255	42	18	3305144	9438010	42	18	3469357	9378889	42
19	3142686	9493341	41	19	3307889	9437048	41	19	3472085	9377880	41
20	3145448	9492426	40	20	3310634	9436085	40	20	3474812	9376869	40
21	3148209	9191511	39	21	3313379	9435122	39	21	3477540	9375858	39
22	3150969	9490595	38	22	3316123	9434157	38	22	3480267	9374846	38
23	3153730	9489678	37	23	3318867	9433192	37	23	3482994	9373833	37
24	3156490	9488760	36	24	3321611	9432227	36	24	3485720	9372820	36
25	3159250	9487842	35	25	3124355	9431260	35	25	3488447	9371806	35
26	3162010	9486922	34	26	3327098	9430293	34	26	3491173	9370790	34
27	3164770	9486002	33	27	3329841	9429324	33	27	3493898	9369774	33
28	3167529	9485081	32	28	3332584	9128355	32	28	3496624	9368758	32
29	3170288	9484159	31	29	3335326	9427386	31	29	3499349	9367740	31
30	3173047	9483237	30	30	3338069	9426415	30	30	3502074	9366722	30
31	3175805	9482313	29	31	3340810	9425444	29	31	3504798	9365703	29
32	3178563	9481389	28	32	3343552	9424471	28	32	3507523	9364683	28
33	3181321	9480464	27	33	3346293	9423498	27	33	3510247	9363662	27
34	3184079	9479538	26	34	3349034	9422525	26	34	3512970	9362641	26
35	3186836	9478612	25	35	3351775	9421550	25	35	3515693	9361618	25
36	3189593	9477684	24	36	3354516	9420575	24	36	3518416	9360595	24
37	3192350	9476756	23	37	3357256	9419598	23	37	3521139	9359571	23
38	3195106	9475827	22	38	3359996	9418021	22	38	3523862	9358547	22
39	3197863	9474897	21	39	3362735	9417644	21	39	3526584	9357521	21
40	3200619	9473966	20	40	3365475	9416665	20	40	3529306	9356495	20
41	3203374	9473035	19	41	3368214	9415686	19	41	3532027	9355468	19
42	3206130	9472103	18	42	3370953	9414705	18	42	3534748	9354440	18
43	3208885	9471170	17	43	3373691	9413724	17	43	3537469	9353412	17
44	3211640	9470236	16	44	3376429	9412743	16	44	3540190	9352382	16
45	3214395	9469301	15	45	3379167	9411760	15	45	3542910	9351352	15
46	3217149	9468366	14	46	3381905	9410777	14	46	3545630	9350321	14
47	3219903	9467430	13	47	3384642	9409793	13	47	3548350	9349289	13
48	3222657	9466493	12	48	3387379	9408808	12	48	3551070	9348257	12
49	3225411	9465555	11	49	3390116	9407822	11	49	3553789	9347223	11
50	3228164	9464616	10	50	3392852	9406835	10	50	3556508	9346189	10
51	3230917	9463677	9	51	3395589	9405848	9	51	3559226	9345154	9
52	3233670	9462736	8	52	3398325	9404860	8	52	3561944	9344119	8
53	3236422	9461795	7	53	3401060	9403871	7	53	3564662	9343082	7
54	3239174	9460854	6	54	3403796	9402881	6	54	3567380	9342045	6
55	3241926	9459911	5	55	3406531	9401891	5	55	3570097	9341007	5
56	3244678	9458968	4	56	3409265	9400899	4	56	3572814	9339968	4
57	3247429	9458023	3	57	3412000	9399907	3	57	3575531	9338928	3
58	3250180	9457078	2	58	3414734	9398914	2	58	3578248	9337888	2
59	3252931	9456132	1	59	3417468	9397921	1	59	3580964	9336846	1
60	3255682	9455186	0	60	3420201	9396926	0	60	3583679	9335804	0
	Cosine	Sine			Cosine	Sine			Cosine	Sine	

Deg. 71.	Deg. 70.	Deg. 69.

	21 Deg.				22 Deg.				23 Deg.		
	Sine	Cosine			Sine	Cosine			Sine	Cosine	
0	3583679	9335804	60	0	3746066	9271839	60	0	3907311	9205049	60
1	3586395	9334761	59	1	3748763	9270748	59	1	3909989	9203912	59
2	3589110	9333718	58	2	3751459	9269658	58	2	3912666	9202774	58
3	3591825	9332673	57	3	3754156	9268566	57	3	3915343	9201635	57
4	3594540	9331628	56	4	3756852	9267474	56	4	3918019	9200496	56
5	3597254	9330582	55	5	3759547	9266380	55	5	3920695	9199356	55
6	3599968	9329535	54	6	3762243	9265286	54	6	3923371	9198215	54
7	3602682	9328488	53	7	3764938	9264192	53	7	3926047	9197073	53
8	3605395	9327439	52	8	3767632	9263096	52	8	3928722	9195931	52
9	3608108	9326390	51	9	3770327	9262000	51	9	3931397	9194788	51
10	3610821	9325340	50	10	3773021	9260902	50	10	3934071	9193644	50
11	3613534	9324260	49	11	3775714	9259805	49	11	3936745	9192499	49
12	3616246	9323228	48	12	3778408	9258706	48	12	3939419	9191353	48
13	3618958	9322186	47	13	3781101	9257606	47	13	3942093	9190207	47
14	3621669	9321133	46	14	3783794	9256506	46	14	3944766	9189060	46
15	3624380	9320079	45	15	3786486	9255405	45	15	3947439	9187912	45
16	3627091	9319024	44	16	3789178	9254303	44	16	3950111	9186763	44
17	3629802	9317969	43	17	3791870	9253201	43	17	3952783	9185614	43
18	3632512	9316912	42	18	3794562	9252097	42	18	3955455	9184464	42
19	3635222	9315855	41	19	3797253	9250993	41	19	3958127	9183313	41
20	3637932	9314797	40	20	3799944	9249888	40	20	3960798	9182161	40
21	3640641	9313739	39	21	3802634	9248782	39	21	3963468	9181009	39
22	3643351	9312679	38	22	3805324	9247676	38	22	3966139	9179855	38
23	3646059	9311619	37	23	3808014	9246568	37	23	3968809	9178701	37
24	3648768	9310558	36	24	3810704	9245460	36	24	3971479	9177546	36
25	3651476	9309496	35	25	3813393	9244351	35	25	3974148	9176391	35
26	3654184	9308434	34	26	3816082	9243242	34	26	3976818	9175234	34
27	3656891	9307370	33	27	3818770	9242131	33	27	3979486	9174077	33
28	3659599	9306306	32	28	3821459	9241020	32	28	3982155	9172919	32
29	3662306	9305241	31	29	3824147	9239908	31	29	3984823	9171760	31
30	3665012	9304176	30	30	3826834	9238795	30	30	3987491	9170601	30
31	3667719	9303109	29	31	3829522	9237682	29	31	3990158	9169440	29
32	3670425	9302042	28	32	3832209	9236567	28	32	3992825	9168279	28
33	3673130	9300974	27	33	3834895	9235452	27	33	3995492	9167118	27
34	3675836	9299905	26	34	3837582	9234336	26	34	3998158	9165955	26
35	3678541	9298835	25	35	3840268	9233220	25	35	4000825	9164791	25
36	3681246	9297765	24	36	3842953	9232102	24	36	4003490	9163627	24
37	3683950	9296694	23	37	3845639	9230984	23	37	4006156	9162462	23
38	3686654	9295622	22	38	3848324	9229865	22	38	4008821	9161297	22
39	3689358	9294549	21	39	3851008	9228745	21	39	4011486	9160130	21
40	3692061	9293475	20	40	3853693	9227624	20	40	4014150	9158963	20
41	3694765	9292401	19	41	3856377	9226503	19	41	4016814	9157795	19
42	3697468	9291326	18	42	3859060	9225381	18	42	4019478	9156626	18
43	3700170	9290250	17	43	3861744	9224258	17	43	4022141	9155456	17
44	3702872	9289173	16	44	3864427	9223134	16	44	4024804	9154286	16
45	3705574	9288096	15	45	3867110	9222010	15	45	4027467	9153115	15
46	3708276	9287017	14	46	3869792	9220884	14	46	4030129	9151943	14
47	3710977	9285938	13	47	3872474	9219758	13	47	4032791	9150770	13
48	3713678	9284858	12	48	3875156	9218632	12	48	4035453	9149597	12
49	3716379	9283778	11	49	3877837	9217504	11	49	4038114	9148422	11
50	3719079	9282696	10	50	3880518	9216375	10	50	4040775	9147247	10
51	3721780	9281614	9	51	3883199	9215246	9	51	4043436	9146072	9
52	3724479	9280531	8	52	3885880	9214116	8	52	4046096	9144895	8
53	3727179	9279447	7	53	3888560	9212986	7	53	4048756	9143718	7
54	3729878	9278363	6	54	3891240	9211854	6	54	4051416	9142540	6
55	3732577	9277277	5	55	3893919	9210722	5	55	4054075	9141361	5
56	3735275	9276191	4	56	3896598	9209589	4	56	4056734	9140181	4
57	3737973	9275104	3	57	3899277	9208455	3	57	4059393	9139001	3
58	3740671	9274016	2	58	3901955	9207320	2	58	4062051	9137819	2
59	3743369	9272928	1	59	3904633	9206185	1	59	4064709	9136637	1
60	3746066	9271839	0	60	3907311	9205049	0	60	4067366	9135455	0
	Cosine	Sine			Cosine	Sine			Cosine	Sine	

Deg. 68.	Deg. 67.	Deg. 66.

24 Deg.

'	Sine	Cosine	'
0	4067366	9135455	60
1	4070024	9134271	59
2	4072681	9133087	58
3	4075337	9131902	57
4	4077993	9130716	56
5	4080649	9129529	55
6	4083305	9128342	54
7	4085960	9127154	53
8	4088615	9125965	52
9	4091269	9124775	51
10	4093923	9123584	50
11	4096577	9122393	49
12	4099230	9121201	48
13	4101883	9120008	47
14	4104536	9118815	46
15	4107189	9117620	45
16	4109841	9116425	44
17	4112492	9115229	43
18	4115144	9114033	42
19	4117795	9112835	41
20	4120445	9111637	40
21	4123096	9110438	39
22	4125745	9109238	38
23	4128395	9108038	37
24	4131044	9106837	36
25	4133693	9105635	35
26	4136342	9104432	34
27	4138990	9103228	33
28	4141638	9102024	32
29	4144285	9100819	31
30	4146932	9099613	30
31	4149579	9098406	29
32	4152226	9097199	28
33	4154872	9095990	27
34	4157517	9094781	26
35	4160163	9093572	25
36	4162808	9092361	24
37	4165453	9091150	23
38	4168097	9089938	22
39	4170741	9088725	21
40	4173385	9087511	20
41	4176028	9086297	19
42	4178671	9085082	18
43	4181313	9083866	17
44	4183956	9082649	16
45	4186597	9081432	15
46	4189239	9080214	14
47	4191880	9078995	13
48	4194521	9077775	12
49	4197161	9076554	11
50	4199801	9075333	10
51	4202441	9074111	9
52	4205080	9072888	8
53	4207719	9071665	7
54	4210358	9070440	6
55	4212996	9069215	5
56	4215634	9067989	4
57	4218272	9066762	3
58	4220909	9065535	2
59	4223546	9064307	1
60	4226183	9063078	0
'	Cosine	Sine	'

Deg. 65.

25 Deg.

'	Sine	Cosine	'
0	4226183	9063078	60
1	4228819	9061848	59
2	4231455	9060618	58
3	4234090	9059386	57
4	4236725	9058154	56
5	4239360	9056922	55
6	4241994	9055688	54
7	4244628	9054454	53
8	4247262	9053219	52
9	4249895	9051983	51
10	4252528	9050746	50
11	4255161	9049509	49
12	4257793	9048271	48
13	4260425	9047032	47
14	4263056	9045792	46
15	4265687	9044551	45
16	4268318	9043310	44
17	4270949	9042068	43
18	4273579	9040825	42
19	4276208	9039582	41
20	4278838	9038338	40
21	4281467	9037093	39
22	4284095	9035847	38
23	4286723	9034600	37
24	4289351	9033353	36
25	4291979	9032105	35
26	4294606	9030856	34
27	4297233	9029606	33
28	4299859	9028356	32
29	4302485	9027105	31
30	4305111	9025853	30
31	4307736	9024600	29
32	4310361	9023347	28
33	4312986	9022092	27
34	4315610	9020838	26
35	4318234	9019582	25
36	4320857	9018325	24
37	4323481	9017068	23
38	4326103	9015810	22
39	4328726	9014551	21
40	4331348	9013292	20
41	4333970	9012031	19
42	4336591	9010770	18
43	4339212	9009508	17
44	4341832	9008246	16
45	4344453	9006982	15
46	4347072	9005718	14
47	4349692	9004453	13
48	4352311	9003188	12
49	4354930	9001921	11
50	4357548	9000654	10
51	4360166	8999386	9
52	4362784	8998117	8
53	4365401	8996848	7
54	4368018	8995578	6
55	4370634	8994307	5
56	4373251	8993035	4
57	4375866	8991763	3
58	4378482	8990489	2
59	4381097	8989215	1
60	4383711	8987940	0
'	Cosine	Sine	'

Deg. 64.

26 Deg.

'	Sine	Cosine	'
0	4383711	8987940	60
1	4386326	8986665	59
2	4388940	8985389	58
3	4391553	8984112	57
4	4394166	8982834	56
5	4396779	8981555	55
6	4399392	8980276	54
7	4402004	8978996	53
8	4404615	8977715	52
9	4407227	8976433	51
10	4409838	8975151	50
11	4412448	8973868	49
12	4415059	8972584	48
13	4417668	8971299	47
14	4420278	8970014	46
15	4422887	8968727	45
16	4425496	8967440	44
17	4428104	8966153	43
18	4430712	8964864	42
19	4433319	8963575	41
20	4435927	8962285	40
21	4438534	8960994	39
22	4441140	8959703	38
23	4443746	8958411	37
24	4446352	8957118	36
25	4448957	8955824	35
26	4451562	8954529	34
27	4454167	8953234	33
28	4456771	8951938	32
29	4459375	8950641	31
30	4461978	8949344	30
31	4464581	8948045	29
32	4467184	8946746	28
33	4469786	8945446	27
34	4472388	8944146	26
35	4474990	8942844	25
36	4477591	8941542	24
37	4480192	8940240	23
38	4482792	8938936	22
39	4485392	8937632	21
40	4487992	8936326	20
41	4490591	8935021	19
42	4493190	8933714	18
43	4495789	8932406	17
44	4498387	8931098	16
45	4500984	8929789	15
46	4503582	8928480	14
47	4506179	8927169	13
48	4508775	8925858	12
49	4511372	8924546	11
50	4513967	8923234	10
51	4516563	8921920	9
52	4519158	8920606	8
53	4521753	8919291	7
54	4524347	8917975	6
55	4526941	8916659	5
56	4529535	8915342	4
57	4532128	8914024	3
58	4534721	8912705	2
59	4537313	8911385	1
60	4539905	8910065	0
'	Cosine	Sine	'

Deg. 63.

	27 Deg.				28 Deg.				29 Deg.		
′	Sine	Cosine	′	′	Sine	Cosine	′	′	Sine	Cosine	′
0	4539905	8910065	60	0	4694716	8829476	60	0	4848096	8746197	60
1	4542497	8908744	59	1	4697284	8828110	59	1	4850640	8744786	59
2	4545088	8907423	58	2	4699852	8826743	58	2	4853184	8743375	58
3	4547679	8906100	57	3	4702419	8825376	57	3	4855727	8741963	57
4	4550269	8904777	56	4	4704986	8824007	56	4	4858270	8740550	56
5	4552859	8903453	55	5	4707553	8822638	55	5	4860812	8739137	55
6	4555449	8902128	54	6	4710119	8821260	54	6	4863354	8737722	54
7	4558038	8900803	53	7	4712685	8819898	53	7	4865895	8736307	53
8	4560627	8899476	52	8	4715250	8818527	52	8	4868436	8734891	52
9	4563216	8898149	51	9	4717815	8817155	51	9	4870977	8733475	51
10	4565804	8896822	50	10	4720380	8815782	50	10	4873517	8732058	50
11	4568392	8895493	49	11	4722944	8814409	49	11	4876057	8730640	49
12	4570979	8894164	48	12	4725508	8813035	48	12	4878597	8729221	48
13	4573566	8892834	47	13	4728071	8811660	47	13	4881136	8727801	47
14	4576153	8891503	46	14	4730634	8810284	46	14	4883674	8726381	46
15	4578739	8890171	45	15	4733197	8808907	45	15	4886212	8724960	45
16	4581325	8888839	44	16	4735759	8807530	44	16	4888750	8723538	44
17	4583910	8887506	43	17	4738321	8806152	43	17	4891288	8722116	43
18	4586496	8886172	42	18	4740882	8804774	42	18	4893825	8720693	42
19	4589080	8884838	41	19	4743443	8803394	41	19	4896361	8719269	41
20	4591665	8883503	40	20	4746004	8802014	40	20	4898897	8717844	40
21	4594248	8882166	39	21	4748564	8800633	39	21	4901433	8716419	39
22	4596832	8880830	38	22	4751124	8799251	38	22	4903968	8714993	38
23	4599415	8879492	37	23	4753683	8797869	37	23	4906503	8713566	37
24	4601998	8878154	36	24	4756242	8796486	36	24	4909038	8712138	36
25	4604580	8876815	35	25	4758801	8795102	35	25	4911572	8710710	35
26	4607162	8875475	34	26	4761359	8793717	34	26	4914105	8709281	34
27	4609744	8874134	33	27	4763917	8792332	33	27	4916638	8707851	33
28	4612325	8872793	32	28	4766474	8790946	32	28	4919171	8706420	32
29	4614906	8871451	31	29	4769031	8789559	31	29	4921704	8704989	31
30	4617486	8870108	30	30	4771588	8788171	30	30	4924236	8703557	30
31	4620066	8868765	29	31	4774144	8786783	29	31	4926767	8702124	29
32	4622646	8867420	28	32	4776700	8785394	28	32	4929298	8700691	28
33	4625225	8866075	27	33	4779255	8784004	27	33	4931829	8699256	27
34	4627804	8864730	26	34	4781810	8782613	26	34	4934359	8697821	26
35	4630382	8863383	25	35	4784364	8781222	25	35	4936889	8696386	25
36	4632960	8862036	24	36	4786919	8779830	24	36	4939419	8694949	24
37	4635538	8860688	23	37	4789472	8778437	23	37	4941948	8693512	23
38	4638115	8859339	22	38	4792026	8777043	22	38	4944476	8692074	22
39	4640692	8857989	21	39	4794579	8775649	21	39	4947005	8690636	21
40	4643269	8856639	20	40	4797131	8774254	20	40	4949532	8689196	20
41	4645845	8855288	19	41	4799683	8772858	19	41	4952060	8687756	19
42	4648420	8853936	18	42	4802235	8771462	18	42	4954587	8686315	18
43	4650996	8852584	17	43	4804786	8770064	17	43	4957113	8684874	17
44	4653571	8851230	16	44	4807337	8768666	16	44	4959639	8683431	16
45	4656145	8849876	15	45	4809888	8767268	15	45	4962165	8681988	15
46	4658719	8848522	14	46	4812438	8765868	14	46	4964690	8680544	14
47	4661293	8847166	13	47	4814987	8764468	13	47	4967215	8679100	13
48	4663866	8845810	12	48	4817537	8763067	12	48	4969740	8677655	12
49	4666439	8844453	11	49	4820086	8761665	11	49	4972264	8676209	11
50	4669012	8843095	10	50	4822634	8760263	10	50	4974787	8674762	10
51	4671584	8841736	9	51	4825182	8758859	9	51	4977310	8673314	9
52	4674156	8840377	8	52	4827730	8757455	8	52	4979833	8671860	8
53	4676727	8839017	7	53	4830277	8756051	7	53	4982355	8670417	7
54	4679298	8837650	6	54	4832824	8754645	6	54	4984877	8668967	6
55	4681869	8836295	5	55	4835370	8753239	5	55	4987399	8667517	5
56	4684439	8834933	4	56	4837916	8751832	4	56	4989920	8666066	4
57	4687009	8833569	3	57	4840462	8750425	3	57	4992441	8664614	3
58	4689578	8832206	2	58	4843007	8749016	2	58	4994961	8663161	2
59	4692147	8830841	1	59	4845552	8747607	1	59	4997481	8661708	1
60	4694716	8829476	0	60	4848096	8746197	0	60	5000000	8660254	0
′	Cosine	Sine	′	′	Cosine	Sine	′	′	Cosine	Sine	′
	Deg. 62.				Deg. 61.				Deg. 60.		

	30 Deg.				31 Deg.				32 Deg.		
′	Sine	Cosine	′	′	Sine	Cosine	′	′	Sine	Cosine	′
0	5000000	8660254	60	0	5150381	8571673	6	0	5299193	8480481	60
1	5002519	8658799	59	1	5152874	8570174	59	1	5301659	8478939	59
2	5005037	8657344	58	2	5155367	8568675	58	2	5304125	8477397	58
3	5007556	8655887	57	3	5157859	8567175	57	3	5306591	8475853	57
4	5010073	8654430	56	4	5160351	8565674	56	4	5309057	8474309	56
5	5012591	8652973	55	5	5162842	8564173	55	5	5311521	8472765	55
6	5015107	8651514	54	6	5165333	8562671	54	6	5313986	8471219	54
7	5017624	8650055	53	7	5167824	8561168	53	7	5316450	8469673	53
8	5020140	8648595	52	8	5170314	8559664	52	8	5318913	8468126	52
9	5022655	8647134	51	9	5172804	8558160	51	9	5321376	8466579	51
10	5025170	8645673	50	10	5175293	8556655	50	10	5323839	8465030	50
11	5027685	8644211	49	11	5177782	8555149	49	11	5326301	8463481	49
12	5030199	8642748	48	12	5180270	8553643	48	12	5328763	8461932	48
13	5032713	8641284	47	13	5182758	8552135	47	13	5331224	8460381	47
14	5035227	8639820	46	14	5185246	8550627	46	14	5333685	8458830	46
15	5037740	8638355	45	15	5187733	8549119	45	15	5336145	8457278	45
16	5040252	8636889	44	16	5190219	8547600	44	16	5338605	8455726	44
17	5042765	8635423	43	17	5192705	8546099	43	17	5341065	8454172	43
18	5045276	8633956	42	18	5195191	8544588	42	18	5343523	8452618	42
19	5047788	8632488	41	19	5197676	8543077	41	19	5345982	8451064	41
20	5050298	8631019	40	20	5200161	8541564	40	20	5348440	8449508	40
21	5052809	8629549	39	21	5202646	8540051	39	21	5350898	8447952	39
22	5055319	8628079	38	22	5205130	8538538	38	22	5353355	8446395	38
23	5057828	8626608	37	23	5207613	8537023	37	23	5355812	8444838	37
24	5060338	8625137	36	24	5210096	8535508	36	24	5358268	8443279	36
25	5062846	8623664	35	25	5212579	8533992	35	25	5360724	8441720	35
26	5065355	8622191	34	26	5215061	8532475	34	26	5363179	8440161	34
27	5067863	8620717	33	27	5217543	8530958	33	27	5365634	8438600	33
28	5070370	8619243	32	28	5220024	8529440	32	28	5368089	8437039	32
29	5072877	8617768	31	29	5222505	8527921	31	29	5370543	8435477	31
30	5075384	8616292	30	30	5224986	8526402	30	30	5372996	8433914	30
31	5077890	8614815	29	31	5227466	8524881	29	31	5375449	8432351	29
32	5080396	8613337	28	32	5229945	8523360	28	32	5377902	8430787	28
33	5082901	8611859	27	33	5232424	8521839	27	33	5380354	8429222	27
34	5085406	8610380	26	34	5234903	8520316	26	34	5382806	8427657	26
35	5087910	8608901	25	35	5237381	8518793	25	35	5385257	8426091	25
36	5090414	8607420	24	36	5239859	8517269	24	36	5387708	8424524	24
37	5092918	8605939	23	37	5242336	8515745	23	37	5390158	8422956	23
38	5095421	8604457	22	38	5244813	8514219	22	38	5392608	8421388	22
39	5097924	8602975	21	39	5247290	8512693	21	39	5395058	8419819	21
40	5100426	8601491	20	40	5249766	8511167	20	40	5397507	8418249	20
41	5102928	8600007	19	41	5252241	8509639	19	41	5399955	8416679	19
42	5105429	8598523	18	42	5254717	8508111	18	42	5402403	8415108	18
43	5107930	8597037	17	43	5257191	8506582	17	43	5404851	8413536	17
44	5110431	8595551	16	44	5259665	8505053	16	44	5407298	8411963	16
45	5112931	8594064	15	45	5262139	8503522	15	45	5409745	8410390	15
46	5115431	8592576	14	46	5264613	8501991	14	46	5412191	8408816	14
47	5117930	8591088	13	47	5267085	8500459	13	47	5414637	8407241	13
48	5120429	8589599	12	48	5269558	8498927	12	48	5417082	8405666	12
49	5122927	8588109	11	49	5272030	8497394	11	49	5419527	8404090	11
50	5125425	8586619	10	50	5274502	8495860	10	50	5421971	8402513	10
51	5127923	8585127	9	51	5276973	8494325	9	51	5424415	8400936	9
52	5130420	8583635	8	52	5279443	8492790	8	52	5426859	8399357	8
53	5132916	8582143	7	53	5281914	8491254	7	53	5429302	8397778	7
54	5135413	8580649	6	54	5284383	8489717	6	54	5431744	8396199	6
55	5137908	8579155	5	55	5286853	8488179	5	55	5434187	8394618	5
56	5140404	8577660	4	56	5289322	8486641	4	56	5436628	8393037	4
57	5142899	8576164	3	57	5291790	8485102	3	57	5439069	8391455	3
58	5145393	8574668	2	58	5294258	8483562	2	58	5441510	8389873	2
59	5147887	8573171	1	59	5296726	8482022	1	59	5443951	8388290	1
60	5150381	8571673	0	60	5299193	8480481	0	60	5446390	8386706	0
′	Cosine	Sine	′	′	Cosine	Sine	′	′	Cosine	Sine	′
	Deg. 59.				Deg. 58.				Deg. 57.		

FF

	33 Deg.				34 Deg.				35 Deg.		
′	Sine	Cosine	′	′	Sine	Cosine	′	′	Sine	Cosine	′
0	5446390	8386706	60	0	5591929	8290376	60	0	5735764	8191520	60
1	5448830	8385121	59	1	5594340	8288749	59	1	5738147	8189852	59
2	5451269	8383536	58	2	5596751	8287121	58	2	5740529	8188182	58
3	5453707	8381950	57	3	5599162	8285493	57	3	5742911	8186512	57
4	5456145	8380363	56	4	5601572	8283864	56	4	5745292	8184841	56
5	5458583	8378775	55	5	5603981	8282234	55	5	5747672	8183169	55
6	5461020	8377187	54	6	5606390	8280603	54	6	5750053	8181497	54
7	5463456	8375598	53	7	5608798	8278972	53	7	5752432	8179824	53
8	5465892	8374009	52	8	5611206	8277340	52	8	5754811	8178151	52
9	5468328	8372418	51	9	5613614	8275708	51	9	5757190	8176476	51
10	5470763	8370827	50	10	5616021	8274074	50	10	5759568	8174801	50
11	5473198	8369236	49	11	5618428	8272440	49	11	5761946	8173125	49
12	5475632	8367643	48	12	5620834	8270806	48	12	5764323	8171449	48
13	5478066	8366050	47	13	5623239	8269170	47	13	5766700	8169772	47
14	5480499	8364456	46	14	5625645	8267534	46	14	5769076	8168094	46
15	5482932	8362802	45	15	5628049	8265897	45	15	5771452	8166416	45
16	5485365	8361266	44	16	5630453	8264260	44	16	5773827	8164736	44
17	5487797	8359670	43	17	5632857	8262622	43	17	5776202	8163056	43
18	5490228	8358074	42	18	5635260	8260983	42	18	5778576	8161376	42
19	5492659	8356476	41	19	5637663	8259343	41	19	5780950	8159695	41
20	5495090	8354878	40	20	5640066	8257703	40	20	5783323	8158013	40
21	5497520	8353279	39	21	5642467	8256062	39	21	5785696	8156330	39
22	5499950	8351680	38	22	5644869	8254420	38	22	5788069	8154647	38
23	5502379	8350080	37	23	5647270	8252778	37	23	5790440	8152963	37
24	5504807	8348479	36	24	5649670	8251135	36	24	5792812	8151278	36
25	5507236	8346877	35	25	5652070	8249491	35	25	5795183	8149593	35
26	5509663	8345275	34	26	5654469	8247847	34	26	5797553	8147906	34
27	5512091	8343672	33	27	5656868	8246202	33	27	5799923	8146220	33
28	5514518	8342068	32	28	5659267	8244556	32	28	5802292	8144532	32
29	5516944	8340463	31	29	5661665	8242909	31	29	5804661	8142844	31
30	5519370	8338858	30	30	5664062	8241262	30	30	5807030	8141155	30
31	5521795	8337252	29	31	5666459	8239614	29	31	5809397	8139466	29
32	5524220	8335646	28	32	5668856	8237965	28	32	5811765	8137775	28
33	5526645	8334038	27	33	5671252	8236316	27	33	5814132	8136084	27
34	5529069	8332430	26	34	5673648	8234666	26	34	5816498	8134393	26
35	5531492	8330822	25	35	5676043	8233015	25	35	5818864	8132701	25
36	5533915	8329212	24	36	5678437	8231364	24	36	5821230	8131008	24
37	5536338	8327602	23	37	5680832	8229712	23	37	5823595	8129314	23
38	5538760	8325991	22	38	5683225	8228059	22	38	5825959	8127620	22
39	5541182	8324380	21	39	5685619	8226405	21	39	5828323	8125925	21
40	5543603	8322768	20	40	5688011	8224751	20	40	5830687	8124229	20
41	5546024	8321155	19	41	5690403	8223096	19	41	5833050	8122532	19
42	5548444	8319541	18	42	5692795	8221440	18	42	5835412	8120835	18
43	5550864	8317927	17	43	5695187	8219784	17	43	5837774	8119137	17
44	5553283	8316312	16	44	5697577	8218127	16	44	5840136	8117439	16
45	5555702	8314696	15	45	5699968	8216469	15	45	5842497	8115740	15
46	5558121	8313080	14	46	5702357	8214811	14	46	5844857	8114040	14
47	5560539	8311463	13	47	5704747	8213152	13	47	5847217	8112339	13
48	5562956	8309845	12	48	5707136	8211492	12	48	5849577	8110638	12
49	5565373	8308226	11	49	5709524	8209832	11	49	5851936	8108936	11
50	5567790	8306607	10	50	5711912	8208170	10	50	5854294	8107234	10
51	5570206	8304987	9	51	5714299	8206509	9	51	5856652	8105530	9
52	5572621	8303366	8	52	5716686	8204846	8	52	5859010	8103826	8
53	5575036	8301745	7	53	5719073	8203183	7	53	5861367	8102122	7
54	5577451	8300123	6	54	5721459	8201519	6	54	5863724	8100416	6
55	5579865	8298500	5	55	5723844	8199854	5	55	5866080	8098710	5
56	5582279	8296877	4	56	5726229	8198189	4	56	5868435	8097004	4
57	5584692	8295252	3	57	5728614	8196523	3	57	5870790	8095296	3
58	5587105	8293628	2	58	5730998	8194856	2	58	5873145	8093588	2
59	5589517	8292002	1	59	5733381	8193189	1	59	5875499	8091879	1
60	5591929	8290376	0	60	5735764	8191520	0	60	5877853	8090170	0
′	Cosine	Sine	′	′	Cosine	Sine	′	′	Cosine	Sine	′

| Deg. 56. | Deg. 55. | Deg. 54. |

	36 Deg.				37 Deg.				38 Deg.		
'	Sine	Cosine	'	'	Sine	Cosine	'	'	Sine	Cosine	'
0	5877853	8090170	60	0	6018150	7986355	60	0	6156615	7880108	60
1	5880206	8088460	59	1	6020473	7984604	59	1	6158907	7878316	59
2	5882558	80867,9	58	2	6022795	7982853	58	2	6161198	7876524	58
3	5884910	8085037	57	3	6025117	7981100	57	3	6163489	7874732	57
4	5887262	8083325	56	4	6027439	7979347	56	4	6165780	7872939	56
5	5889613	8081612	55	5	6029760	7977594	55	5	6168069	7871145	55
6	5891964	8079899	54	6	6032080	7975839	54	6	6170359	7869350	54
7	5894314	8078185	53	7	6034400	7974084	53	7	6172648	7867555	53
8	5896663	8076470	52	8	6036719	7972329	52	8	6174936	7865759	52
9	5899012	8074754	51	9	6039038	7970572	51	9	6177224	7863963	51
10	5901361	8073038	50	10	6041356	7968815	50	10	6179511	7862165	50
11	5903709	8071321	49	11	6043674	7967058	49	11	6181798	7860367	49
12	5906057	8069603	48	12	6045991	7965299	48	12	6184084	7858569	48
13	5908404	8067885	47	13	6048308	7963540	47	13	6186370	7856770	47
14	5910750	8066166	46	14	6050624	7961780	46	14	6188655	7854970	46
15	5913096	8064446	45	15	6052940	7960020	45	15	6190939	7853169	45
16	5915442	8062726	44	16	6055255	7958259	44	16	6193224	7851368	44
17	5917787	8061005	43	17	6057570	7956497	43	17	6195507	7849566	43
18	5920132	8059283	42	18	6059884	7954735	42	18	6197790	7847764	42
19	5922476	8057560	41	19	6062198	7952972	41	19	6200073	7845961	41
20	5924819	8055837	40	20	6064511	7951208	40	20	6202355	7844157	40
21	5927163	8054113	39	21	6066824	7949444	39	21	6204636	7842352	39
22	5929505	8052389	38	22	6069136	7947678	38	22	6206917	7840547	38
23	5931847	8050664	37	23	6071447	7945913	37	23	6209198	7838741	37
24	5934189	8048938	36	24	6073758	7944146	36	24	6211478	7836935	36
25	5936530	8047211	35	25	6076069	7942379	35	25	6213757	7835127	35
26	5938871	8045484	34	26	6078379	7940611	34	26	6216036	7833320	34
27	5941211	8043756	33	27	6080689	7938843	33	27	6218314	7831511	33
28	5943550	8042028	32	28	6082998	7937074	32	28	6220592	7829702	32
29	5945889	8040299	31	29	6085306	7935304	31	29	6222870	7827892	31
30	5948228	8038569	30	30	6087614	7933533	30	30	6225146	7826082	30
31	5950566	8036838	29	31	6089922	7931762	29	31	6227423	7824270	29
32	5952904	8035107	28	32	6092229	7929990	28	32	6229698	7822459	28
33	5955241	8033375	27	33	6094535	7928218	27	33	6231974	7820646	27
34	5957577	8031642	26	34	6096841	7926445	26	34	6234248	7818833	26
35	5959913	8029909	25	35	6099147	7924671	25	35	6236522	7817019	25
36	5962249	8028175	24	36	6101452	7922896	24	36	6238796	7815205	24
37	5964584	8026440	23	37	6103756	7921121	23	37	6241069	7813390	23
38	5966918	8024705	22	38	6106060	7919345	22	38	6243342	7811574	22
39	5969252	8022969	21	39	6108363	7917569	21	39	6245614	7809757	21
40	5971586	8021232	20	40	6110666	7915792	20	40	6247885	7807940	20
41	5973919	8019495	19	41	6112969	7914014	19	41	6250156	7806123	19
42	5976251	8017756	18	42	6115270	7912235	18	42	6252427	7804304	18
43	5978583	8016018	17	43	6117572	7910456	17	43	6254696	7802485	17
44	5980915	8014278	16	44	6119873	7908676	16	44	6256966	7800665	16
45	5983246	8012538	15	45	6122173	7906896	15	45	6259235	7798845	15
46	5985577	8010797	14	46	6124473	7905115	14	46	6261503	7797024	14
47	5987906	8009056	13	47	6126772	7903333	13	47	6263771	7795202	13
48	5990236	8007314	12	48	6129071	7901550	12	48	6266038	7793380	12
49	5992565	8005571	11	49	6131369	7899767	11	49	6268305	7791557	11
50	5994893	8003827	10	50	6133666	7897983	10	50	6270571	7789733	10
51	5997221	8002083	9	51	6135964	7896198	9	51	6272837	7787909	9
52	5999549	8000338	8	52	6138260	7894413	8	52	6275102	7786084	8
53	6001876	7998593	7	53	6140556	7892627	7	53	6277366	7784258	7
54	6004202	7996847	6	54	6142852	7890841	6	54	6279631	7782431	6
55	6006528	7995100	5	55	6145147	7889054	5	55	6281894	7780604	5
56	6008854	7993352	4	56	6147442	7887266	4	56	6284157	7778777	4
57	6011179	7991604	3	57	6149736	7885477	3	57	6286420	7776949	3
58	6013503	7989855	2	58	6152029	7883688	2	58	6288682	7775120	2
59	6015827	7988105	1	59	6154322	7881898	1	59	6290943	7773290	1
60	6018150	7986355	0	60	6156615	7880108	0	60	6293204	7771460	0
'	Cosine	Sine	'	'	Cosine	Sine	'	'	Cosine	Sine	'

Deg. 53.	Deg. 52.	Deg. 51.

39 Deg.				40 Deg.				41 Deg.		
′	Sine	Cosine	′	′	Sine	Cosine	′	′	Sine	Cosine	′
0	6293204	7771460	60	0	6427876	7660444	60	0	6560590	7547096	60
1	6295464	7769629	59	1	6430104	7658574	59	1	6562785	7545187	59
2	6297724	7767797	58	2	6432332	7656704	58	2	6564980	7543278	58
3	6299983	776595 5	57	3	6434559	7654832	57	3	6567174	7541368	57
4	6302242	7764132	56	4	6436785	7652960	56	4	6569367	7539457	56
5	6304500	7762298	55	5	6439011	7651087	55	5	6571560	7537546	55
6	6306758	7760464	54	6	6441236	7649214	54	6	6573752	7535634	54
7	6309015	7758029	53	7	6443461	7647340	53	7	6575944	7533721	53
8	6311272	7756794	52	8	6445685	7615465	52	8	6578135	7531808	52
9	6313528	7754957	51	9	6447909	7643590	51	9	6580326	7529894	51
10	6315784	7753121	50	10	6450132	7641714	50	10	6582516	7527980	50
11	6318039	7751283	49	11	6452355	7639838	49	11	6584706	7526065	49
12	6320293	7749445	48	12	6454577	7637960	48	12	6586895	7524149	48
13	6322547	7747606	47	13	6456798	7636082	47	13	6589083	7522233	47
14	6324800	7745767	46	14	6459019	7634204	46	14	6591271	7520316	46
15	6327053	7743926	45	15	6461240	7632325	45	15	6593458	7518398	45
16	6329306	7742086	44	16	6463460	7630445	44	16	6595645	7516480	44
17	6331557	7740244	43	17	6465679	7628564	43	17	6597831	7514561	43
18	6333809	7738402	42	18	6467898	7626683	42	18	6600017	7512641	42
19	6336059	7736559	41	19	6470116	7624802	41	19	6602202	7510721	41
20	6338310	7734716	40	20	6472334	7622919	40	20	6604386	7508800	40
21	6340559	7732872	39	21	6474551	7621036	39	21	6606570	7506879	39
22	6342808	7731027	38	22	6476767	7619152	38	22	6608754	7504957	38
23	6345057	7729182	37	23	6478984	7617268	37	23	6610936	7503034	37
24	6347305	7727336	36	24	6481199	7615383	36	24	6613119	7501111	36
25	6349553	7725489	35	25	6483414	7613497	35	25	6615300	7499187	35
26	6351800	7723642	34	26	6485628	7611611	34	26	6617482	7497262	34
27	6354046	7721794	33	27	6487842	7609724	33	27	6619662	7495337	33
28	6356292	7719945	32	28	6490056	7607837	32	28	6621842	7493411	32
29	6358537	7718096	31	29	6492268	7605949	31	29	6624022	7491484	31
30	6360782	7716246	30	30	6494480	7604060	30	30	6626200	7489557	30
31	6363026	7714395	29	31	6496692	7602170	29	31	6628379	7487629	29
32	6365270	7712544	28	32	6498903	7600280	28	32	6630557	7485701	28
33	6367513	7710692	27	33	6501114	7598389	27	33	6632734	7483772	27
34	6369756	7708840	26	34	6503324	7596498	26	34	6634910	7481842	26
35	6371998	7706986	25	35	6505533	7594606	25	35	6637087	7479912	25
36	6374240	7705132	24	36	6507742	7592713	24	36	6639262	7477981	24
37	6376481	7703278	23	37	6509951	7590820	23	37	6641437	7476049	23
38	6378721	7701423	22	38	6512158	7588926	22	38	6643612	7474117	22
39	6380961	7699567	21	39	6514366	7587031	21	39	6645785	7472184	21
40	6383201	7697710	20	40	6516572	7585136	20	40	6647959	7470251	20
41	6385440	7695853	19	41	6518778	7583240	19	41	6650131	7468317	19
42	6387678	7693996	18	42	6520984	7581343	18	42	6652304	7466382	18
43	6389916	7692137	17	43	6523189	7579446	17	43	6654475	7464446	17
44	6392153	7690278	16	44	6525394	7577548	16	44	6656646	7462510	16
45	6394390	7688418	15	45	6527598	7575650	15	45	6658817	7460574	15
46	6396626	7686558	14	46	6529801	7573751	14	46	6660987	7458636	14
47	6398862	7684697	13	47	6532004	7571851	13	47	6663156	7456699	13
48	6401097	7682835	12	48	6534206	7569951	12	48	6665325	7454760	12
49	6403332	7680973	11	49	6536408	7568050	11	49	6667493	7452821	11
50	6405566	7679110	10	50	6538609	7566148	10	50	6669661	7450881	10
51	6407799	7677246	9	51	6540810	7564246	9	51	6671828	7448941	9
52	6410032	7675382	8	52	6543010	7562343	8	52	6673994	7446999	8
53	6412264	7673517	7	53	6545209	7560439	7	53	6676160	7445058	7
54	6414496	7671652	6	54	6547408	7558535	6	54	6678326	7443115	6
55	6416728	7669785	5	55	6549607	7556630	5	55	6680490	7441173	5
56	6418958	7667918	4	56	6551804	7554724	4	56	6682655	7439229	4
57	6421189	7666051	3	57	6554002	7552818	3	57	6684818	7437285	3
58	6423418	7664183	2	58	6556198	7550911	2	58	6686981	7435340	2
59	6425647	7662314	1	59	6558305	7549004	1	59	6689144	7433394	1
60	6427876	7660444	0	60	6560590	7547096	0	60	6691306	7431448	0
′	Cosine	Sine	′	′	Cosine	Sine	′	′	Cosine	Sine	′
Deg. 50.				Deg. 49.				Deg. 48.			

42 Deg.				43 Deg.				44 Deg.			
'	Sine	Cosine	'	'	Sine	Cosine	'	'	Sine	Cosine	'
0	6691306	7431448	60	0	6819984	7313537	6	0	6946584	7193398	60
1	6693468	7429502	59	1	6822111	7311553	59	1	6948676	7191377	59
2	6695628	7427554	58	2	6824237	7309568	58	2	6950767	7189355	58
3	6697789	7425606	57	3	6826363	7307583	57	3	6952858	7187333	57
4	6699948	7423658	56	4	6828489	7305597	56	4	6954949	7185310	56
5	6702108	7421708	55	5	6830613	7303610	55	5	6957039	7183287	55
6	6704266	7419758	54	6	6832738	7301623	54	6	6959128	7181263	54
7	6706424	7417808	53	7	6834861	7299635	53	7	6961217	7179238	53
8	6708582	7415857	52	8	6836984	7297646	52	8	6963305	7177213	52
9	6710739	7413905	51	9	6839107	7295657	51	9	6965392	7175187	51
10	6712895	7411953	50	10	6841229	7293668	50	10	6967479	7173161	50
11	6715051	7410000	49	11	6843350	7291677	49	11	6969565	7171134	49
12	6717206	7408046	48	12	6845471	7289686	48	12	6971651	7169106	48
13	6719361	7406092	47	13	6847591	7287695	47	13	6973736	7167078	47
14	6721515	7404137	46	14	6849711	7285703	46	14	6975821	7165049	46
15	6723668	7402181	45	15	6851830	7283710	45	15	6977905	7163019	45
16	6725821	7400225	44	16	6853948	7281716	44	16	6979988	7160989	44
17	6727973	7398268	43	17	6856066	7279722	43	17	6982071	7158959	43
18	6730125	7396311	42	18	6858184	7277728	42	18	6984153	7156927	42
19	6732276	7394353	41	19	6860300	7275732	41	19	6986234	7154895	41
20	6734427	7392394	40	20	6862416	7273736	40	20	6988315	7152863	40
21	6736577	7390435	39	21	6864532	7271740	39	21	6990396	7150830	39
22	6738727	7388475	38	22	6866647	7269743	38	22	6992476	7148796	38
23	6740876	7386515	37	23	6868761	7267745	37	23	6994555	7146762	37
24	6743024	7384553	36	24	6870875	7265747	36	24	6996633	7144727	36
25	6745172	7382592	35	25	6872988	7263748	35	25	6998711	7142691	35
26	6747319	7380629	34	26	6875101	7261748	34	26	7000789	7140655	34
27	6749466	7378666	33	27	6877213	7259748	33	27	7002866	7138618	33
28	6751612	7376703	32	28	6879325	7257747	32	28	7004942	7136581	32
29	6753757	7374738	31	29	6881435	7255746	31	29	7007018	7134543	31
30	6755902	7372773	30	30	6883546	7253744	30	30	7009093	7132504	30
31	6758046	7370808	29	31	6885655	7251741	29	31	7011167	7130465	29
32	6760190	7368842	28	32	6887765	7249738	28	32	7013241	7128426	28
33	6762333	7366875	27	33	6889873	7247734	27	33	7015314	7126385	27
34	6764476	7364908	26	34	6891981	7245729	26	34	7017387	7124344	26
35	6766618	7362940	25	35	6894089	7243724	25	35	7019459	7122303	25
36	6768760	7360971	24	36	6896195	7241719	24	36	7021531	7120260	24
37	6770901	7359002	23	37	6898302	7239712	23	37	7023601	7118218	23
38	6773041	7357032	22	38	6900407	7237705	22	38	7025672	7116174	22
39	6775181	7355061	21	39	6902512	7235698	21	39	7027741	7114130	21
40	6777320	7353090	20	40	6904617	7233690	20	40	7029811	7112086	20
41	6779459	7351118	19	41	6906721	7231681	19	41	7031879	7110041	19
42	6781597	7349146	18	42	6908824	7229671	18	42	7033947	7107995	18
43	6783734	7347173	17	43	6910927	7227661	17	43	7036014	7105948	17
44	6785871	7345199	16	44	6913029	7225651	16	44	7038081	7103901	16
45	6788007	7343225	15	45	6915131	7223640	15	45	7040147	7101854	15
46	6790143	7341250	14	46	6917232	7221628	14	46	7042213	7099806	14
47	6792278	7339275	13	47	6919332	7219615	13	47	7044278	7097757	13
48	6794413	7337299	12	48	6921432	7217602	12	48	7046342	7095707	12
49	6796547	7335322	11	49	6923531	7215589	11	49	7048406	7093657	11
50	6798681	7333345	10	50	6925630	7213574	10	50	7050469	7091607	10
51	6800813	7331367	9	51	6927728	7211559	9	51	7052532	7089556	9
52	6802946	7329388	8	52	6929825	7209544	8	52	7054594	7087504	8
53	6805078	7327409	7	53	6931922	7207528	7	53	7056655	7085451	7
54	6807209	7325429	6	54	6934018	7205511	6	54	7058716	7083398	6
55	6809339	7323449	5	55	6936114	7203494	5	55	7060776	7081345	5
56	6811469	7321467	4	56	6938209	7201476	4	56	7062835	7079291	4
57	6813599	7319486	3	57	6940304	7199457	3	57	7064894	7077236	3
58	6815728	7317503	2	58	6942398	7197438	2	58	7066953	7075180	2
59	6817856	7315521	1	59	6944491	7195418	1	59	7069011	7073124	1
60	6819984	7313537	0	60	6946584	7193398	0	60	7071068	7071068	0
'	Cosine	Sine	'	'	Cosine	Sine	'	'	Cosine	Sine	'

Deg. 47.   Deg. 46.   Deg. 45.

TANGENTS.

′	0°	1°	2°	3°	4°	5°	6°	′
0	0·0000000	0·0174551	0·0349208	0·0524078	0·0699268	0·0874887	0·1051042	60
1	·0002909	·0177400	·0352120	·0526995	·0702191	·0877818	·1053983	59
2	·0005818	·0180370	·0355033	·0529912	·0705115	·0880749	·1056925	58
3	·0008727	·0183280	·0357945	·0532829	·0708038	·0883681	·1059866	57
4	·0011636	·0186190	·0360858	·0535746	·0710961	·0886612	·1062808	56
5	·0014544	·0189100	·0363771	·0538663	·0713885	·0889544	·1065750	55
6	·0017453	·0192010	·0366683	·0541581	·0716809	·0892476	·1068692	54
7	·0020362	·0194920	·0369596	·0544498	·0719733	·0895408	·1071634	53
8	·0023271	·0197830	·0372509	·0547416	·0722657	·0898341	·1074576	52
9	·0026180	·0200740	·0375422	·0550333	·0725581	·0901273	·1077519	51
10	0·0029089	0·0203650	0·0378335	0·0553251	0·0728505	0·0904206	0·1080462	50
11	·0031998	·0206560	·0381248	·0556169	·0731430	·0907138	·1083405	49
12	·0034907	·0209470	·0384161	·0559087	·0734354	·0910071	·1086348	48
13	·0037816	·0212380	·0387074	·0562005	·0737279	·0913004	·1089291	47
14	·0040725	·0215291	·0389988	·0564923	·0740203	·0915938	·1092234	46
15	·0043634	·0218201	·0392901	·0567841	·0743128	·0918871	·1095178	45
16	·0046542	·0221111	·0395814	·0570759	·0746053	·0921804	·1098122	44
17	·0049451	·0224021	·0398728	·0573678	·0748979	·0924738	·1101066	43
18	·0052360	·0226932	·0401641	·0576596	·0751904	·0927672	·1104010	42
19	·0055269	·0229842	·0404555	·0579515	·0754829	·0930605	·1106955	41
20	0·0058178	0·0232753	0·0407469	0·0582434	0·0757755	0·0933540	0·1109899	40
21	·0061087	·0235663	·0410383	·0585352	·0760680	·0936474	·1112814	39
22	·0063996	·0238574	·0413296	·0588271	·0763606	·0939409	·1115789	38
23	·0066905	·0241484	·0416210	·0591190	·0766532	·0942344	·1118734	37
24	·0069814	·0244395	·0419124	·0594109	·0769458	·0945278	·1121680	36
25	·0072723	·0247305	·0422038	·0597029	·0772384	·0948213	·1124625	35
26	·0075632	·0250216	·0424952	·0599918	·0775311	·0951148	·1127571	34
27	·0078541	·0253127	·0427866	·0602867	·0778237	·0954084	·1130517	33
28	·0081450	·0256038	·0430781	·0605787	·0781164	·0957019	·1133463	32
29	·0084360	·0258948	·0433695	·0608706	·0784090	·0959955	·1136410	31
30	0·0087269	0·0261859	0·0436609	0·0611626	0·0787017	0·0962890	0·1139356	30
31	·0090178	·0264770	·0439524	·0614546	·0789944	·0965826	·1142303	29
32	·0093087	·0267681	·0442438	·0617466	·0792871	·0968763	·1145250	28
33	·0095996	·0270592	·0445353	·0620386	·0795798	·0971699	·1148197	27
34	·0098905	·0273503	·0448268	·0623306	·0798726	·0974635	·1151144	26
35	·0101814	·0276414	·0451183	·0626226	·0801653	·0977572	·1154092	25
36	·0104724	·0279325	·0454097	·0629117	·0804581	·0980509	·1157039	24
37	·0107633	·0282236	·0457012	·0632067	·0807509	·0983446	·1159987	23
38	·0110542	·0285148	·0459927	·0634988	·0810437	·0986383	·1162936	22
39	·0113451	·0288059	·0462842	·0637008	·0813305	·0989320	·1165884	21
40	0·0116361	0·0290970	0·0465757	0·0640829	0·0816293	0·0992257	0·1168832	20
41	·0119270	·0293882	·0468673	·0643750	·0819221	·0995194	·1171781	19
42	·0122179	·0296793	·0471588	·0646671	·0822150	·0998133	·1174730	18
43	·0125088	·0299705	·0474503	·0649592	·0825078	·1001071	·1177679	17
44	·0127998	·0302616	·0477419	·0652513	·0828007	·1004009	·1180628	16
45	·0130907	·0305528	·0480334	·0655435	·0830936	·1006947	·1183578	15
46	·0133817	·0308439	·0483250	·0658356	·0833865	·1009886	·1186528	14
47	·0136726	·0311351	·0486166	·0661278	·0836794	·1012824	·1189478	13
48	·0139635	·0314263	·0489082	·0664199	·0839723	·1015763	·1192428	12
49	·0142545	·0317174	·0491997	·0667121	·0842653	·1018702	·1195378	11
50	0·0145454	0·0320086	0·0494913	0·0670043	0·0845583	0·1021641	0·1198329	10
51	·0148364	·0322998	·0497829	·0672965	·0848512	·1024580	·1201279	9
52	·0151273	·0325910	·0500746	·0675887	·0851442	·1027520	·1204230	8
53	·0154183	·0328822	·0503662	·0678809	·0854372	·1030460	·1207182	7
54	·0157093	·0331734	·0506578	·0681732	·0857302	·1033399	·1210133	6
55	·0160002	·0334646	·0509495	·0684654	·0860233	·1036340	·1213085	5
56	·0162912	·0337558	·0512411	·0687577	·0863163	·1039280	·1216036	4
57	·0165821	·0340471	·0515328	·0690499	·0866094	·1042220	·1218988	3
58	·0168731	·0343383	·0518244	·0693422	·0869025	·1045161	·1221941	2
59	·0171641	·0346295	·0521161	·0696345	·0871956	·1048101	·1224893	1
60	0·0174551	0·0349208	0·0524078	0·0699268	0·0874887	0·1051042	0·1227846	0
′	89°	88°	87°	86°	85°	84°	83°	′

CO-TANGENTS.

TANGENTS.

′	7°	8°	9°	10°	11°	12°	13°	′
0	0·1227846	0·1405408	0·1583844	0·1763270	0·1943803	0·2125566	0·2308682	60
1	·1230798	·1408375	·1586826	·1766269	·1946822	·2128606	·2311746	59
2	·1233752	·1411342	·1589809	.1769269	·1949841	·2131647	·2314811	58
3	·1236705	·1414308	·1592791	·1772269	·1952861	·2134688	·2317876	57
4	·1239658	·1417276	·1595774	·1775270	·1955881	·2137730	·2320941	56
5	·1242612	·1420243	·1598757	·1778270	·1958901	·2140772	·2324007	55
6	·1245566	·1423211	·1601740	·1781271	·1961922	·2143814	·2327073	54
7	·1248520	·1426179	·1604724	·1784273	·1964943	·2146857	·2330140	53
8	·1251474	·1429147	·1607708	·1787274	·1967964	·2149900	·2333207	52
9	·1254429	·1432115	·1610692	·1790276	·1970986	·2152944	·2336274	51
10	0·1257384	0·1435084	0·1613677	0·1793279	0·1974008	0·2155988	0·2339342	50
11	·1260339	·1438053	·1616662	·1796281	·1977031	·2159032	·2342410	49
12	·1263294	·1441022	·1619647	·1799284	·1980053	·2162077	·2345479	48
13	·1266249	·1443991	·1622632	·1802287	·1983076	·2165122	·2348548	47
14	·1269205	·1446961	·1625618	·1805291	·1986100	·2168 67	·2351617	46
15	·1272161	·1449931	·1628603	·1808295	·1989124	·2171213	·2354687	45
16	·1275117	·1452901	·1631590	·1811299	·1992148	·2174259	·2357758	44
17	·1278073	·1455872	·1634576	·1814303	·1995172	·2177306	·2360829	43
18	·1281030	·1458842	·1637563	·1817308	·1998197	·2180353	·2363900	42
19	·1283986	·1461813	·1640550	·1820313	·2001222	·2183400	·2366971	41
20	0·1286943	0·1464784	0·1643537	0·1823319	0·2004248	0·2186448	0·2370044	40
21	·1289900	·1467756	·1646525	·1826324	·2007274	·2189496	·2373116	39
22	·1292858	·1470727	·1649513	·1829330	·2010300	·2192544	·2376189	38
23	·1295815	·1473699	·1652501	·1832337	·2013327	·2195593	·2379262	37
24	·1298773	1476672	·1655489	·1835343	·2016354	·2198643	·2382336	36
25	·1301731	·1479644	·1658478	·1838350	·2019381	·2201692	·2385410	35
26	·1304690	·1482617	·1661467	·1841358	·2022409	·2204742	·2388485	34
27	·1307648	·1485590	·1664456	·1844365	·2025437	·2207793	·2391560	33
28	·1310607	·1488563	·1667446	·1847373	·2028465	·2210844	·2394635	32
29	·1313566	·1491536	·1670436	·1850382	·2031494	·2213895	·2397711	31
30	0·1316525	0·1494510	0·1673426	0·1853390	0·2034523	0·2216947	0·2400788	30
31	·1319484	·1497484	·1676417	·1856399	·2037552	·2219999	·2403864	29
32	·1322444	·1500458	·1679407	·1859409	·2040582	·2223051	·2406942	28
33	·1325404	·1503433	·1682398	·1862418	·2043612	·2226104	·2410019	27
34	·1328364	·1506408	·1685390	·1865428	·2046643	·2229157	·2413097	26
35	·1331324	·1509383	·1688381	·1868439	·2049674	·2232211	·2416176	25
36	·1334285	·1512358	·1691373	·1871449	·2052705	·2235265	·2419255	24
37	·1337246	·1515333	·1694366	·1874460	·2055737	·2238319	·2422334	23
38	·1340207	·1518309	·1697358	·1877471	·2058769	·2241374	·2425414	22
39	·1343168	·1521285	·1700351	·1880483	·2061801	·2244429	·2428494	21
40	0·1346129	0·1524262	0·1703344	0·1883495	0·2064834	0·2247485	0·2431575	20
41	·1349091	·1527238	·1706338	·1886507	·2067867	·2250541	·2434656	19
42	·1352053	·1530215	·1709331	·1889520	·2070900	·2253597	·2437737	18
43	·1355015	·1533192	·1712325	·1892533	·2073934	·2256654	·2440819	17
44	·1357978	·1536170	·1715320	·1895546	·2076968	·2259711	·2443902	16
45	·1360940	·1539147	·1718314	·1898559	·2080003	·2262769	·2446984	15
46	·1363903	·1542125	·1721309	·1901573	·2083038	·2265827	·2450068	14
47	·1366866	·1545103	·1724304	·1904587	·2086073	·2268885	·2453151	13
48	·1369830	·1548082	·1727300	·1907602	·2089109	·2271944	·2456236	12
49	·1372793	·1551061	·1730296	·1910617	·2092145	·2275003	·2459320	11
50	0·1375757	0·1554040	0·1733292	0·1913632	0·2095181	0·2278063	0·2462405	10
51	·1378721	1557019	·1736288	·1916648	·2098218	·2281123	·2465491	9
52	·1381685	·1559998	·1739285	·1919664	·2101255	·2284184	·2468577	8
53	·1384650	·1562978	·1742282	·1922680	·2104293	·2287244	·2471663	7
54	·1387615	·1565958	·1745279	·1925696	·2107331	·2290306	·2474750	6
55	·1390580	·1568939	·1748277	·1928713	.2110369	·2293367	·2477837	5
56	·1393545	·1571919	·1751275	·1931731	·2113407	·2296429	·2480925	4
57	·1396510	·1574900	·1754273	·1934748	·2116446	·2299492	·2484013	3
58	·1399476	·1577881	·1757272	·1937766	·2119486	·2302555	·2487102	2
59	·1402442	·1580863	·1760271	·1940784	·2122525	·2305618	·2490191	1
60	0·1405408	0·1583844	0·1763270	0·1943803	0·2125566	0·2308682	0·2493280	0
′	82°	81°	80°	79°	78°	77°	76°	′

CO-TANGENTS.

TANGENTS.

'	14°	15°	16°	17°	18°	19°	20°	'
0	0·2493280	0·2679492	0·2867454	0·3057307	0·3249197	0·3443276	0·3639702	60
1	·2496370	·2682610	·2870602	·3060488	·3252413	·3446530	·3642997	59
2	·2499460	·2685728	·2873751	·3063670	·3255630	·3449785	·3646292	58
3	·2502551	·2688847	·2876900	·3066852	·3258848	·3453040	·3649588	57
4	·2505642	·2691067	·2880050	·3070034	·3262066	·3456296	·3652885	56
5	·2508734	·2695087	·2883201	·3073218	·3265284	3459553	·3656182	55
6	·2511826	·2698207	·2886352	·3076402	·3268504	·3462810	·3659480	54
7	·2514919	·2701328	·2889503	·3079586	·3271724	·3466068	·3662779	53
8	·2518012	·2704449	·2892655	·3082771	·3274944	·3469327	·3666079	52
9	·2521106	·2707571	·2895808	·3085957	·3278165	·3472586	·3669379	51
10	0·2524200	0·2710694	·2898961	0·3089143	0·3281387	0·3475846	0·3672680	50
11	·2527294	·2713817	·2902114	·3092330	·3284610	·3479107	·3675981	49
12	·2530389	·2716940	·2905269	·3095517	·3287833	·3482368	·3679284	48
13	·2533484	·2720064	·2908423	·3098705	·3291056	·3485630	·3682587	47
14	·2536580	·2723188	·2911578	·3101893	·3294281	·3488893	·3685890	46
15	·2539676	·2726313	·2914734	·3105083	·3297505	·3492156	·3689195	45
16	·2542773	·2729438	·2917890	·3108272	·3300731	·3495420	·3692500	44
17	·2545870	·2732564	·2921047	·3111462	·3303957	·3498685	·3695806	43
18	·2548968	·2735690	·2924205	·3114653	·3307184	·3501950	·3699112	42
19	·2552066	·2738817	·2927363	·3117845	·3310411	·3505216	·3702420	41
20	0·2555165	0·2741945	0·2930521	0·3121036	0·3313639	0·3508483	0·3705728	40
21	·2558264	·2745072	·2933680	·3124229	·3316868	·3511750	·3709036	39
22	·2561363	·2748201	·2936839	·3127422	·3320097	·3515018	·3712346	38
23	·2564463	·2751330	·2939999	·3130616	·3323327	·3518287	·3715656	37
24	·2567564	·2754459	·2943160	·3133810	·3326557	·3521556	·3718967	36
25	·2570664	·2757589	·2946321	·3137005	·3329788	·3524826	·3722278	35
26	·2573766	·2760719	·2949483	·3140200	·3333020	·3528096	·3725590	34
27	·2576868	·2763850	·2952645	·3143396	·3336252	·3531368	·3728903	33
28	·2579970	·2766981	·2955808	·3146593	·3339485	·3534640	·3732217	32
29	·2583073	·2770113	·2958971	·3149790	·3342719	·3537912	·3735532	31
30	0·2586176	0·2773245	0·2962135	0·3152988	0·3345953	0·3541186	0·3738847	30
31	·2589280	·2776378	·2965299	·3156186	·3349188	·3544460	·3742163	29
32	·2592384	·2779512	·2968464	·3159385	·3352424	·3547734	·3745479	28
33	·2595488	·2782646	·2971630	·3162585	·3355660	·3551010	·3748797	27
34	·2598593	·2785780	·2974796	·3165785	·3358896	·3554286	·3752115	26
35	·2601699	·2788915	·2977962	·3168986	·3362134	·3557562	·3755433	25
36	·2604805	·2792050	·2981129	·3172187	·3365372	·3560840	·3758753	24
37	·2607911	·2795186	·2984297	·3175389	·3368610	·3564118	·3762073	23
38	·2611018	·2798322	·2987465	·3178591	·3371850	·3567397	·3765394	22
39	·2614126	·2801459	·2990634	·3181794	·3375090	·3570676	·3768716	21
40	0·2617234	0·2804597	0·2993803	0·3184998	0·3378330	0·3573956	0·3772038	20
41	·2620342	·2807735	·2996973	·3188202	·3381571	·3577237	·3775361	19
42	·2623451	·2810873	·3000144	·3191407	·3384813	·3580518	·3778685	18
43	·2626560	·2814012	·3003315	·3194613	·3388056	·3583801	·3782010	17
44	·2629670	·2817152	·3006486	·3197819	·3391299	·3587083	·3785335	16
45	·2632780	·2820292	·3009658	·3201025	·3394543	·3590367	·3788661	15
46	·2635891	·2823432	·3012831	·3204232	·3397787	·3593651	·3791988	14
47	·2639002	·2826573	·3016004	·3207440	·3401032	·3596936	·3795315	13
48	·2642114	·2829715	·3019178	·3210649	·3404278	·3600222	·3798644	12
49	·2645226	·2832857	·3022352	·3213858	·3407524	·3603508	·3801973	11
50	0·2648339	0·2835999	0·3025527	0·3217067	0·3410771	0·3606795	0·3805302	10
51	·2651452	·2839143	·3028703	·3220278	·3414019	·3610082	·3808633	9
52	·2654566	·2842286	·3031879	·3223489	·3417267	·3613371	·3811964	8
53	·2657680	·2845430	·3035055	·3226700	·3420516	·3616660	·3815296	7
54	·2660794	·2848575	·3038232	·3229912	·3423765	·3619949	·3818629	6
55	·2663909	·2851720	·3041410	·3233125	·3427015	·3623240	·3821962	5
56	·2667025	·2854866	·3044588	·3236338	·3430266	·3626531	·3825296	4
57	·2670141	·2858012	·3047767	·3239552	·3433518	·3629823	·3828631	3
58	·2673257	·2861159	·3050946	·3242766	·3436770	·3633115	·3831967	2
59	·2676374	·2864306	·3054126	·3245981	·3440023	·3636408	·3835303	1
60	0·2679492	0·2867454	0·3057307	0·3249 97	0·3443276	0·3639702	0·3838640	0
'	75°	74°	73°	72°	71°	70°	69°	'

CO-TANGENTS.

TANGENTS.

′	21°	22°	23°	24°	25°	26°	27°	′
0	0·3838640	0·4040262	0 4244748	0·4452287	0·4663077	0·4877326	0·5095254	60
1	·3841978	·4043646	·4248182	·4455773	·4666618	·4880927	·5098919	59
2	·3845317	·4047031	·4251616	·4459260	·4670161	·4884530	·5102585	58
3	·3848656	·4050417	·4255051	·4462747	·4673705	·4888133	·5106252	57
4	·3851996	·4053804	·4258487	·4466236	·4677250	·4891737	·5109919	56
5	·3855337	·4057191	·4261924	·4469726	·4680796	·4895343	·5113588	55
6	·3858679	·4060579	·4265361	·4473216	·4684342	·4898949	·5117259	54
7	·3862021	·4063968	·4268800	·4476708	·4687890	·4902557	·5120930	53
8	·3865364	·4067358	·4272239	·4480200	·4691439	·4906166	·5124602	52
9	·3868708	·4070748	·4275680	·4483693	·4694988	·4909775	·5128275	51
10	0·3872053	0·4074139	0·4279121	0·4487187	0·4698539	0·4913386	0·5131950	50
11	·3875398	·4077531	·4282563	·4490682	·4702090	·4916997	·5135625	49
12	·3878744	·4080924	·4286005	·4494178	·4705643	·4920610	·5139302	48
13	·3882091	·4084318	·4289449	·4497675	·4709196	·4924224	·5142980	47
14	·3885439	·4087713	·4292894	·4501173	·4712751	·4927838	·5146658	46
15	·3888787	·4091108	·4296339	·4504672	·4716306	·4931454	·5150338	45
16	·3892136	·4094504	·4299785	·4508171	·4719863	·4935071	·5154019	44
17	·3895486	·4097901	·4303232	·4511672	·4723420	·4938689	·5157702	43
18	·3898837	·4101299	·4306680	·4515173	·4726978	·4942308	·5161385	42
19	·3902189	·4104697	·4310129	·4518676	·4730538	·4945928	·5165069	41
20	0·3905541	0·4108097	0·4313579	0·4522179	0·4734098	0·4949549	0·5168755	40
21	·3908894	·4111497	·4317030	·4525683	·4737659	·4953171	·5172441	39
22	·3912247	·4114898	·4320481	·4529188	·4741222	·4956795	·5176129	38
23	·3915602	·4118300	·4323933	·4532694	·4744785	·4960418	·5179818	37
24	·3918957	·4121703	·4327386	·4536201	·4748349	·4964043	·5183508	36
25	·3922313	·4125106	·4330840	·4539709	·4751914	·4967669	·5187199	35
26	·3925670	·4128510	·4334295	·4543218	·4755481	·4971297	·5190801	34
27	·3929027	·4131915	·4337751	·4546728	·4759048	·4974925	·5194584	33
28	·3932386	·4135321	·4341208	·4550238	·4762616	·4978554	·5198278	32
29	·3935745	·4138728	·4344665	·4553750	·4766185	·4982185	·5201974	31
30	0·3939105	0·4142136	0·4348124	0·4557263	0·4769755	0·4985816	0·5205671	30
31	·3942465	·4145544	·4351583	·4560776	·4773326	·4989449	·5209368	29
32	·3945827	·4148953	·4355043	·4564290	·4776899	·4993082	·5213067	28
33	·3949189	·4152363	·4358504	·4567806	·4780472	·4996717	·5216767	27
34	·3952552	·4155774	·4361966	·4571322	·4784046	·5000352	·5220468	26
35	·3955916	·4159186	·4365429	·4574839	·4787621	·5003989	·5224170	25
36	·3959280	·4162598	·4368893	·4578357	·4791197	·5007627	·5227874	24
37	·3962645	·4166012	·4372357	·4581877	·4794774	·5011266	·5231578	23
38	·3966011	·4169426	·4375823	·4585397	·4798352	·5014906	·5235284	22
39	·3969378	·4172841	·4379289	·4588918	·4801932	·5018547	·5238990	21
40	0·3972746	0·4176257	0·4382756	0·4592439	0·4805512	0·5022189	0·5242698	20
41	·3976114	·4179673	·4386224	·4595962	·4809093	·5025832	·5246407	19
42	·3979483	·4183091	·4389693	·4599486	·4812675	·5029476	·5250117	18
43	·3982853	·4186509	·4393163	·4603011	·4816258	·5033121	·5253829	17
44	·3986224	·4189928	·4396634	·4606537	·4819842	·5036768	·5257541	16
45	·3989595	·4193348	·4400105	·4610063	·4823427	·5040415	·5261255	15
46	·3992968	·4196769	·4403578	·4613591	·4827014	·5044063	·5264969	14
47	·3996341	·4200190	·4407051	·4617119	·4830601	·5047713	·5268685	13
48	·3999715	·4203613	·4410526	·4620649	·4834189	·5051363	·5272402	12
49	·4003089	·4207036	·4414001	·4624179	·4837778	·5055015	·5276120	11
50	0·4006465	0·4210460	0·4417477	0·4627710	0·4841368	0·5058668	0·5279839	10
51	·4009841	·4213885	·4420954	·4631243	·4844959	·5062322	·5283560	9
52	·4013218	·4217311	·4424432	·4634776	·4848552	·5065977	·5287281	8
53	·4016596	·4220738	·4427910	·4638310	·4852145	·5069633	·5291004	7
54	·4019974	·4224165	·4431390	·4641845	·4855739	·5073290	·5294727	6
55	·4023354	·4227594	·4434871	·4645382	·4859334	·5076948	·5298452	5
56	·4026734	·4231023	·4438352	·4648919	·4862931	·5080607	·5302178	4
57	·4030115	·4234453	·4441834	·4652457	·4866528	·5084267	·5305906	3
58	·4033496	·4237884	·4445118	·4655996	·4870126	·5087929	·5309634	2
59	·4036879	·4241316	·4448802	·4659536	·4873726	·5091591	·5313364	1
60	0·4040262	0·4244748	0·4452287	0·4663077	0·4877326	0·5095254	0·5317094	0
′	68°	67°	66°	65°	64°	63°	62°	′

CO-TANGENTS.

TANGENTS.

′	28°	29°	30°	31°	32°	33°	34°	′
0	0·5317094	·5543091	0·5773503	0·6008606	0·6248694	0·6494076	0·6745085	60
1	·5320826	·5546894	·5777382	·6012566	·6252739	·6498212	·6749318	59
2	·5324559	·5550698	·5781262	·6016527	·6256786	·6502350	·6753553	58
3	·5328293	·5554504	·5785144	·6020490	·6260834	·6506490	·6757790	57
4	·5332029	·5558311	·5789027	·6024454	·6264884	·6510631	·6762028	56
5	·5335765	·5562119	·5792912	·6028419	·6268935	·6514774	·6766268	55
6	·5339503	·5565929	·5796797	·6032386	·6272988	·6518918	·6770509	54
7	·5343242	·5569739	·5800684	·6036354	·6277042	·6523064	·6774752	53
8	·5346981	·5573551	·5804573	·6040323	·6281098	·6527211	·6778997	52
9	·5350723	·5577364	·5808462	·6044294	·6285155	·6531360	·6783243	51
10	0·5354465	0·5581179	0·5812353	0·6048266	0·6289214	0·6535511	0·6787492	50
11	·5358208	·5584994	·5816245	·6052240	·6293274	·6539663	·6791741	49
12	·5361953	·5588811	·5820139	·6056215	·6297336	·6543817	·6795993	48
13	·5365699	·5592629	·5824034	·6060192	·6301399	·6547972	·6800246	47
14	·5369446	·5596449	·5827930	·6064170	·6305164	·6552129	·6804501	46
15	·5373194	·5600269	·5831828	·6068149	·6309530	·6556287	·6808758	45
16	·5376943	·5604091	·5835726	·6072130	·6313598	·6560447	·6813016	44
17	·5380694	·5607914	·5839627	·6076112	·6317667	·6564609	·6817276	43
18	·5384445	·5611738	·5843528	·6080095	·6321738	·6568772	·6821537	42
19	·5388198	·5615564	·5847431	·6084080	·6325810	·6572937	·6825801	41
20	0·5391952	0·5619391	0·5851335	0·6088067	0·6329883	0·6577103	0·6830066	40
21	·5395707	·5623219	·5855241	·6092054	·6333959	·6581271	·6834333	39
22	·5399464	·5627048	·5859148	·6096043	·6338035	·6585441	·6838601	38
23	·5403221	·5630879	·5863056	·6100034	·6342113	·6589612	·6842871	37
24	·5406980	·5634710	·5866965	·6104026	·6346193	·6593785	·6847143	36
25	·5410740	·5638543	·5870876	·6108019	·6350274	·6597960	·6851416	35
26	·5414501	·5642378	·5874788	·6112014	·6354357	·6602136	·6855692	34
27	·5418263	·5646213	·5878702	·6116011	·6358441	·6606313	·6859969	33
28	·5422027	·5650050	·5882616	·6120008	·6362527	·6610492	·6864247	32
29	·5425791	·5653888	·5886533	·6124007	·6366614	·6614673	·6868528	31
30	0·5429557	0·5657728	0·5890450	0·6128008	0·6370703	0·6618856	0·6872810	30
31	·5433324	·5661568	·5894369	·6132010	·6374793	·6623040	·6877093	29
32	·5437092	·5665410	·5898289	·6136013	·6378885	·6627225	·6881379	28
33	·5440862	·5669254	·5902211	·6140018	·6382978	·6631413	·6885666	27
34	·5444632	·5673098	·5906134	·6144024	·6387073	·6635601	·6889955	26
35	·5448404	·5676944	·5910058	·6148032	·6391169	·6639792	·6894246	25
36	·5452177	·5680791	·5913984	·6152041	·6395267	·6643984	·6898538	24
37	·5455951	·5684639	·5917910	·6156052	·6399366	·6648178	·6902832	23
38	·5459727	·5688488	·5921839	·6160064	·6403467	·6652373	·6907128	22
39	·5463503	·5692339	·5925768	·6164077	·6407569	·6656570	·6911425	21
40	0·5467281	0·5696191	0·5929699	0·6168092	0·6411673	0·6660769	0·6915725	20
41	·5471060	·5700045	·5933632	·6172108	·6415779	·6664969	·6920026	19
42	·5474840	·5703899	·5937565	·6176126	·6419886	·6669171	·6924328	18
43	·5478621	·5707755	·5941501	·6180145	·6423994	·6673374	·6928633	17
44	·5482404	·5711612	·5945437	·6184166	·6428105	·6677580	·6932939	16
45	·5486188	·5715471	·5949375	·6188188	·6432216	·6681786	·6937247	15
46	·5489973	·5719331	·5953314	·6192211	·6436329	·6685995	·6941557	14
47	·5493759	·5723192	·5957255	·6196236	·6440444	·6690205	·6945868	13
48	·5497547	·5727054	·5961196	·6200263	·6444560	·6694417	·6950181	12
49	·5501335	·5730918	·5965140	·6204291	·6448678	·6698630	·6954496	11
50	0·5505125	0·5734783	·5969084	0·6208320	0·6452797	0·6702845	0·6958813	10
51	·5508916	·5738649	·5973030	·6212351	·6456918	·6707061	·6963131	9
52	·5512708	·5742516	·5976978	·6216383	·6461041	·6711280	·6967451	8
53	·5516502	·5746385	·5980926	·6220417	·6465165	·6715500	·6971773	7
54	·5520297	·5750255	·5984877	·6224452	·6469290	·6719721	·6976097	6
55	·5524093	·5754126	·5988828	·6228488	·6473417	·6723944	·6980422	5
56	·5527890	·5757999	·5992781	·6232527	·6477546	·6728169	·6984749	4
57	·5531688	·5761873	·5996735	·6236566	·6481676	·6732306	·6989078	3
58	·5535488	·5765748	·6000691	·6240607	·6485808	·6736624	·6993409	2
59	·5539288	·5769625	·6004648	·6244650	·6489941	·6740854	·6997741	1
60	0·5543091	0·5773503	0·6008606	0·6248694	0·6494076	0·6745085	0·7002075	0
′	61°	60°	59°	58°	57°	56°	55°	′

CO-TANGENTS.

TANGENTS.

′	35°	36°	37°	38°	39°	40°	41°	′
0	0·7002075	0·7265425	0·7535541	0·7812856	0·8097840	0·8390996	0·8692867	60
1	·7006411	·7269871	·7540102	·7817542	·8102658	·8395955	·8697976	59
2	·7010749	·7274318	·7544666	·7822229	·8107478	·8400915	·8703087	58
3	·7015089	·7278767	·7549232	·7826919	·8112300	·8405878	·8708200	57
4	·7019430	·7283218	·7553799	·7831611	·8117124	·8410844	·8713316	56
5	·7023773	·7287671	·7558369	·7836305	·8121951	·8415812	·8718435	55
6	·7028118	·7292125	·7562941	·7841002	·8126780	·8420782	·8723556	54
7	·7032464	·7296582	·7567514	·7845700	·8131611	·8425755	·8728680	53
8	·7036813	·7301041	·7572090	·7850400	·8136444	·8430730	·8733806	52
9	·7041163	·7305501	·7576668	·7855103	·8141280	·8435708	·8738935	51
10	0·7045515	0·7309963	0·7581248	0·7859808	0·8146118	0·8440688	0·8744067	50
11	·7049869	·7314428	·7585829	·7864515	·8150958	·8445670	·8749201	49
12	·7054224	·7318894	·7590413	·7869224	·8155801	·8450655	·8754338	48
13	·7058581	·7323362	·7594999	·7873935	·8160646	·8455643	·8759478	47
14	·7062940	·7327832	·7599587	·7878649	·8165493	·8460633	·8764620	46
15	·7067301	·7332303	·7604177	·7883364	·8170343	·8465625	·8769765	45
16	·7071664	·7336777	·7608769	·7888082	·8175195	·8470620	·8774912	44
17	·7076028	·7341253	·7613363	·7892802	·8180049	·8475617	·8780062	43
18	·7080395	·7345730	·7617959	·7897524	·8184905	·8480617	·8785215	42
19	·7084763	·7350210	·7622557	·7902248	·8189764	·8485619	·8790370	41
20	0·7089133	0·7354691	0·7627157	0·7906975	0·8194625	0·8490624	0·8795528	40
21	·7093504	·7359174	·7631759	·7911703	·8199488	·8495631	·8800688	39
22	·7097878	·7363362	·7636363	·7916434	·8204354	·8500640	·8805852	38
23	·7102253	·7368147	·7640969	·7921167	·8209222	·8505653	·8811017	37
24	·7106630	·7372636	·7645577	·7925902	·8214093	·8510667	·8816186	36
25	·7111009	·7377127	·7650188	·7930640	·8218965	·8515684	·8821357	35
26	·7115390	·7381620	·7654800	·7935379	·8223840	·8520704	·8826531	34
27	·7119772	·7386115	·7659414	·7940121	·8228718	·8525726	·8831707	33
28	·7124157	·7390611	·7664031	·7944865	·8233597	·8530750	·8836886	32
29	·7128543	·7395110	·7668649	·7949611	·8238479	·8535777	·8842068	31
30	0·7132931	0·7399611	0·7673270	0·7954359	0·8243364	0·8540807	0·8847253	30
31	·7137320	·7404113	·7677893	·7959110	·8248251	·8545839	·8852440	29
32	·7141712	·7408618	·7682517	·7963862	·8253140	·8550873	·8857630	28
33	·7146106	·7413124	·7687144	·7968617	·8258031	·8555910	·8862822	27
34	·7150501	·7417633	·7691773	·7973374	·8262925	·8560950	·8868017	26
35	·7154898	·7422143	·7696404	·7978134	·8267821	·8565992	·8873215	25
36	·7159297	·7426655	·7701037	·7982895	·8272719	·8571037	·8878415	24
37	·7163698	·7431170	·7705672	·7987659	·8277620	·8576084	·8883619	23
38	·7168100	·7435686	·7710309	·7992425	·8282523	·8581133	·8888825	22
39	·7172505	·7440204	·7714948	·7997193	·8287429	·8586185	·8894033	21
40	0·7176911	0·7444724	0·7719589	0·8001963	0·8292337	0·8591240	0·8899244	20
41	·7181319	·7449246	·7724233	·8006736	·8297247	·8596297	·8904458	19
42	·7185729	·7453770	·7728878	·8011511	·8302160	·8601357	·8909675	18
43	·7190141	·7458296	·7733526	·8016288	·8307075	·8606419	·8914894	17
44	·7194554	·7462824	·7738176	·8021067	·8311992	·8611484	·8920116	16
45	·7198970	·7467354	·7742827	·8025849	·8316912	·8616551	·8925341	15
46	·7203387	·7471886	·7747481	·8030632	·8321834	·8621621	·8930569	14
47	·7207806	·7476420	·7752137	·8035418	·8326759	·8626694	·8935799	13
48	·7212227	·7480956	·7756795	·8040206	·8331686	·8631768	·8941032	12
49	·7216650	·7485494	·7761455	·8044997	·8336615	·8636846	·8946268	11
50	0·7221075	0·7490033	0·7766118	0·8049790	0·8341547	0·8641926	0·8951506	10
51	·7225502	·7494575	·7770782	·8054584	·8346481	·8647009	·8956747	9
52	·7229930	·7499119	·7775448	·8059382	·8351418	·8652094	·8961991	8
53	·7234361	·7503665	·7780117	·8064181	·8356357	·8657181	·8967238	7
54	·7238793	·7508212	·7784788	·8068983	·8361208	·8662272	·8972487	6
55	·7243227	·7512762	·7789460	·8073787	·8366242	·8667365	·8977739	5
56	·7247663	·7517314	·7794135	·8078593	·8371188	·8672460	·8982994	4
57	·7252101	·7521867	·7798812	·8083401	·8376136	·8677558	·8988251	3
58	·7256540	·7526423	·7803492	·8088212	·8381087	·8682659	·8993512	2
59	·7260982	·7530981	·7808173	·8093025	·8386041	·8687762	·8998775	1
60	0·7265425	0·7535541	0·7812856	0·8097840	0·8390996	0·8692867	0·9004040	0
′	54°	53°	52°	51°	50°	49°	48°	′

CO-TANGENTS.

TANGENTS.

′	42°	43°	44°	45°	46°	47°	48°	′
0	0·9004040	0·9325151	0·9656888	1·0000000	1·0355303	1·0723687	1·1106125	60
1	·9009309	·9330591	·9662511	1·0005819	1 0361333	1·0729943	1·1112624	59
2	·9014580	·9336034	·9668137	1·0011642	1·0367367	1·0736203	1·1119127	58
3	·9019854	·9341479	·9673767	1·0017409	1·0373404	1·0742467	1·11·5635	57
4	·9025131	·9346928	·9679399	1·0023298	1·0379445	1·0748734	1·1132146	56
5	·9030411	·9352380	·9685035	1·0029131	1·0385489	1·0755006	1·1138662	55
6	·9035693	·9357834	·9690674	1·0034968	1·0391538	1·0761282	1·1145182	54
7	·9040979	·9363292	·9696316	1·0040807	1·0397589	1·0767561	1·1151706	53
8	·9046267	·9368753	·9701962	1·0046651	1·0403645	1·0773845	1·1158235	52
9	·9051557	·9374216	·9707610	1·0052497	1·0409704	1·0780132	1·1164768	51
10	0·9056851	0·9379683	0·9713262	1·0058348	1·0415767	1·0786423	1·1171305	50
11	·9062147	·9385153	.9718917	1·0064201	1·0421833	1·0792718	1·1177846	49
12	·9067446	·9390625	.9724575	1·0070058	1·0427904	1·099018	1·1184391	48
13	·9072748	·9396101	.9730236	1·0075918	1·0433977	1·0805321	1·1190941	47
14	·9078053	·9401579	.9735901	1·0081782	1·0440055	1·0811628	1·1197495	46
15	·9083360	·9407061	.9741569	1·0087649	1·0446136	1·0817939	1·1204053	45
16	·9088671	·9412545	·9747240	1·0093520	1·0452221	1·0824254	1·1210616	44
17	·9093984	·9418033	·9752914	1·0099394	1·0458310	1·0830573	1·1217183	43
18	·9099300	·9423523	·9758591	1·0105272	1·0464402	1·0836896	1·1223754	42
19	·9104619	·9429017	·9764272	1·0111153	1·0470498	1·0843223	1·1230329	41
20	0·9109940	0·9434513	0·9769956	1·0117038	1·0476598	1·0849554	1·1236909	40
21	·9115265	·9440013	·9775643	1·0122925	1·0482702	1·0855889	1·1243493	39
22	·9120592	·9445516	·9781333	1·0128817	1·0488809	1·0862228	1·1250081	38
23	·9125922	·9451021	·9787027	1·0134712	1·0494920	1·0868571	1·1256674	37
24	·9131255	·9456530	·9792724	1·0140610	1·0501034	1·0874918	1·1263271	36
25	·9136591	·9462042	·9798424	1·0146512	1·0507153	1·0881269	1·1269872	35
26	·9141929	·9467556	·9804127	1·0152418	1·0513275	1·0887624	1·1276478	34
27	·9147270	·9473074	·9809833	1·0158326	1·0519401	1·0893984	1·1283088	33
28	·9152615	·9478595	·9815543	1·0164239	1·0525531	1·0900347	1·1289702	32
29	·9157962	·9484119	·9821256	1·0170155	1·0531664	1·0906714	1·1296321	31
30	0·9163312	0·9489646	0·9826973	1·0176074	1·0537801	1·0913085	1·1302944	30
31	·9168665	·9495176	·9832692	1·0181997	1·0543942	1·0919460	1·1309571	29
32	·9174020	·9500709	·9838415	1·0187923	1·0550087	1·0925840	1·1316203	28
33	·9179379	·9506245	·9844141	1·0193853	1·0556235	1·0932223	1·1322839	27
34	·9184740	·9511784	·9849871	1·0199786	1 0562388	1·0938610	1·1329479	26
35	·9190104	·9517326	·9855603	1·0205723	1·0568544	1·0945002	1·1336124	25
36	·9195471	·9522871	·9861339	1·0211664	1·0574704	1·0951397	1·1342773	24
37	·9200841	·9528420	·9867079	1·0217608	1·0580867	1·0957797	1·1349427	23
38	·9206214	·9533971	·9872821	1·0223555	1·0587035	1·0964201	1·1356085	22
39	·9211590	·9539526	·9878567	1·0229506	1·0593206	1·0970609	1·1362747	21
40	0·9216969	0·9545083	0·9884316	1·0235461	1·0599381	1·0977020	1·1369414	20
41	·9222350	·9550644	·9890069	1·0241419	1·0605560	1·0983436	1·1376086	19
42	·9227734	·9556208	·9895825	1·0247381	1.0611742	1·0989857	1·1382761	18
43	·9233122	·9561774	·9901584	1·0253346	1·0617929	1·0996281	1·1389441	17
44	·9238512	·9567344	·9907346	1·0259315	1·0624119	1·1002709	1·1396126	16
45	·9243905	·9572917	·9913112	1·0265287	1·0630313	1·1009141	1·1402815	15
46	·9249301	·9578494	·9918881	1·0271263	1·0636511	1·1015578	1·1409508	14
47	·9254700	·9584073	·9924654	1·0277243	1·0642713	1·1022019	1·1416206	13
48	·9260102	·9589655	·9930429	1·0283226	1·0648918	1·1028463	1·1422908	12
49	·9265506	·9595241	·9936208	1·0289212	1·0655128	1·1034912	1·1429615	11
50	0·9270914	0·9600829	0·9941991	1·0295203	1·0661341	1·1041365	1·1436326	10
51	·9276324	·9606421	·9947777	1·0301196	1·0667558	1·1047823	1·1443041	9
52	·9281738	·9612016	·9953566	1·0307194	1·0673779	1·1054284	1·1449762	8
53	·9287154	·9617614	·9959358	1·0313195	1·0680004	1·1060750	1·1456486	7
54	·9292573	·9623215	·9965154	1·0319199	1·0686233	1·1067219	1·1463215	6
55	·9297996	·9628819	·9970953	1·0325208	1·0692466	1·1073693	1·1469949	5
56	·9303421	·9634427	·9976756	1·0331220	1·0698702	1·1080171	1·1476687	4
57	·9308849	·9640037	·9982562	1·0337235	1·0704943	1·1086653	1·1483429	3
58	·9314280	·9645651	·9988371	1·0343254	1·0711187	1·1093140	1·1490176	2
59	·9319714	·9651268	·9994184	1·0349277	1·0717435	1·1099630	1·1496928	1
60	0·9325151	0·9656888	1·0000000	1·0355303	1·0723687	1·1106125	1·1503684	0
′	47°	46°	45°	44°	43°	42°	41°	′

CO-TANGENTS.

TANGENTS.

′	49°	50°	51°	52°	53°	54°	55°	′
0	1·1503684	1·1917536	1·2348972	1·2799416	1·3270448	1·3763819	1·4281480	60
1	1·1510445	1·1924579	1·2356319	1·2807094	1·3278483	1·3772242	1·4290326	59
2	1·1517210	1·1931626	1·2363672	1·2814776	1·3286524	1·3780672	1·4299178	58
3	1·1523979	1·1938679	1·2371030	1·2822465	1·3294571	1·3789108	1·4308039	57
4	1·1530754	1·1945736	1·2378393	1·2830160	1·3302624	1·3797551	1·4316906	56
5	1·1537532	1·1952799	1·2385762	1·2837860	1·3310684	1·3806001	1·4325781	55
6	1·1544316	1·1959866	1·2393136	1·2845566	1·3318750	1·3814458	1·4334664	54
7	1·1551104	1·1966938	1·2400515	1·2853277	1·3326822	1·3822922	1·4343554	53
8	1·1557896	1·1974015	1·2407900	1·2860995	1·3334900	1·3831392	1·4352451	52
9	1·1564693	1·1981097	1·2415290	1·2868718	1·3342984	1·3839869	1·4361356	51
10	1·1571495	1·1988184	1·2422685	1·2876447	1·3351075	1·3848353	1·4370268	50
11	1·1578301	1·1995276	1·2430086	1·2884182	1·3359172	1·3856844	1·4379187	49
12	1·1585112	1·2002373	1·2437492	1·2891922	1·3367276	1·3865342	1·4388114	48
13	1·1591927	1·2009475	1·2444903	1·2899669	1·3375386	1·3873847	1·4397049	47
14	1·1598747	1·2016581	1·2452320	1·2907421	1·3383502	1·3882358	1·4405991	46
15	1·1605571	1·2023693	1·2459742	1·2915179	1·3391624	1·3890876	1·4414940	45
16	1·1612400	1·2030810	1·2467169	1·2922943	1·3399753	1·3899401	1·4423897	44
17	1·1619234	1·2037932	1·2474602	1·2930713	1·3407888	1·3907934	1·4432862	43
18	1·1626073	1·2045058	1·2482040	1·2938488	1·3416029	1·3916473	1·4441834	42
19	1·1632916	1·2052190	1·2489484	1·2946270	1·3424177	1·3925019	1·4450814	41
20	1·1639763	1·2059327	1·2496933	1·2954057	1·3432331	1·3933571	1·4459801	40
21	1·1646615	1·2066468	1·2504388	1·2961850	1·3440492	1·3942131	1·4468796	39
22	1·1653472	1·2073615	1·2511848	1·2969649	1·3448658	1·3950698	1·4477798	38
23	1·1660334	1·2080767	1·2519313	1·2977454	1·3456832	1·3959272	1·4486808	37
24	1·1667200	1·2087924	1·2526784	1·2985265	1·3465011	1·3967852	1·4495825	36
25	1·1674071	1·2095085	1·2534260	1·2993081	1·3473198	1·3976440	1·4504850	35
26	1·1680947	1·2102252	1·2541742	1·3000904	1·3481390	1·3985034	1·4513883	34
27	1·1687827	1·2109424	1·2549229	1·3008733	1·3489589	1·3993636	1·4522923	33
28	1·1694712	1·2116601	1·2556721	1·3016567	1·3497794	1·4002245	1·4531971	32
29	1·1701601	1·2123783	1·2564219	1·3024407	1·3506006	1·4010860	1·4541027	31
30	1·1708496	1·2130970	1·2571723	1·3032254	1·3514224	1·4019483	1·4550090	30
31	1·1715395	1·2138162	1·2579232	1·3040106	1·3522449	1·4028113	1·4559161	29
32	1·1722298	1·2145359	1·2586747	1·3047964	1·3530680	1·4036749	1·4568240	28
33	1·1729207	1·2152562	1·2594267	1·3055828	1·3538918	1·4045393	1·4577326	27
34	1·1736120	1·2159769	1·2601792	1·3063699	1·3547162	1·4054044	1·4586420	26
35	1·1743038	1·2166982	1·2609323	1·3071575	1·3555413	1·4062702	1·4595522	25
36	1·1749960	1·2174199	1·2616860	1·3079457	1·3563670	1·4071367	1·4604632	24
37	1·1756888	1·2181422	1·2624402	1·3087345	1·3571934	1·4080039	1·4613749	23
38	1·1763820	1·2188650	1·2631950	1·3095239	1·3580204	1·4088718	1·4622874	22
39	1·1770756	1·2195883	1·2639503	1·3103140	1·3588481	1·4097405	1·4632007	21
40	1·1777698	1·2203121	1·2647062	1·3111046	1·3596764	1·4106098	1·4641147	20
41	1·1784644	1·2210364	1·2654626	1·3118958	1·3605054	1·4114799	1·4650296	19
42	1·1791595	1·2217613	1·2662196	1·3126876	1·3613350	1·4123506	1·4659452	18
43	1·1798551	1·2224866	1·2669772	1·3134801	1·3621653	1·4132221	1·4668616	17
44	1·1805512	1·2232125	1·2677353	1·3142731	1·3629963	1·4140943	1·4677788	16
45	1·1812477	1·2239389	1·2684940	1·3150668	1·3638279	1·4149673	1·4686967	15
46	1·1819447	1·2246658	1·2692532	1·3158610	1·3646602	1·4158409	1·4696155	14
47	1·1826422	1·2253932	1·2700130	1·3166559	1·3654931	1·4167153	1·4705350	13
48	1·1833402	1·2261211	1·2707733	1·3174513	1·3663267	1·4175904	1·4714553	12
49	1·1840387	1·2268496	1·2715342	1·3182474	1·3671610	1·4184662	1·4723764	11
50	1·1847376	1·2275786	1·2722957	1·3190441	1·3679959	1·4193427	1·4732983	10
51	1·1854370	1·2283081	1·2730578	1·3198414	1·3688315	1·4202200	1·4742210	9
52	1·1861369	1·2290381	1·2738204	1·3206393	1·3696678	1·4210979	1·4751445	8
53	1·1868373	1·2297687	1·2745835	1·3214379	1·3705047	1·4219766	1·4760688	7
54	1·1875382	1·2304997	1·2753473	1·3222370	1·3713423	1·4228561	1·4769938	6
55	1·1882395	1·2312313	1·2761116	1·3230368	1·3721806	1·4237362	1·4779197	5
56	1·1889414	1·2319634	1·2768765	1·3238371	1·3730195	1·4246171	1·4788463	4
57	1·1896437	1·2326961	1·2776419	1·3246381	1·3738591	1·4254988	1·4797738	3
58	1·1903465	1·2334292	1·2784079	1·3254397	1·3746994	1·4263811	1·4807021	2
59	1·1910498	1·2341629	1·2791745	1·3262420	1·3755403	1·4272642	1·4816311	1
60	1·1917536	1·2348972	1·2799416	1·3270448	1·3763819	1·4281480	1·4825610	0
′	40°	39°	38°	37°	36°	35°	34°	′

CO-TANGENTS.

TANGENTS.

′	56°	57°	58°	59°	60°	61°	62°	′
0	1·4825610	1·5398650	1·6003345	1·6642795	1·7320508	1·8040478	1·8807265	60
1	1·4834916	1·5408460	1·6013709	1 6653766	1·7332149	1·8052860	1·8820470	59
2	1·4844231	1·5418280	1·6024082	1· 6664748	1·7343803	1·8065256	1·8833690	58
3	1·4853554	1·5428108	1·6034465	1·6675741	1·7355468	1·8077664	1·8846924	57
4	1·4862884	1·5437946	1·6044858	1·6686744	1·7367144	1·8090086	1·8860172	56
5	1·4872223	1·5447792	1·6055260	1·6697758	1·7378833	1·8102521	1·8873436	55
6	1·4881570	1·5457647	1·6065672	1·6708782	1·7390533	1·8114969	1·8886713	54
7	1·4890925	1·5467510	1·6076094	1·6719818	1·7402245	1·8127430	1·8900006	53
8	1·4900288	1·5477383	1·6086525	1·6730864	1·7413969	1·8139904	1·8913313	52
9	1·4909659	1·5487264	1·6096966	1·6741921	1·7425705	1·8152391	1·8926635	51
10	1·4919039	1·5497155	1·6107417	1·6752988	1·7437453	1·8164892	1·8939971	50
11	1·4928426	1·5507054	1·6117878	1·6764067	1·7449213	1·8177405	1·8953322	49
12	1·4937822	1·5516963	1·6128349	1·6775156	1·7460984	1·8189932	1·8966688	48
13	1·4947225	1·5526880	1·6138829	1·6786256	1·7472768	1·8202473	1·8980068	47
14	1·4956637	1·5536806	1·6149320	1·6797367	1·7484564	1·8215026	1·8993464	46
15	1·4966058	1·5546741	1·6159820	1·6808489	1·7496371	1·8227593	1·9006874	45
16	1·4975486	1·5556685	1·6170330	1·6819621	1·7508191	1·8240173	1·9020299	44
17	1·4984923	1·5566639	1·6180850	1·6830765	1·7520023	1·8252767	1·9033738	43
18	1·4994367	1·5576601	1·6191380	1·6841919	1·7531866	1·8265374	1·9047193	42
19	1·5003821	1·5586572	1·6201920	1·6853085	1·7543722	1·8277994	1·9060663	41
20	1·5013282	1·5596552	1·6212469	1·6864261	1·7555590	1·8290628	1·9074147	40
21	1·5022751	1·5606542	1·6223029	1·6875449	1·7567470	1·8303275	1·9087647	39
22	1·5032229	1·5616540	1·6233599	1·6886647	1·7579362	1·8315936	1·9101162	38
23	1·5041716	1·5626548	1·6244178	1·6897856	1·7591267	1·8328610	1·9114691	37
24	1·5051210	1·5636564	1·6254768	1·6909077	1·7603183	1·8341297	1·9128236	36
25	1·5060713	1·5646590	1·6265368	1·6920308	1·7615112	1·8353999	1·9141795	35
26	1·5070224	1·5656625	1·6275977	1·6931550	1·7627053	1·8366713	1·9155370	34
27	1·5079743	1·5666669	1·6286597	1·6942804	1·7639007	1·8379442	1·9168960	33
28	1·5089271	1·5676722	1·6297227	1·6954069	1·7650972	1·8392184	1·9182565	32
29	1·5098807	1·5686784	1·6307867	1·6965344	1·7662950	1·8404940	1·9196186	31
30	1·5108352	1·5696856	1·6318517	1·6976631	1·7674940	1·8417709	1·9209821	30
31	1·5117905	1·5706936	1·6329177	1·6987929	1·7686943	1·8430492	1·9223472	29
32	1·5127466	1·5717026	1·6339847	1·6999238	1·7698958	1·8443289	1·9237138	28
33	1·5137036	1·5727126	1·6350528	1·7010559	1·7710985	1·8456099	1·9250819	27
34	1·5146614	1·5737234	1·6361218	1·7021890	1·7723024	1·8468923	1·9264516	26
35	1·5156201	1·5747352	1·6371919	1·7033233	1·7735076	1·8481761	1·9278228	25
36	1·5165796	1·5757479	1·6382630	1·7044587	1·7747141	1·8494613	1·9291956	24
37	1·5175400	1·5767615	1·6393351	1·7055953	1·7759218	1·8507479	1·9305699	23
38	1·5185012	1·5777760	1·6404082	1·7067329	1·7771307	1·8520358	1·9319457	22
39	1·5194632	1·5787915	1·6414824	1·7078717	1·7783409	1·8533252	1·9333231	21
40	1·5204261	1·5798079	1·6425576	1·7090116	1·7795524	1·8546159	1·9347020	20
41	1·5213899	1·5808253	1·6436338	1·7101527	1·7807651	1·8559080	1·9360825	19
42	1·5223545	1·5818436	1·6447111	1·7112949	1·7819790	1·8572015	1·9374645	18
43	1·5233200	1·5828628	1·6457893	1·7124382	1·7831943	1·8584965	1·9388481	17
44	1·5242863	1·5838830	1·6468687	1·7135827	1·7844107	1·8597928	1·9402333	16
45	1·5252535	1·5849041	1·6479490	1·7147283	1·7856285	1·8610905	1·9416200	15
46	1·5262215	1·5859261	1·6490304	1·7158751	1·7868475	1·8623896	1·9430083	14
47	1·5271904	1·5869491	1·6501128	1·7170230	1·7880678	1·8636902	1·9443981	13
48	1·5281602	1·5879731	1·6511963	1·7181720	1·7892893	1·8649921	1·9457896	12
49	1·5291308	1·5889979	1·6522808	1·7193222	1·7905121	1·8662955	1·9471826	11
50	1·5301023	1·5900238	1·6533663	1·7204736	1·7917362	1·8676003	1·9485772	10
51	1·5310746	1·5910505	1·6544529	1·7216261	1·7929616	1·8689065	1·9499733	9
52	1·5320479	1·5920783	1·6555405	1·7227797	1·7941883	1·8702141	1·9513711	8
53	1·5330219	1·5931070	1·6566292	1·7239346	1·7954162	1·8715231	1·9527704	7
54	1·5339969	1·5941366	1·6577189	1·7250905	1·7966454	1·8728336	1·9541713	6
55	1·5349727	1·5951672	1·6588097	1·7262477	1·7978759	1·8741455	1·9555739	5
56	1·5359494	1·5961987	1·6599016	1·7274060	1·7991077	1·8754588	1·9569780	4
57	1·5369270	1·5972312	1·6609945	1·7285654	1·8003408	1·8767736	1·9583837	3
58	1·5379054	1·5982647	1·6620884	1·7297260	1·8015751	1·8780898	1·9597910	2
59	1·5388848	1·5992991	1·6631834	1·7308878	1·8028108	1·8794074	1·9612000	1
60	1·5398650	1·6003345	1·6642795	1·7320508	1·8040478	1·8807265	1·9626105	0
′	33°	32°	31°	30°	29°	28°	27°	′

CO-TANGENTS.

TANGENTS.

′	63°	64°	65°	66°	67°	68°	69°	′
0	1·9626105	2·0503038	2·1445069	2·2460368	2·3558524	2·4750869	2·6050891	60
1	1·9640427	2·0518185	2·1461366	2·2477962	2·3577590	2·4771612	2·6073558	59
2	1·9654364	2·0533349	2·1477683	2·2495580	2·3596683	2·4792386	2·6096259	58
3	1·9668518	2·0548531	2·1494021	2·2513221	2·3615801	2·4813190	2·6118995	57
4	1·9682688	2·0563732	2·1510378	2·2530885	2·3634946	2·4834023	2·6141766	56
5	1·9696874	2·0578950	2·1526757	2·2548572	2·3654118	2·4854887	2·6164571	55
6	1·9711077	2·0594187	2 1543156	2·2566283	2·3673316	2·4875781	2·6187411	54
7	1·9725296	2·0609442	2·1559575	2·2584016	2·3692540	2·4896706	2·6210286	53
8	1·9739531	2·0624716	2·1576015	2·2601773	2·3711791	2·4917660	2·6233196	52
9	1·9753782	2·0640008	2·1592476	2·2619554	2 3731068	2·4938645	2·6256141	51
10	1·9768050	2·0655318	2·1608958	2·2637357	2·3750372	2·4959661	2·6279121	50
11	1·9782334	2·0670646	2·1625460	2·2655184	2·3769703	2·4980707	2·6302136	49
12	1·9796635	2·0685994	2·1641983	2·2673035	2·3789060	2·5001784	2·6325186	48
13	1·9810952	2·0701359	2·1658527	2·2690909	2·3808444	2·5022891	2·6348271	47
14	1·9825286	2·0716743	2·1675091	2·2708807	2·3827855	2·5044029	2·6371392	46
15	1·9839636	2·0732146	2·1691677	2·2726729	2·3847293	2·5065198	2·6394549	45
16	1 9854003	2·0747567	2·1708283	2·2744674	2·3866758	2·5086398	2·6417741	44
17	1·9868387	2·0763007	2·1724911	2·2762643	2·3886250	2·5107629	2·6440969	43
18	1·9882787	2·0778465	2·1741559	2·2780636	2·3905769	2·5128890	2·6464232	42
19	1·9897204	2·0793942	2·1758229	2·2798653	2·3925316	2·5150183	2·6487531	41
20	1·9911637	2·0809438	2·1774920	2·2816693	2·3944889	2·5171507	2·6510867	40
21	1·9926087	2·0824953	2 1791631	2·2834758	2·3964490	2·5192863	2·6534238	39
22	1·9940554	2·0840487	2·1808364	2·2852846	2·3984118	2·5214249	2·6557645	38
23	1·9955038	2·0855039	2·1825119	2·2870959	2·4003774	2·5235667	2·6581089	37
24	1·9969539	2·0871610	2·1841894	2·2889096	2·4023457	2·5257117	2·6604569	36
25	1·9984056	2·0887200	2·1858691	2·2907257	2·4043168	2·5278598	2·6628085	35
26	1·9998590	2·0902809	2·1875510	2·2925442	2·4062906	2·5300111	2·6651638	34
27	2·0013142	2·0918437	2·1892349	2·2943651	2·4082672	2·5321655	2·6675227	33
28	2·0027710	2·0934085	2·1909210	2·2961885	2·4102465	2·5343231	2·6698853	32
29	2·0042295	2·0949751	2·1926093	2·2980143	2·4122286	2·5364839	2·6722516	31
30	2·0056897	2·0965436	2·1942997	2·2998425	2·4142136	2·5386479	2·6746215	30
31	2·0071516	2·0981140	2·1959923	2·3016732	2·4162013	2·5408151	2·6769951	29
32	2·0086153	2·0996864	2·1976871	2·3035064	2·4181918	2·5429855	2·6793725	28
33	2 0100806	2·1012607	2·1993840	2·3053420	2·4201851	2·5451591	2·6817535	27
34	2·0115477	2·1028369	2·2010831	2·3071801	2·4221812	2·5473359	2·6841383	26
35	2·0130164	2·1044150	2·2027843	2·3090206	2·4241801	2·5495160	2·6865267	25
36	2·0144869	2·1059951	2·2044878	2·3108637	2·4261819	2·5516992	2·6889190	24
37	2·0159592	2·1075771	2·2061934	2·3127092	2·4281864	2·5538858	2·6913149	23
38	2·0174331	2·1091611	2·2079012	2·3145571	2·4301938	2·5560756	2·6937147	22
39	2·0189088	2·1107470	2·2096112	2·3164076	2·4322041	2·5582686	2·6961181	21
40	2·0203862	2·1123348	2·2113234	2·3182606	2·4342172	2·5604649	2·6985254	20
41	2·0218654	2·1139246	2·2130379	2·3201160	2·4362331	2·5626645	2·7009364	19
42	2·0233462	2·1155164	2·2147545	2·3219740	2·4382519	2·5648674	2·7033513	18
43	2·0248289	2·1171101	2·2164733	2·3238345	2·4402736	2·5670735	2·7057699	17
44	2·0263133	2·1187057	2·2181944	2·3256975	2·4422982	2·5692830	2·7081923	16
45	2·0277994	2·1203034	2·2199177	2·3275630	2·4443256	2·5714957	2·7106186	15
46	2·0292873	2·1219030	2·2216432	2·3294311	2·4463559	2·5737118	2·7130487	14
47	2·0307769	2·1235046	2·2233709	2·3313017	2·4483891	2·5759312	2·7154826	13
48	2·0322683	2·1251082	2·2251009	2·3331748	2·4504252	2·5781539	2·7179204	12
49	2·0337615	2·1267137	2·2268331	2·3350505	2·4524642	2·5803800	2·7203620	11
50	2·0352565	2·1283213	2·2285676	2·3369287	2·4545061	2·5826094	2·7228076	10
51	2 0367532	2·1299308	2·2303043	2·3388095	2·4565510	2·5848421	2·7252569	9
52	2·0382517	2·1315423	2·2320433	2·3406928	2·4585987	2·5870782	2·7277102	8
53	2·0397519	2·1331559	2·2337845	2·3425787	2·4606494	2·5893177	2·7301674	7
54	2·0412540	2·1347714	2·2355280	2·3444672	2·4627030	2·5915606	2·7326284	6
55	2·0427578	2·1363890	2·2372738	2 3463582	2·4647596	2·5938068	2·7350934	5
56	2·0442634	2·1380085	2·2390218	2·3482519	2·4668191	2·5960564	2·7375623	4
57	2·0457708	2·1396301	2·2407721	2·3501481	2·4688816	2·5983095	2·7400352	3
58	2·0472800	2·1412537	2·2425247	2·3520469	2·4709470	2·6005659	2·7425120	2
59	2·0487910	2·1428793	2·2442796	2·3539483	2·4730155	2·6028258	2·7449927	1
60	2·0503038	2·1445069	2·2460368	2·3558524	2·4750869	2·6050891	2·7474774	0
′	26°	25°	24°	23°	22°	21°	20°	′

CO-TANGENTS.

TANGENTS.

'	70°	71°	72°	73°	74°	75°	76°	'
0	2·7474774	2·9042109	3·0776835	3·2708526	3·4874144	3·7320508	4·0107809	60
1	2·7499661	2·9069576	3·0807325	3·2742588	3·4912470	3·7363980	4·0157570	59
2	2·7524588	2·9097089	3·0837869	3·2776715	3·4950874	3·7407546	4·0207446	58
3	2·7549554	2·9124649	3·0868468	3·2810907	3·4989356	3·7451207	4·0257440	57
4	2·7574561	2·9152256	3·0899122	3·2845164	3·5027916	3·7494963	4·0307550	56
5	2·7599608	2·9179909	3·0929831	3·2879487	3·5066555	3·7538815	4·0357779	55
6	2·7624695	2·9207610	3·0960596	3·2913876	3·5105273	3·7582763	4·0408125	54
7	2·7649822	2·9235358	3·0991416	3·2948330	3·5144070	3·7626807	4·0458590	53
8	2·7674990	2·9263152	3·1022291	3·2982851	3·5182946	3·7670947	4·0509174	52
9	2·7700199	2·9290995	3·1053223	3·3017438	3·5221902	3·7715185	4·0559877	51
10	2·7725448	2·9318885	3·1084210	3·3052091	3·5260938	3·7759519	4·0610700	50
11	2·7750738	2·9346822	3·1115254	3·3086811	3·5300054	3·7803951	4·0661643	49
12	2·7776069	2·9374807	3·1146353	3·3121598	3·5339251	3·7848481	4·0712707	48
13	2·7801440	2·9402840	3·1177509	3·3156452	3·5378528	3·7893109	4·0763892	47
14	2·7826853	2·9430921	3·1208722	3·3191373	3·5417886	3·7937835	4·0815199	46
15	2·7852307	2·9459050	3·1239991	3·3226362	3·5457325	3·7982661	4·0866627	45
16	2·7877802	2·9487227	3·1271317	3·3261419	3·5496846	3·8027585	4·0918178	44
17	2·7903339	2·9515453	3·1302701	3·3296543	3·5536449	3·8072609	4·0969852	43
18	2·7928917	2·9543727	3·1334141	3·3331736	3·5576133	3·8117733	4·1021649	42
19	2·7954537	2·9572050	3·1365639	3·3366997	3·5615900	3·8162957	4·1073569	41
20	2·7980198	2·9600422	3·1397194	3·3402326	3·5655749	3·8208281	4·1125614	40
21	2·8005901	2·9628842	3·1428807	3·3437724	3·5695681	3·8253707	4·1177784	39
22	2·8031646	2·9657312	3·1460478	3·3473191	3·5735696	3·8299233	4·1230079	38
23	2·8057433	2·9685831	3·1492207	3·3508728	3·5775794	3·8344861	4·1282499	37
24	2·8083263	2·9714399	3·1523994	3·3544333	3·5815975	3·8390591	4·1335046	36
25	2·8109134	2·9743016	3·1555840	3·3580008	3·5856241	3·8436424	4·1387719	35
26	2·8135048	2·9771683	3·1587744	3·3615753	3·5896590	3·8482358	4·1440519	34
27	2·8161004	2·9800400	3·1619706	3·3651568	3·5937024	3·8528396	4·1493446	33
28	2·8187003	2·9829167	3·1651728	3·3687453	3·5977543	3·8574537	4·1546501	32
29	2·8213045	2·9857983	3·1683808	3·3723408	3·6018146	3·8620782	4·1599685	31
30	2·8239129	2·9886850	3·1715948	3·3759434	3·6058835	3·8667131	4·1652998	30
31	2·8265256	2·9915766	3·1748147	3·3795531	3·6099609	3·8713584	4·1706440	29
32	2·8291426	2·9944734	3·1780406	3·3831699	3·6140469	3·8760142	4·1760011	28
33	2·8317639	2·9973751	3·1812724	3·3867938	3·6181415	3·8806805	4·1813713	27
34	2·8343896	3·0002820	3·1845102	3·3904249	3·6222447	3·8853574	4·1867546	26
35	2·8370196	3·0031939	3·1877540	3·3940631	3·6263566	3·8900448	4·1921510	25
36	2·8396539	3·0061109	3·1910039	3·3977085	3·6304771	3·8947429	4·1975606	24
37	2·8422926	3·0090330	3·1942598	3·4013612	3·6346064	3·8994517	4·2029835	23
38	2·8449356	3·0119603	3·1975217	3·4050210	3·6387444	3·9041710	4·2084196	22
39	2·8475831	3·0148926	3·2007897	3·4086882	3·6428911	3·9089011	4·2138690	21
40	2·8502349	3·0178301	3·2040638	3·4123626	3·6470467	3·9136420	4·2193318	20
41	2·8528911	3·0207728	3·2073440	3·4160443	3·6512111	3·9183937	4·2248080	19
42	2·8555517	3·0237207	3·2106304	3·4197333	3·6553844	3·9231563	4·2302977	18
43	2·8582158	3·0266737	3·2139228	3·4234297	3·6595665	3·9279297	4·2358009	17
44	2·8608863	3·0296320	3·2172215	3·4271334	3·6637575	3·9327141	4·2413177	16
45	2·8635602	3·0325954	3·2205263	3·4308446	3·6679575	3·9375092	4·2468482	15
46	2·8662386	3·0355641	3·2238373	3·4345631	3·6721665	3·9423157	4·2523923	14
47	2·8689215	3·0385381	3·2271546	3·4382891	3·6763845	3·9471331	4·2579501	13
48	2·8716088	3·0415173	3·2304780	3·4420226	3·6806115	3·9519615	4·2635218	12
49	2·8743007	3·0445018	3·2338078	3·4457635	3·6848475	3·9568011	4·2691072	11
50	2·8769970	3·0474915	3·2371438	3·4495120	3·6890927	3·9616518	4·2747066	10
51	2·8796979	3·0504866	3·2404860	3·4532679	3·6933469	3·9665137	4·2803199	9
52	2·8824033	3·0534870	3·2438346	3·4570315	3·6976104	3·9713868	4·2859472	8
53	2·8851132	3·0564928	3·2471895	3·4608026	3·7018830	3·9762712	4·2915885	7
54	2·8878277	3·0595038	3·2505508	3·4645813	3·7061648	3·9811669	4·2972440	6
55	2·8905467	3·0625203	3·2539184	3·4683676	3·7104558	3·9860739	4·3029136	5
56	2·8932704	3·0655421	3·2572924	3·4721616	3·7147561	3·9909924	4·3085974	4
57	2·8959986	3·0685694	3·2606728	3·4759632	3·7190658	3·9959223	4·3142955	3
58	2·8987314	3·0716020	3·2640596	3·4797726	3·7233847	4·0008636	4·3200079	2
59	2·9014688	3·0746400	3·2674529	3·4835896	3·7277131	4·0058165	4·3257347	1
60	2·9042109	3·0776835	3·2708526	3·4874144	3·7320508	4·0107809	4·3314759	0
'	19°	18°	17°	16°	15°	14°	13°	'

CO-TANGENTS.

TANGENTS.

′	77°	78°	79°	30°	81°	82°	83°	′
0	4·3314759	4·7046301	5·1445540	5·6712818	6·3137515	7·1153697	8·1443464	60
1	4·3372316	4·7113686	5·1525557	5·6809446	6·3256601	7·1301190	8·1639786	59
2	4·3430018	4·7181256	5·1605813	5·6906394	6·3376126	7·1455308	8·1837041	58
3	4·3487866	4·7249012	5·1686311	5·7003663	6·3496092	7·1607056	8·2035239	57
4	4·3545861	4·7316954	5·1767051	5·7101256	6·3616502	7·1759437	8·2234384	56
5	4·3604003	4·7385083	5 1848035	5·7199173	6·3737359	7·1912456	8·2434485	55
6	4·3662293	4·7453401	5·1929264	5·7297416	6·3858665	7·2066116	8·2635547	54
7	4·3720731	4·7521907	5·2010738	5·7395988	6·3980422	7·2220422	8·2837579	53
8	4·3779317	4·7590603	5·2092459	5·7494889	6·4102633	7·2375378	8·3040586	52
9	4·3838054	4·7659490	5·2174428	5·7594122	6·4225301	7·2530987	8·3244577	51
10	4·3896940	4·7728568	5·2256647	5·7693688	6·4348428	7·2687255	8·3449558	50
11	4·3955977	4·7797837	5·2339116	5·7793588	6·4472017	7·2844184	8·3655536	49
12	4·4015164	4·7867300	5·2421836	5·7893825	6·4596070	7·3001780	8·3862519	48
13	4·4074504	4·7936957	5·2504809	5·7994400	6·4720591	7·3160047	8·4070515	47
14	4·4133996	4·8006808	5·2588035	5·8095315	6·4845581	7·3318089	8·4279531	46
15	4·4193641	4·8076854	5·2671517	5·8190572	6·4971043	7·3478610	8·4489573	45
16	4·4253439	4·8147096	5·2755255	5·8298172	6·5096981	7·3638916	8·4700651	44
17	4·4313392	4·8217536	5·2839251	5·8400117	6·5223396	7·3799909	8·4912772	43
18	4·4373500	4·8288174	5·2923505	5·8502410	6·5350293	7·3961595	8·5125943	42
19	4·4433762	4·8359010	5·3008018	5·8605051	6·5477672	7·4123978	8·5340172	41
20	4·4494181	4·8430045	5·3092793	5·8708042	6·5605538	7·4287064	8·5555468	40
21	4·4554756	4·8501282	5·3177830	5·8811386	6·5733892	7·4450855	8·5771838	39
22	4·4615489	4·8572719	5·3263131	5·8915084	6·5862739	7·4615357	8·5989290	38
23	4·4676379	4·8644359	5·3348696	5·9019138	6·5992080	7·4780576	8·6207833	37
24	4·4737428	4·8716201	5·3434527	5·9123550	6·6121919	7·4946514	8·6427475	36
25	4·4798636	4·8788248	5·3520626	5·9228322	6·6252258	7·5113178	8·6648223	35
26	4·4860004	4·8860409	5·3606993	5·9333455	6·6383100	7·5280571	8·6870088	34
27	4·4921532	4·8932956	5·3693630	5·9438952	6·6514449	7·5448699	8·7093077	33
28	4·4983221	4·9005620	5·3780538	5·9544815	6·6646307	7·5617567	8·7317198	32
29	4·5045072	4·9078491	5·3867718	5·9651045	6·6778677	7·5787179	8·7542461	31
30	4·5107085	4·9151570	5·3955172	5·9757644	6·6911502	7·5957541	8·7768874	30
31	4·5169261	4·9224859	5·4042901	5·9864614	6·7044966	7·6128657	8·7996446	29
32	4·5231601	4·9298358	5·4130906	5·9971957	6·7178891	7·6300533	8·8225186	28
33	4·5294105	4·9372068	5·4219188	6·0079676	6·7313341	7·6473174	8·8455103	27
34	4·5356773	4·9445990	5·4307750	6·0187772	6·7448318	7·6646584	8·8686200	26
35	4·5419608	4·9520125	5·4396592	6·0296247	6·7583826	7·6820769	8·8918505	25
36	4·5482608	4·9594474	5·4485715	6·0405103	6·7719867	7·6995735	8·9152009	24
37	4·5545776	4·9669037	5·4575121	6·0514343	6·7856446	7·7171486	8·9386726	23
38	4·5609111	4·9743817	5·4664812	6·0623967	6·7993565	7·7348028	8·9622668	22
39	4·5672615	4·9818813	5·4754788	6·0733979	6·8131227	7·7525366	8·9859843	21
40	4·5736287	4·9894027	5·4845052	6·0844381	6·8269437	7·7703506	9·0098261	20
41	4·5800129	4·9969459	5·4935604	6·0955174	6·8408196	7·7882453	9·0337933	19
42	4·5864141	5·0045111	5·5026446	6·1066360	6·8547508	7·8062212	9·0578867	18
43	4·5928325	5·0120984	5·5117579	6·1177943	6·8687378	7·8242790	9·0821074	17
44	4·5992680	5·0197078	5·5209005	6·1289923	6·8827807	7·8424191	9·1064564	16
45	4·6057207	5·0273395	5·5300724	6·1402303	6·8968799	7·8606423	9·1309348	15
46	4·6121908	5·0349935	5·5392740	6·1515085	6·9110359	7·8789489	9·1555436	14
47	4·6186783	5·0426700	5·5485052	6·1628272	6·9252489	7·8973396	9·1802838	13
48	4·6251832	5·0503690	5·5577663	6·1741865	6·9395192	7·9158151	9·2051564	12
49	4·6317056	5·0580907	5·5670574	6·1855867	6·9538473	7·9343758	9·2301627	11
50	4·6382457	5·0658352	5·5763786	6·1970279	6·9682335	7·9530224	9·2553035	10
51	4·6448034	5·0736025	5·5857302	6·2085106	6·9826781	7·9717555	9·2805802	9
52	4·6513788	5·0813928	5·5951121	6·2200347	6·9971806	7·9905756	9·3059936	8
53	4·6579721	5·0892061	5·6045247	6·2316007	7·0117441	8·0094835	9·3315450	7
54	4·6645832	5·0970426	5·6139680	6·2432086	7·0263662	8·0284796	9·3572355	6
55	4·6712124	5·1049024	5·6234421	6·2548588	7·0410482	8·0475647	9·3830663	5
56	4·6778595	5·1127855	5·6329474	6·2665515	7·0557905	8·0667394	9·4090384	4
57	4·6845248	5·1206921	5·6424838	6·2782868	7·0705934	8·0860042	9·4351531	3
58	4·6912083	5·1286224	5·6520516	6·2900651	7·0854573	8·1053599	9·4614116	2
59	4·6979100	5·1365763	5·6616509	6·3018866	7·1003826	8·1248071	9·4878149	1
60	4·7046301	5·1445540	5·6712818	6·3137515	7·1153697	8·1443464	9·5143645	0
′	12°	11°	10°	9°	8°	7°	6°	′

CO-TANGENTS.

GG

TANGENTS.

′	84°	85°	86°	87°	88°	89°	′
0	9·5143645	11·430052	14·300666	19·081137	28·636253	57·289962	60
1	9·5410613	11·468474	14·360696	19·187930	28·877089	58·261174	59
2	9·5679068	11·507154	14·421230	19·295922	29·122005	59·265872	58
3	9·5949022	11·546093	14·482273	19·405133	29·371106	60·305820	57
4	9·6220486	11·585294	14·543833	19·515584	29·624499	61·382905	56
5	9·6493475	11·624761	14·605916	19·627296	29·882299	62·499154	55
6	9·6768000	11·664495	14·668529	19·740291	30·144619	63·656741	54
7	9·7044075	11·704500	14·731679	19·854591	30·411580	64·858008	53
8	9·7321713	11·744779	14·795372	19·970219	30·683307	66·105473	52
9	9·7600927	11·785333	14·859616	20·087199	30·959928	67·401854	51
10	9·7881732	11·826167	14·924417	20·205553	31·241577	68·750087	50
11	9·8164140	11·867282	14·989784	20·325308	31·528392	70·153346	49
12	9·8448166	11·908682	15·055723	20·446486	31·820516	71·615070	48
13	9·8733823	11·950370	15·122242	20·569115	32·118099	73·138991	47
14	9·9021125	11·992349	15·189349	20·693220	32·421295	74·729165	46
15	9·9310088	12·034622	15·257052	20·818828	32·730264	76·390009	45
16	9·9600724	12·077192	15·325358	20·945966	33·045173	78·126342	44
17	9·9893050	12·120062	15·394276	21·074664	33·366194	79·943430	43
18	10·018708	12·163236	15·463814	21·204949	33·693509	81·847041	42
19	10·048283	12·206716	15·533981	21·336851	34·027303	83·843507	41
20	10·078031	12·250505	15·604784	21·470401	34·367771	85·939791	40
21	10·107954	12·294609	15·676233	21·605630	34·715115	88·143572	39
22	10·138054	12·339028	15·748337	21·742569	35·069546	90·463336	38
23	10·168332	12·383768	15·821105	21·881251	35·431282	92·908487	37
24	10·198789	12·428831	15·894545	22·021710	35·800553	95·489475	36
25	10·229428	12·474221	15·968667	22·163980	36·177596	98·217943	35
26	10·260249	12·510942	16·043482	22·308097	36·562509	101·10690	34
27	10·291255	12·565997	16·118998	22·454096	36·956001	104·17094	33
28	10·322447	12·612390	16·195225	22·602015	37·357892	107·42648	32
29	10·353827	12·659125	16·272174	22·751892	37·768613	110·89205	31
30	10·385397	12·706205	16·349855	22·903766	38·188459	114·58865	30
31	10·417158	12·753634	16·428279	23·057677	38·617718	118·54018	29
32	10·449112	12·801417	16·507456	23·213666	39·056771	122·77396	28
33	10·481261	12·849557	16·587396	23·371777	39·505895	127·32134	27
34	10·513607	12·898058	16·668112	23·532052	39·965460	132·21851	26
35	10·546151	12·946924	16·749614	23·694537	40·435837	137·50745	25
36	10·578895	12·996160	16·831915	23·859277	40·917412	143·23712	24
37	10·611841	13·045769	16·915025	24·026320	41·410588	149·46502	23
38	10·644992	13·095757	16·998957	24·195714	41·915790	156·25908	22
39	10·678348	13·146127	17·083724	24·367509	42·433464	163·70019	21
40	10·711913	13·196883	17·169337	24·541758	42·964077	171·88540	20
41	10·745687	13·248031	17·255809	24·718512	43·508122	180·93220	19
42	10·779673	13·299574	17·343155	24·897826	44·066113	190·98419	18
43	10·813872	13·351518	17·431385	25·079757	44·638596	202·21875	17
44	10·848288	13·403867	17·520516	25·264361	45·226141	214·85762	16
45	10·882921	13·456625	17·610559	25·451700	45·829351	229·18166	15
46	10·917775	13·509799	17·701529	25·641832	46·448862	245·55198	14
47	10·952850	13·563391	17·793442	25·834823	47·085343	264·44080	13
48	10·988150	13·617409	17·886310	26·030736	47·739501	286·47773	12
49	11·023676	13·671856	17·980150	26·229638	48·412084	312·52137	11
50	11·059431	13·726738	18·074977	26·431600	49·103881	343·77371	10
51	11·095416	13·782060	18·170807	26·636690	49·815726	381·97099	9
52	11·131635	13·837827	18·267654	26·844984	50·548506	429·71757	8
53	11·168089	13·894045	18·365537	27·056557	51·303157	491·10600	7
54	11·204780	13·950719	18·464471	27·271486	52·080673	572·95721	6
55	11·241712	14·007856	18·564473	27·489853	52·882109	687·54887	5
56	11·278885	14·065459	18·665562	27·711740	53·708587	859·43630	4
57	11·316304	14·123536	18·767754	27·937233	54·561300	1145·9153	3
58	11·353970	14·182092	18·871068	28·166422	55·441517	1718·8732	2
59	11·391885	14·241134	18·975523	28·399397	56·350590	3437·7467	1
60	11·430052	14·300666	19·081137	28·636253	57·289962	Infinite.	0
′	5°	4°	3°	2°	1°	0°	′

CO-TANGENTS.

SECANTS.

′	0°	1°	2°	3°	4°	5°	6°	′
0	1.0000000	1·0001523	1·0006095	1·0013723	1·0024419	1·0038198	1·0055083	60
1	1·0000000	1·0001574	1·0006198	1·0013877	1·0024623	1·0038454	1·0055391	59
2	1·0000002	1·0001627	1·0006300	1·0014030	1·0024829	1·0038711	1·0055699	58
3	1·0000004	1·0001679	1·0006404	1·0014185	1·0025035	1·0038969	1·0056009	57
4	1·0000007	1·0001733	1·0006509	1·0014341	1·0025241	1·0039227	1·0056319	56
5	1·0000011	1·0001788	1·0006614	1·0014497	1·0025449	1·0039486	1·0056631	55
6	1·0000015	1·0001843	1·0006721	1·0014655	1·0025658	1·0039747	1·0056943	54
7	1·0000021	1·0001900	1·0006828	1·0014813	1·0025867	1·0040008	1·0057256	53
8	1·0000027	1·0001957	1·0006936	1·0014972	1·0026078	1·0040270	1·0057570	52
9	1·0000034	1·0002015	1·0007045	1·0015132	1·0026289	1·0040533	1·0057885	51
10	1·0000042	1·0002073	1·0007154	1·0015293	1·0026501	1·0040796	1·0058200	50
11	1·0000051	1·0002133	1·0007265	1·0015454	1·0026714	1·0041061	1·0058517	49
12	1·0000061	1·0002194	1·0007376	1·0015617	1·0026928	1·0041326	1·0058834	48
13	1·0000072	1·0002255	1·0007489	1·0015780	1·0027142	1·0041592	1·0059153	47
14	1·0000083	1·0002317	1·0007602	1·0015944	1·0027358	1·0041859	1·0059472	46
15	1·0000095	1·0002380	1·0007716	1·0016109	1·0027574	1·0042127	1·0059792	45
16	1·0000108	1·0002444	1·0007830	1·0016275	1·0027791	1·0042396	1·0060113	44
17	1·0000122	1·0002509	1·0007916	1·0016442	1·0028009	1·0042666	1·0060435	43
18	1·0000137	1·0002575	1·0008063	1·0016609	1·0028228	1·0042937	1·0060757	42
19	1·0000153	1·0002641	1·0008180	1·0016778	1·0028448	1·0043208	1·0061081	41
20	1·0000169	1·0002708	1·0008298	1·0016947	1·0028669	1·0043480	1·0061405	40
21	1·0000187	1·0002776	1·0008417	1·0017117	1·0028890	1·0043753	1·0061731	39
22	1·0000205	1·0002845	1·0008537	1·0017288	1·0029112	1·0044028	1·0062057	38
23	1·0000224	1·0002915	1·0008658	1·0017460	1·0029336	1·0044302	1·0062384	37
24	1·0000244	1·0002986	1·0008779	1·0017633	1·0029560	1·0044578	1·0062712	36
25	1·0000264	1·0003058	1·0008902	1·0017806	1·0029785	1·0044855	1·0063040	35
26	1·0000286	1·0003130	1·0009025	1·0017981	1·0030010	1·0045132	1·0063370	34
27	1·0000308	1·0003203	1·0009149	1·0018156	1·0030237	1·0045411	1·0063701	33
28	1·0000332	1·0003277	1·0009274	1·0018332	1·0030464	1·0045690	1·0064032	32
29	1·0000356	1·0003352	1·0009400	1·0018509	1·0030693	1·0045970	1·0064364	31
30	1·0000381	1·0003428	1·0009527	1·0018687	1·0030922	1·0046251	1·0064697	30
31	1·0000407	1·0003505	1·0009654	1·0018866	1·0031152	1·0046533	1·0065031	29
32	1·0000433	1·0003582	1·0009783	1·0019045	1·0031383	1·0046815	1·0065366	28
33	1·0000461	1·0003660	1·0009912	1·0019225	1·0031615	1·0047099	1·0065702	27
34	1·0000489	1·0003739	1·0010042	1·0019407	1·0031847	1·0047383	1·0066039	26
35	1·0000518	1·0003820	1·0010173	1·0019589	1·0032081	1·0047669	1·0066376	25
36	1·0000548	1·0003900	1·0010305	1·0019772	1·0032315	1·0047955	1·0066714	24
37	1·0000579	1·0003982	1·0010438	1·0019956	1·0032551	1·0048242	1·0067054	23
38	1·0000611	1·0004065	1·0010571	1·0020140	1·0032787	1·0048530	1·0067394	22
39	1·0000644	1·0004148	1·0010705	1·0020326	1·0033024	1·0048819	1·0067735	21
40	1·0000677	1·0004232	1·0010841	1·0020512	1·0033261	1·0049108	1·0068077	20
41	1·0000711	1·0004317	1·0010977	1·0020699	1·0033500	1·0049399	1·0068419	19
42	1·0000746	1·0004403	1·0011114	1·0020887	1·0033740	1·0049690	1·0068763	18
43	1·0000782	1·0004490	1·0011251	1·0021076	1·0033980	1·0049982	1·0069108	17
44	1·0000819	1·0004578	1·0011390	1·0021266	1·0034221	1·0050275	1·0069453	16
45	1·0000857	1·0004666	1·0011529	1·0021457	1·0034463	1·0050569	1·0069799	15
46	1·0000895	1·0004756	1·0011670	1·0021648	1·0034706	1·0050864	1·0070146	14
47	1·0000935	1·0004846	1·0011811	1·0021841	1·0034950	1·0051160	1·0070494	13
48	1·0000975	1·0004937	1·0011953	1·0022034	1·0035195	1·0051456	1·0070843	12
49	1·0001016	1·0005029	1·0012096	1·0022228	1·0035440	1·0051754	1·0071193	11
50	1·0001058	1·0005121	1·0012239	1·0022423	1·0035687	1·0052052	1·0071544	10
51	1·0001101	1·0005215	1·0012384	1·0022619	1·0035934	1·0052351	1·0071895	9
52	1·0001144	1·0005309	1·0012529	1·0022815	1·0036182	1·0052651	1·0072248	8
53	1·0001189	1·0005405	1·0012676	1·0023013	1·0036431	1·0052952	1·0072601	7
54	1·0001234	1·0005501	1·0012823	1·0023211	1·0036681	1·0053254	1·0072955	6
55	1·0001280	1·0005598	1·0012971	1·0023410	1·0036932	1·0053557	1·0073310	5
56	1·0001327	1·0005666	1·0013120	1·0023610	1·0037183	1·0053860	1·0073666	4
57	1·0001375	1·0005794	1·0013269	1·0023811	1·0037436	1·0054164	1·0074023	3
58	1·0001423	1·0005894	1·0013420	1·0024013	1·0037689	1·0054470	1·0074380	2
59	1·0001473	1·0005994	1·0013571	1·0024216	1·0037943	1·0054776	1·0074739	1
60	1·0001523	1·0006095	1·0013723	1·0024419	1·0038198	1·0055083	1·0075098	0
′	89°	88°	87°	86°	85°	84°	83°	′

CO-SECANTS.

GG*

SECANTS.

′	7°	8°	9°	10°	11°	12°	13°	′
0	1·0075098	1·0098276	1·0124651	1·0154266	1·0187167	1·0223406	1·0263041	60
1	1·0075459	1·0098689	1·0125118	1·0154787	1·0187743	1·0224039	1 0263731	59
2	1·0075820	1·0099103	1·0125586	1·0155310	1·0188321	1·0224672	1·0264421	58
3	1·0076182	1·0099518	1·0126055	1·0155833	1·0188899	1·0225307	1·0265113	57
4	1·0076545	1·0099934	1·0126524	1·0156357	1·0189478	1·0225942	1·0265806	56
5	1·0076908	1 010035 I	1·0126995	1·0156882	1 0190059	1·0226578	1·0266499	55
6	1·0077273	1·0100769	1·0127466	1·0157408	1·0190640	1·0227216	1·0267194	54
7	1·0077639	1·0101187	1·0127939	1·0157934	1·0191222	1·0227854	1·0267889	53
8	1·0078005	1·0101607	1·0128412	1·0158462	1·0191805	1·0228493	1·0268586	52
9	1·0078372	1·0102027	1·0128886	1·0158991	1·0192389	1·0229133	1·0269283	51
10	1·0078741	1·0102449	1·0129361	1·0159520	1·0192973	1·0229774	1·0269982	50
11	1·0079110	1·0102871	1·0129837	1·0160050	1·0193559	1·0230416	1·0270681	49
12	1·0079480	1·0103294	1·0130314	1·0160582	1·0194146	1·0231059	1·0271381	48
13	1·0079851	1·0103718	1·0130791	1·0161114	1·0194734	1·0231703	1·0272082	47
14	1·0080222	1·0104143	1·0131270	1·0161647	1·0195322	1·0232348	1·0272785	46
15	1·0080595	1·0104568	1·0131750	1·0162181	1·0195912	1·0232994	1·0273488	45
16	1·0080968	1·0104995	1·0132230	1·0162716	1·0196502	1·0233641	1·0274192	44
17	1·0081343	1·0105422	1·0132711	1·0163252	1·0197093	1·0234288	1·0274897	43
18	1·0081718	1 0105851	1·0133194	1·0163789	1·0197686	1·0234937	1·0275603	42
19	1·0082094	1·0106280	1·0133677	1·0164327	1·0198279	1·0235587	1·0276310	41
20	1·0082471	1·0106710	1·0134161	1·0164865	1·0198873	1·0236237	1·0277018	40
21	1·0082849	1·0107141	1·0134646	1·0165405	1·0199468	1·0236889	1·0277727	39
22	1·0083228	1·0107573	1·0135132	1·0165946	1·0200064	1·0237541	1·0278437	38
23	1·0083607	1·0108006	1·0135618	1·0166487	1·0200661	1·0238195	1·0279148	37
24	1·0083988	1·0108440	1·0136106	1·0167029	1·0201259	1·0238849	1·0279860	36
25	1·0084369	1·0108875	1·0136595	1·0167573	1·0201858	1·0239504	1·0280573	35
26	1·0084752	1·0109310	1·0137084	1·0168117	1·0202457	1·0240161	1·0281287	34
27	1·0085135	1·0109747	1·0137574	1·0168662	1·0203058	1·0240818	1·0282002	33
28	1·0085519	1·0110184	1·0138066	1·0169208	1·0203660	1·0241476	1·0282717	32
29	1·0085904	1·0110622	1·0138558	1·0169755	1·0204262	1·0242135	1·0283434	31
30	1·0086290	1·0111061	1·0139051	1·0170303	1·0204866	1·0242795	1·0284152	30
31	1·0086676	1·0111501	1·0139545	1·0170851	1·0205470	1·0243456	1·0284871	29
32	1·0087064	1·0111942	1·0140040	1·0171401	1·0206075	1·0244118	1·0285590	28
33	1 0087452	1·0112384	1·0140536	1·0171952	1·0206682	1·0244781	1·0286311	27
34	1·0087842	1·0112827	1·0141032	1·0172503	1·0207289	1·0245445	1·0287033	26
35	1·0088232	1·0113270	1·0141530	1·0173056	1·0207897	1·0246110	1·0287755	25
36	1·0088623	1·0113715	1·0142029	1·0173609	1·0208506	1·0246776	1·0288479	24
37	1·0089015	1·0114160	1·0142528	1·0174163	1·0209116	1·0247442	1·0289203	23
38	1·0089408	1·0114606	1·0143028	1·0174719	1·0209727	1·0248110	1·0289929	22
39	1·0089802	1·0115054	1·0143530	1·0175275	1·0210339	1·0248779	1·0290655	21
40	1·0090196	1·0115502	1·0144032	1·0175832	1·0210952	1·0249448	1·0291383	20
41	1 0090592	1·0115951	1·0144535	1·0176390	1·0211566	1·0250119	1·0292111	19
42	1·0090988	1 0116400	1·0145039	1 0176949	1·0212180	1·0250790	1·0292840	18
43	1·0091386	1·0116851	1·0145544	1·0177509	1·0212795	1·0251463	1·0293571	17
44	1·0091784	1·0117303	1·0146050	1·0178069	1·0213413	1·0252136	1·0294302	16
45	1·0092183	1·0117755	1·0146556	1·0178631	1·0214030	1·0252811	1·0295034	15
46	1·0092583	1·0118229	1·0147064	1·0179194	1·0214619	1·0253486	1·0295768	14
47	1·0092984	1·0118663	1·014 572	1·0179757	1·0215268	1·0254162	1·0296502	13
48	1 0093386	1·0119118	1·0148082	1·0180321	1·0215888	1·0254839	1·0297237	12
49	1·0093788	1·0119575	1·0148592	1·0180887	1·0216510	1·0255518	1·0297973	11
50	1·0094192	1·0120032	1·0149103	1·0181453	1·0217132	1·0256197	1·0298711	10
51	1·0094596	1·0120489	1·0149616	1·0182020	1·0217755	1·0256877	1·0299449	9
52	1·0095001	1·0120948	1·0150129	1·0182588	1·0218379	1·0257558	1·0300188	8
53	1·0095408	1·0121408	1·0150643	1·0183158	1·0219004	1·0258240	1·0300928	7
54	1·0095815	1·0121869	1·0151158	1·0183728	1·0219630	1·0258923	1·0301669	6
55	1 0096223	1·0122330	1·0151673	1·0184298	1·0220257	1·0259607	1·0302411	5
56	1·0096631	1·0122793	1·0152190	1·0184870	1·0220885	1·0260292	1·0303154	4
57	1·0097041	1·0123256	1·0152708	1·0185443	1·0221514	1·0260978	1·0303898	3
58	1·0097452	1·0123720	1·0153226	1·0186017	1·0222144	1·0261665	1·0304643	2
59	1·0097863	1·0124185	1·0153746	1·0186591	1·0222774	1·0262352	1·0305389	1
60	1·0098276	1·0124651	1·0154266	1·0187167	1·0223406	1·0263041	1·0306136	0
′	82°	81°	80°	79°	78°	77°	76°	′

CO-SECANTS.

SECANTS.

′	14°	15°	16°	17°	18°	19°	20°	′
0	1·0306136	1·0352762	1·0402994	1·0456918	1·0514622	1·0576207	1·0641778	60
1	1·0306884	1·0353569	1·0403863	1·0457848	1·0515617	1·0577267	1·0642905	59
2	1·0307633	1·0354378	1·0404732	1·0458780	1·0516612	1·0578328	1·0644033	58
3	1·0308383	1·0355187	1·0405602	1·0459712	1·0517608	1·0579390	1·0645163	57
4	1·0309134	1·0355998	1·0406473	1·0460646	1·0518606	1·0580453	1·0646294	56
5	1·0309886	1·0356809	1·0407346	1·0461581	1·0519605	1·0581517	1·0647425	55
6	1·0310639	1·0357621	1·0408219	1·0462516	1·0520604	1·0582583	1·0648558	54
7	1·0311393	1·0358435	1·0409094	1·0463453	1·0521605	1·0583649	1·0649693	53
8	1·0312147	1·0359249	1·0409969	1·0464391	1·0522607	1·0584717	1·0650828	52
9	1·0312903	1·0360065	1·0410845	1·0465330	1·0523610	1·0585786	1·0651964	51
10	1·0313660	1·0360881	1·0411723	1·0466270	1·0524614	1·0586855	1·0653102	50
11	1·0314418	1·0361699	1·0412601	1·0467211	1·0525619	1·0587926	1·0654240	49
12	1·0315177	1·0362517	1·0413481	1·0468153	1·0526625	1·0588999	1·0655380	48
13	1·0315936	1·0363337	1·0414362	1·0469096	1·0527633	1·0590072	1·0656521	47
14	1·0316697	1·0364157	1·0415243	1·0470040	1·0528641	1·0591146	1·0657663	46
15	1·0317459	1·0364979	1·0416126	1·0470986	1·0529651	1·0592221	1·0658807	45
16	1·0318222	1·0365801	1·0417009	1·0471932	1·0530661	1·0593298	1·0659951	44
17	1·0318985	1·0366625	1·0417894	1·0472879	1·0531673	1·0594376	1·0661097	43
18	1·0319750	1·0367449	1·0418780	1·0473828	1·0532686	1·0595454	1·0662243	42
19	1·0320516	1·0368275	1·0419667	1·0474777	1·0533699	1·0596534	1·0663391	41
20	1·0321282	1·0369101	1·0420554	1·0475728	1·0534714	1·0597615	1·0664540	40
21	1·0322050	1·0369929	1·0421443	1·0476679	1·0535730	1·0598697	1·0665690	39
22	1·0322818	1·0370757	1·0422333	1·0477632	1·0536747	1·0599781	1·0666842	38
23	1·0323588	1·0371587	1·0423224	1·0478586	1·0537705	1·0600865	1·0667994	37
24	1·0324359	1·0372417	1·0424116	1·0479540	1·0538785	1·0601951	1·0669118	36
25	1·0325130	1·0373249	1·0425009	1·0480496	1·0539805	1·0603037	1·0670302	35
26	1·0325903	1·0374082	1·0425903	1·0481453	1·0540826	1·0604125	1·0671458	34
27	1·0326676	1·0374915	1·0426798	1·0482411	1·0541849	1·0605214	1·0672615	33
28	1·0327451	1·0375750	1·0427694	1·0483370	1·0542873	1·0606304	1·0673774	32
29	1·0328227	1·0376585	1·0428591	1·0484330	1·0543897	1·0607395	1·0674933	31
30	1·0329003	1·0377422	1·0429489	1·0485291	1·0544923	1·0608487	1·0676094	30
31	1·0329781	1·0378260	1·0430388	1·0486253	1·0545950	1·0609580	1·0677255	29
32	1·0330559	1·0379098	1·0431289	1·0487217	1·0546978	1·0610675	1·0678418	28
33	1·0331339	1·0379938	1·0432190	1·0488181	1·0548007	1·0611770	1·0679582	27
34	1·0332119	1·0380779	1·0433092	1·0489146	1·0549037	1·0612867	1·0680747	26
35	1·0332901	1·0381621	1·0433995	1·0490113	1·0550068	1·0613965	1·0681914	25
36	1·0333683	1·0382463	1·0434900	1·0491080	1·0551101	1·0615064	1·0683081	24
37	1·0334467	1·0383307	1·0435805	1·0492049	1·0552134	1·0616164	1·0684250	23
38	1·0335251	1·0384152	1·0436712	1·0493019	1·0553169	1·0617265	1·0685420	22
39	1·0336037	1·0384998	1·0437619	1·0493989	1·0554204	1·0618367	1·0686591	21
40	1·0336823	1·0385844	1·0438528	1·0494961	1·0555241	1·0619471	1·0687763	20
41	1·0337611	1·0386692	1·0439437	1·0495934	1·0556279	1·0620575	1·0688936	19
42	1·0338390	1·0387541	1·0440348	1·0496908	1·0557318	1·0621681	1·0690110	18
43	1·0339188	1·0388391	1·0441259	1·0497883	1·0558358	1·0622788	1·0691286	17
44	1·0339979	1·0389242	1·0442172	1·0498859	1·0559399	1·0623896	1·0692463	16
45	1·0340770	1·0390094	1·0443086	1·0499836	1·0560441	1·0625005	1·0693641	15
46	1·0341563	1·0390947	1·0444001	1·0500815	1·0561485	1·0626115	1·0694820	14
47	1·0342356	1·0391800	1·0444917	1·0501794	1·0562529	1·0627227	1·0696000	13
48	1·0343151	1·0392655	1·0445833	1·0502774	1·0563575	1·0628339	1·0697182	12
49	1·0343946	1·0393511	1·0446751	1·0503756	1·0564621	1·0629453	1·0698364	11
50	1·0344743	1·0394368	1·0447670	1·0504738	1·0565669	1·0630568	1·0699548	10
51	1·0345540	1·0395226	1·0448590	1·0505722	1·0566718	1·0631684	1·0700733	9
52	1·0346338	1·0396085	1·0449511	1·0506706	1·0567768	1·0632801	1·0701919	8
53	1·0347138	1·0396945	1·0450433	1·0507692	1·0568819	1·0633919	1·0703106	7
54	1·0347938	1·0397806	1·0451357	1·0508679	1·0569871	1·0635038	1·0704295	6
55	1·0348740	1·0398669	1·0452281	1·0509667	1·0570924	1·0636158	1·0705484	5
56	1·0349542	1·0399532	1·0453206	1·0510656	1·0571978	1·0637280	1·0706675	4
57	1·0350346	1·0400396	1·0454132	1·0511646	1·0573034	1·0638403	1·0707867	3
58	1·0351150	1·0401261	1·0455060	1·0512637	1·0574090	1·0639527	1·0709060	2
59	1·0351955	1·0402127	1·0455988	1·0513629	1·0575148	1·0640652	1·0710254	1
60	1·0352762	1·0402994	1·0456918	1·0514622	1·0576207	1·0641778	1·0711450	0
′	75°	74°	73°	72°	71°	70°	69°	′

CO-SECANTS.

SECANTS.

′	21°	22°	23°	24°	25°	26°	27°	′
0	1·0731450	1·0785347	1·0863604	1·0946363	1·1033779	1·1126019	1·1223262	60
1	1·0712647	1·0786616	1·0864946	1·0947781	1·1035277	1·1127599	1·1224927	59
2	1·0713844	1·0787885	1·0866289	1·0949201	1·1036775	1·1129179	1·1226592	58
3	1·0715043	1·0789156	1·0867634	1·0950622	1·1038275	1·1130761	1·1228259	57
4	1·0716244	1·0790427	1·0868979	1·0952044	1·1039777	1·1132345	1·1229928	56
5	1·0717445	1·0791700	1·0870326	1·0953407	1·1041279	1·1133929	1·1231598	55
6	1·0718647	1·0792975	1·0871675	1·0954892	1·1042783	1·1135516	1·1233269	54
7	1·0719851	1·0794250	1·0873024	1·0956318	1·1044289	1·1137103	1·1234912	53
8	1·0721056	1·0795527	1·0874375	1·0957746	1·1045795	1·1138692	1·1236616	52
9	1·0722262	1·0796805	1·0875727	1·0959174	1·1047303	1·1140282	1·1238292	51
10	1·0723469	1·0798084	1·0877080	1·0960604	1·1048813	1·1141874	1·1239969	50
11	1·0724678	1·0799364	1·0878435	1·0962036	1·1050324	1·1143467	1·1241648	49
12	1·0725887	1·0800646	1·0879791	1·0963468	1·1051836	1·1145062	1·1243328	48
13	1·0727098	1·0801928	1·0881148	1·0964902	1·1053349	1·1146658	1·1245010	47
14	1·0728310	1·0803212	1·0882500	1·0966337	1·1054864	1·1148255	1·1246693	46
15	1·0729523	1·0804497	1·0883866	1·0967774	1·1056380	1·1149854	1·1248377	45
16	1·0730737	1·0805784	1·0885226	1·0969212	1·1057898	1·1151454	1·1250063	44
17	1·0731953	1·0807071	1·0886589	1·0970651	1·1059417	1·1153056	1·1251750	43
18	1·0733170	1·0808360	1·0887952	1·0972091	1·1060937	1·1154659	1·1253439	42
19	1·0734388	1·0809650	1·0889317	1·0973533	1·1062458	1·1156263	1·1255130	41
20	1·0735607	1·0810942	1·0890682	1·0974976	1·1063981	1·1157869	1·1256821	40
21	1·0736827	1·0812234	1·0892050	1·0976420	1·1065506	1·1159476	1·1258514	39
22	1·0738048	1·0813528	1·0893418	1·0977866	1·1067031	1·1161084	1·1260209	38
23	1·0739271	1·0814823	1·0894788	1·0979313	1·1068558	1·1162694	1·1261905	37
24	1·0740495	1·0816119	1·0896159	1·0980761	1·1070087	1·1164306	1·1263603	36
25	1·0741720	1·0817417	1·0897531	1·0982211	1·1071616	1·1165919	1·1265302	35
26	1·0742946	1·0818715	1·0898904	1·0983662	1·1073147	1·1167533	1·1267003	34
27	1·0744173	1·0820015	1·0900279	1·0985114	1·1074680	1·1169148	1·1268705	33
28	1·0745402	1·0821316	1·0901655	1·0986568	1·1076214	1·1170766	1·1270408	32
29	1·0746631	1·0822618	1·0903032	1·0988023	1·1077749	1·1172384	1·1272113	31
30	1·0747862	1·0823922	1·0904411	1·0989479	1·1079285	1·1174004	1·1273819	30
31	1·0749095	1·0825227	1·0905791	1·0990936	1·1080823	1·1175625	1·1275527	29
32	1·0750328	1·0826533	1·0907172	1·0992395	1·1082363	1·1177248	1·1277237	28
33	1·0751562	1·0827840	1·0908554	1·0993855	1·1083903	1·1178872	1·1278918	27
34	1·0752798	1·0829149	1·0909938	1·0995317	1·1085445	1·1180498	1·1280660	26
35	1·0754035	1·0830458	1·0911323	1·0996779	1·1086989	1·1182124	1·1282374	25
36	1·0755273	1·0831769	1·0912709	1·0998243	1·1088533	1·1183753	1·1284089	24
37	1·0756512	1·0833081	1·0914097	1·0999709	1·1090079	1·1185383	1·1285806	23
38	1·0757753	1·0834395	1·0915485	1·1001175	1·1091627	1·1187014	1·1287524	22
39	1·0758995	1·0835709	1·0916876	1·1002644	1·1093176	1·1188647	1·1289244	21
40	1·0760237	1·0837025	1·0918267	1·1004113	1·1094726	1·1190281	1·1290965	20
41	1·0761481	1·0838342	1·0919659	1·1005584	1·1096277	1·1191916	1·1292687	19
42	1·0762727	1·0839661	1·0921053	1·1007056	1·1097830	1·1193553	1·1294412	18
43	1·0763973	1·0840980	1·0922448	1·1008529	1·1099385	1·1195191	1·1296137	17
44	1·0765221	1·0842301	1·0923845	1·1010004	1·1100940	1·1196831	1·1297864	16
45	1·0766470	1·0843623	1·0925243	1·1011480	1·1102498	1·1198472	1·1299593	15
46	1·0767720	1·0844947	1·0926642	1·1012957	1·1104056	1·1200115	1·1301323	14
47	1·0768971	1·0846271	1·0928042	1·1014436	1·1105616	1·1201759	1·1303055	13
48	1·0770224	1·0847597	1·0929444	1·1015916	1·1107177	1·1203405	1·1304788	12
49	1·0771477	1·0848924	1·0930846	1·1017397	1·1108740	1·1205051	1·1306522	11
50	1·0772732	1·0850252	1·0932251	1·1018879	1·1110304	1·1206700	1·1308258	10
51	1·0773988	1·0851582	1·0933656	1·1020363	1·1111869	1·1208350	1·1309996	9
52	1·0775246	1·0852913	1·0935063	1·1021849	1·1113436	1·1210001	1·1311735	8
53	1·0776504	1·0854245	1·0936471	1·1023335	1·1115004	1·1211653	1·1313475	7
54	1·0777764	1·0855578	1·0937880	1·1024823	1·1116573	1·1213308	1·1315217	6
55	1·0779025	1·0856912	1·0939291	1·1026313	1·1118144	1·1214963	1·1316961	5
56	1·0780287	1·0858248	1·0940702	1·1027803	1·1119716	1·1216620	1·1318706	4
57	1·0781550	1·0859585	1·0942116	1·1029295	1·1121290	1·1218278	1·1320452	3
58	1·0782815	1·0860924	1·0943530	1·1030789	1·1122865	1·1219938	1·1322200	2
59	1·0784080	1·0862263	1·0944946	1·1032283	1·1124442	1·1221600	1·1323950	1
60	1·0785347	1·0863604	1·0946363	1·1033779	1·1126019	1·1223262	1·1325701	0
′	68°	67°	66°	65°	64°	63°	62°	′

CO-SECANTS.

SECANTS.

′	28°	29°	30°	31°	32°	33°	34°	′
0	1·1325701	1·1433541	1·1547005	1.1666334	1·1791784	1·1921633	1·2062179	60
1	1·1327453	1·1435385	1·1548945	1·1668374	1·1793928	1·1925886	1·2064547	59
2	1·1329207	1·1437231	1·1550887	1·1670416	1·1796074	1·1928142	1·2066917	58
3	1·1330962	1·1439078	1·1552830	1·1672459	1·1798222	1·1930399	1·2069288	57
4	1·1332719	1·1440927	1·1554775	1·1674504	1·1800372	1·1932658	1·2071662	56
5	1·1334478	1·1442778	1·1556722	1·1676551	1·1802523	1·1934918	1·2074037	55
6	1·1336238	1·1444630	1·1558670	1·1678599	1·1804676	1·1937181	1·2076415	54
7	1·1337999	1·1446484	1·1560620	1·1680649	1·1806831	1·1939446	1·2078794	53
8	1·1339762	1·1448339	1·1562572	1·1682701	1·1808988	1·1941712	1·2081175	52
9	1·1341527	1·1450196	1·1564525	1·1684755	1·1811146	1·1943980	1·2083559	51
10	1·1343293	1·1452055	1·1566480	1·1686810	1·1813307	1·1946251	1·2085944	50
11	1·1345060	1·1453915	1·1568436	1·1688867	1·1815469	1·1948523	1·2088331	49
12	1·1346829	1·1455776	1·1570394	1·1690926	1·1817633	1·1950796	1·2090720	48
13	1·1348600	1·1457639	1·1572354	1·1692986	1.1819798	1·1953072	1·2093112	47
14	1·1350372	1·1459504	1·1574315	1·1695048	1·1821966	1·1955350	1·2095505	46
15	1·1352146	1·1461371	1·1576278	1·1697112	1·1824135	1·1957629	1·2097900	45
16	1·1353921	1·1463238	1·1578243	1·1699178	1·1826306	1·1959911	1·2100297	44
17	1·1355697	1·1465108	1·1580209	1·1701245	1·1828479	1·1962194	1·2102696	43
18	1·1357476	1·1466979	1·1582177	1·1703314	1·1830654	1·1964479	1·2105097	42
19	1·1359255	1·1468852	1·1584146	1·1705385	1·1832830	1·1966767	1·2107500	41
20	1·1361036	1·1470726	1·1586118	1·1707457	1·1835008	1·1969056	1·2109905	40
21	1·1362819	1·1472602	1·1588091	1·1709531	1·1837188	1·1971346	1·2112312	39
22	1·1364603	1·1474479	1·1590065	1·1711607	1·1839370	1·1973639	1·2114721	38
23	1·1366389	1·1476358	1·1592041	1·1713685	1·1841554	1·1975934	1·2117132	37
24	1·1368176	1·1478239	1·1594019	1·1715764	1·1843739	1·1978230	1·2119545	36
25	1·1369965	1·1480121	1·1595999	1·1717845	1·1845927	1·1980529	1·2121960	35
26	1·1371755	1·1482005	1·1597980	1·1719928	1·1848116	1·1982829	1·2124377	34
27	1·1373547	1·1483890	1·1599963	1·1722013	1·1850307	1·1985131	1·2126795	33
28	1·1375341	1·1485777	1·1601947	1·1724099	1·1852500	1·1987435	1·2129216	32
29	1·1377135	1·1487665	1·1603933	1·1726187	1·1854694	1·1989741	1·2131639	31
30	1·1378932	1·1489555	1·1605921	1·1728277	1·1856890	1·1992049	1·2134064	30
31	1·1380730	1·1491447	1·1607911	1·1730368	1·1859089	1·1994359	1·2136491	29
32	1·1382529	1·1493340	1·1609902	1·1732462	1·1861289	1·1996671	1·2138920	28
33	1·1384330	1·1495235	1·1611894	1·1734557	1·1863490	1·1998985	1·2141351	27
34	1·1386133	1·1497132	1·1613889	1·1736653	1·1865694	1·2001300	1·2143784	26
35	1·1387937	1·1499030	1·1615885	1·1738752	1·1867900	1·2003618	1·2146218	25
36	1·1389742	1·1500930	1·1617883	1·1740852	1·1870107	1·2005937	1·2148655	24
37	1·1391550	1·1502831	1·1619882	1·1742954	1·1872316	1·2008258	1·2151094	23
38	1·1393358	1·1504734	1·1621883	1·1745058	1·1874527	1·2010582	1·2153535	22
39	1·1395169	1·1506638	1·1623886	1·1747163	1·1876740	1·2012907	1·2155978	21
40	1·1396980	1·1508544	1·1625891	1·1749270	1·1878954	1·2015234	1·2158423	20
41	1·1398794	1·1510452	1·1627897	1·1751379	1·1881171	1·2017563	1·2160870	19
42	1·1400608	1·1512361	1·1629905	1·1753490	1·1883389	1·2019894	1·2163319	18
43	1·1402425	1·1514272	1·1631914	1·1755603	1·1885609	1·2022226	1·2165770	17
44	1·1404243	1·1516185	1·1633925	1·1757717	1·1887831	1·2024561	1·2168223	16
45	1·1406062	1·1518099	1·1635938	1·1759833	1·1890055	1·2026898	1·2170678	15
46	1·1407883	1·1520015	1·1637953	1·1761951	1·1892280	1·2029236	1·2173135	14
47	1·1409706	1·1521932	1·1639968	1·1764070	1·1894508	1·2031577	1·2175594	13
48	1·1411530	1·1523851	1·1641987	1·1766191	1·1896737	1·2033919	1·2178055	12
49	1·1413356	1·1525772	1·1644007	1·1768314	1·1898968	1·2036264	1·2180518	11
50	1·1415183	1·1527694	1·1646028	1·1770439	1·1901201	1·2038610	1·2182983	10
51	1·1417012	1·1529618	1·1648051	1·1772566	1·1903436	1·2040958	1·2185450	9
52	1·1418842	1·1531543	1·1650076	1·1774694	1·1905673	1·2043308	1·2187919	8
53	1·1420674	1·1533470	1·1652102	1·1776824	1·1907911	1·2045660	1·2190390	7
54	1·1422507	1·1535399	1·1654130	1·1778956	1·1910152	1·2048014	1·2192864	6
55	1·1424342	1·1537329	1·1656160	1·1781089	1·1912394	1·2050370	1·2195339	5
56	1·1426179	1·1539261	1·1658191	1·1783225	1·1914638	1·2052728	1·2197816	4
57	1·1428017	1·1541195	1·1660224	1·1785362	1·1916884	1·2055088	1·2200296	3
58	1·1429857	1·1543130	1·1662259	1·1787501	1·1919132	1·2057450	1·2202777	2
59	1·1431698	1·1545067	1·1664296	1·1789642	1·1921381	1·2059814	1·2205260	1
60	1·1433541	1·1547005	1·1666334	1·1791784	1·1923633	1·2062179	1·2207746	0
′	61°	60°	59°	58°	57°	56°	55°	′

CO-SECANTS.

460   NATURAL SECANTS AND CO-SECANTS

SECANTS.

′	35°	36°	37°	38°	39°	40°	41°	′
0	1·2207746	1·2360680	1·2521357	1·2600182	1·2867596	1·3054073	1·3250130	60
1	1·2210233	1·2363293	1·2524102	1·2603067	1·2870628	1·3057261	1·3253482	59
2	1·2212723	1·2365909	1·2526850	1·2695955	1·2873663	1·3060451	1·3256837	58
3	1·2215215	1·2368526	1·2529601	1·2698845	1·2876700	1·3063644	1·3260194	57
4	1·2217708	1·2371146	1·2532353	1·2701737	1·2879740	1·3066839	1·3263554	56
5	1·2220204	1·2373768	1·2535108	1.2704632	1·2882782	1·3070038	1·3266918	55
6	1·2222702	1·2376393	1·2537865	1·2707529	1·2885827	1·3073239	1·3270284	54
7	1·2225202	1·2379019	1·2540625	1·2710429	1·2888875	1·3076442	1·3273653	53
8	1·2227703	1·2381647	1·2543387	1·2713331	1·2891925	1·3079649	1·3277024	52
9	1·2230207	1·2384278	1·2546151	1·2716235	1·2894977	1·3082858	1·3280399	51
10	1·2232713	1·2386911	1·2548917	1·2719142	1·2898032	1·3086069	1·3283776	50
11	1·2235722	1·2389546	1·2551685	1·2722052	1·2901090	1·3089284	1·3287156	49
12	1·2237732	1·2392183	1·2554456	1·2724963	1·2904150	1·3092501	1·3290539	48
13	1·2240244	1·2394823	1·2557229	1·2727877	1·2907213	1·3095720	1·3293925	47
14	1·2242758	1·2397464	1·2560005	1·2730794	1·2910278	1·3098943	1·3297314	46
15	1·2245274	1·2400108	1·2562782	1·2733712	1·2913346	1·3102168	1·3300706	45
16	1·2247793	1·2402754	1·2565562	1·2736634	1·2916416	1·3105396	1·3304100	44
17	1.2250313	1·2405402	1·2568345	1·2739557	1·2919489	1·3108626	1·3307497	43
18	1·2252836	1·2408052	1·2571129	1·2742484	1·2922564	1·3111860	1·3310897	42
19	1·2255361	1·2410704	1·2573916	1·2745412	1·2925642	1·3115095	1·3314301	41
20	1·2257887	1·2413359	1·2576705	1·2748343	1·2928723	1·3118334	1·3317707	40
21	1·2260416	1·2416016	1·2570497	1·2751276	1·2931806	1·3121575	1·3321115	39
22	1·2262947	1·2418675	1·2582291	1·2754212	1·2934892	1·3124820	1·3324527	38
23	1·2265480	1·2421336	1·2585087	1·2757151	1·2937980	1·3128066	1·3327942	37
24	1·2268015	1·2423999	1·2587885	1·2760091	1·2941071	1·3131316	1·3331359	36
25	1·2270552	1·2426665	1·2590686	1·2763034	1·2944164	1·3134568	1·3334779	35
26	1·2273091	1·2429333	1·2593489	1·2765980	1·2947260	1·3137823	1·3338203	34
27	1·2275633	1·2432003	1·2596294	1·2768928	1·2950359	1·3141081	1·3341629	33
28	1·2278176	1·2434675	1·2599102	1·2771878	1·2953460	1·3144341	1·3345058	32
29	1·2280722	1·2437349	1·2601912	1·2774831	1·2956564	1·3147604	1·3348489	31
30	1·2283269	1·2440026	1·2604724	1·2777787	1·2959670	1·3150870	1·3351924	30
31	1·2285819	1·2442704	1·2607539	1·2780744	1·2962779	1·3154139	1·3355362	29
32	1·2288371	1·2445385	1·2610356	1·2783705	1·2965890	1·3157410	1·3358802	28
33	1·2290924	1·2448069	1·2613175	1·2786667	1·2969004	1·3160684	1·3362246	27
34	1·2293480	1·2450754	1·2615997	1·2789632	1·2972121	1·3163961	1·3365692	26
35	1·2296039	1·2453442	1·2618820	1·2792600	1·2975240	1·3167240	1·3369141	25
36	1·2298599	1·2456131	1·2621617	1·2795570	1·2978362	1·3170523	1·3372594	24
37	1·2301161	1·2458823	1·2624475	1·2798543	1·2981487	1·3173808	1·3376049	23
38	1·2303725	1·2461518	1·2627306	1·2801518	1·2984614	1·3177006	1·3379507	22
39	1·2306292	1·2464214	1·2630140	1·2804495	1·2987743	1·3180386	1·3382968	21
40	1·2308861	1·2466913	1·2632975	1·2807475	1·2990876	1·3183680	1·3386432	20
41	1·2311432	1·2469614	1·2635813	1·2810457	1·2994011	1·3186976	1·3389898	19
42	1·2314004	1·2472317	1·2638653	1·2813412	1·2997148	1·3190274	1·3393368	18
43	1·2316579	1·2475022	1·2641496	1·2816430	1·3000288	1·3193576	1·3396841	17
44	1·2319156	1·2477730	1·2644341	1·2819419	1·3003431	1·3196881	1·3400316	16
45	1·2321736	1·2480440	1·2647188	1·2822412	1·3006576	1·3200188	1·3403795	15
46	1·2324317	1·2483152	1·2650038	1·2825407	1·3009724	1·3203498	1·3407276	14
47	1·2326900	1·2485866	1·2652890	1·2828404	1·3012875	1·3206810	1·3410761	13
48	1·2329486	1·2488583	1·2655745	1·2831401	1·3016028	1·3210126	1·3414248	12
49	1·2332074	1·2491302	1·2658601	1·2834406	1·3019184	1·3213444	1·3417738	11
50	1·2334664	1·2494023	1·2661460	1·2837411	1·3022343	1·3216765	1·3421232	10
51	1·2337256	1·2496746	1·2664322	1·2840118	1·3025504	1·3220089	1·3424728	9
52	1·2339850	1·2499471	1·2667186	1·2843428	1·3028667	1·3223416	1·3428227	8
53	1·2342446	1·2502199	1·2670052	1·2846440	1·3031834	1·3226745	1·3431729	7
54	1·2345044	1·2504929	1·2672921	1·2849455	1·3035003	1·3230078	1·3435234	6
55	1·2347645	1·2507661	1·2675792	1·2852472	1·3038175	1·3233413	1·3438742	5
56	1·2350248	1·2510396	1·2678665	1·2855492	1·3041349	1·3236750	1·3442253	4
57	1·2352852	1·2513133	1·2681541	1·2858514	1·3044526	1·3240091	1·3445767	3
58	1·2355459	1·2515872	1·2684419	1·2861539	1·3047706	1·3243435	1·3449284	2
59	1·2358069	1·2518613	1·2687299	1·2864566	1·3050888	1·3246781	1·3452804	1
60	1·2360680	1·2521357	1·2690182	1·2867596	1·3054073	1·3250130	1·3456327	0
′	54°	53°	52°	51°	50°	49°	48°	′

CO-SECANTS.

SECANTS.

′	42°	43°	44°	45°	46°	47°	48°	′
0	1·3456327	1·3673275	1·3901636	1·4142136	1·4395565	1·4662792	1·4944765	60
1	1·3459853	1·3676985	1·3905543	1·4146251	1·4399904	1·4667368	1·4949596	59
2	1·3463382	1·3680699	1·3909453	1·4150370	1·4404246	1·4671948	1·4954431	58
3	1·3466914	1·3684416	1·3913366	1·4154493	1·4408592	1·4676532	1·4959270	57
4	1·3470449	1·3688136	1·3917283	1·4158619	1·4412941	1·4681120	1·4964113	56
5	1·3473987	1·3691859	1·3921203	1·4162749	1·4417295	1·4685713	1·4968961	55
6	1·3477528	1·3695586	1·3925127	1·4166883	1·4421652	1·4690309	1·4973813	54
7	1·3481072	1·3699315	1·3929054	1·4171020	1·4426013	1·4694910	1·4978670	53
8	1·3484619	1·3703048	1·3932985	1·4175161	1·4430379	1·4699514	1·4983531	52
9	1·3488168	1·3706784	1·3936918	1·4179306	1·4434748	1·4704123	1·4988397	51
10	1·3491721	1·3710523	1·3940856	1·4183454	1·4439120	1·4708736	1·4993267	50
11	1·3495277	1·3714266	1·3944796	1·4187605	1·4443497	1·4713354	1·4998141	49
12	1·3498836	1·3718011	1·3948740	1·4191761	1·4447878	1·4717975	1·5003020	48
13	1·3502398	1·3721760	1·3952688	1·4195920	1·4452262	1·4722600	1·5007903	47
14	1·3505963	1·3725512	1·3956639	1·4200082	1·4456651	1·4727230	1·5012791	46
15	1·3509531	1·3729268	1·3960593	1·4204248	1·4461043	1·4731864	1·5017683	45
16	1·3513102	1·3733026	1·3964551	1·4208418	1·4465439	1·4736502	1·5022580	44
17	1·3516677	1·3736788	1·3968512	1·4212592	1·4469839	1·4741144	1·5027481	43
18	1·3520254	1·3740553	1·3972477	1·4216769	1·4474243	1·4745790	1·5032387	42
19	1·3523834	1·3744321	1·3976445	1·4220950	1·4478651	1·4750440	1·5037297	41
20	1·3527417	1·3748092	1·3980416	1·4225134	1·4483063	1·4755095	1·5042211	40
21	1·3531003	1·3751867	1·3984391	1·4229323	1·4487478	1·4759754	1·5047131	39
22	1·3534593	1·3755645	1·3988369	1·4233514	1·4491898	1·4764417	1·5052054	38
23	1·3538185	1·3759426	1·3992351	1·4237710	1·4496322	1·4769084	1·5056982	37
24	1·3541780	1·3763210	1·3996336	1·4241909	1·4500749	1·4773755	1·5061915	36
25	1·3545379	1·3766998	1·4000325	1·4246112	1·4505181	1·4778431	1·5066852	35
26	1·3548980	1·3770789	1·4004317	1·4250319	1·4509616	1·4783111	1·5071793	34
27	1·3552585	1·3774583	1·4008313	1·4254529	1·4514055	1·4787795	1·5076739	33
28	1·3556193	1·3778380	1·4012312	1·4258743	1·4518408	1·4792483	1·5081600	32
29	1·3559803	1·3782181	1·4016315	1·4262961	1·4522946	1·4797176	1·5086645	31
30	1·3563417	1·3785985	1·4020321	1·4267182	1·4527397	1·4801872	1·5091605	30
31	1·3567034	1·3789792	1·4024330	1·4271407	1·4531852	1·4806573	1·5096569	29
32	1·3570654	1·3793602	1·4028343	1·4275636	1·4536311	1·4811278	1·5101538	28
33	1·3574277	1·3797416	1·4032360	1·4279868	1·4540774	1·4815988	1·5106511	27
34	1·3577903	1·3801233	1·4036380	1·4284105	1·4545241	1·4820702	1·5111489	26
35	1·3581532	1·3805053	1·4040403	1·4288345	1·4549712	1·4825420	1·5116472	25
36	1·3585164	1·3808877	1·4044430	1·4292588	1·4554187	1·4830142	1·5121459	24
37	1·3588800	1·3812704	1·4048461	1·4296836	1·4558666	1·4834868	1·5126450	23
38	1·3592438	1·3816534	1·4052494	1·4301087	1·4563149	1·4839599	1·5131446	22
39	1·3596080	1·3820367	1·4056532	1·4305342	1·4567636	1·4844334	1·5136447	21
40	1·3599725	1·3824204	1·4060573	1·4309600	1·4572127	1·4849073	1·5141452	20
41	1·3603372	1·3828044	1·4064617	1·4313863	1·4576621	1·4853817	1·5146462	19
42	1·3607023	1·3831887	1·4068665	1·4318129	1·4581120	1·4858565	1·5151477	18
43	1·3610677	1·3835734	1·4072717	1·4322399	1·4585623	1·4863317	1·5156496	17
44	1·3614334	1·3839584	1·4076772	1·4326772	1·4590130	1·4868073	1·5161520	16
45	1·3617995	1·3843437	1·4080831	1·4330950	1·4594641	1·4872834	1·5166548	15
46	1·3621658	1·3847294	1·4084893	1·4335231	1·4599156	1·4877599	1·5171581	14
47	1·3625324	1·3851153	1·4088958	1·4339516	1·4603675	1·4882369	1·5176619	13
48	1·3628994	1·3855017	1·4093028	1·4343805	1·4608198	1·4887142	1·5181661	12
49	1·3632667	1·3858883	1·4097100	1·4348097	1·4612726	1·4891920	1·5186708	11
50	1·3636343	1·3862753	1·4101177	1·4352393	1·4617257	1·4896703	1·5191759	10
51	1·3640022	1·3866626	1·4105257	1·4356693	1·4621792	1·4901489	1·5196815	9
52	1·3643704	1·3870503	1·4109340	1·4360997	1·4626321	1·4906280	1·5201876	8
53	1·3647389	1·3874383	1·4113427	1·4365305	1·4630875	1·4911076	1·5206942	7
54	1·3651078	1·3878266	1·4117517	1·4369616	1·4635422	1·4915876	1·5212012	6
55	1·3654770	1·3882153	1·4121612	1·4373932	1·4639973	1·4920680	1·5217087	5
56	1·3658464	1·3886043	1·4125709	1·4378251	1·4644529	1·4925488	1·5222166	4
57	1·3662162	1·3889936	1·4129810	1·4382574	1·4649089	1·4930301	1·5227250	3
58	1·3665863	1·3893832	1·4133915	1·4386900	1·4653652	1·4935118	1·5232339	2
59	1·3669567	1·3897733	1·4138024	1·4391231	1·4658220	1·4939940	1·5237433	1
60	1·3673275	1·3901636	1·4142136	1·4395565	1·4662792	1·4944765	1·5242531	0
′	47°	46°	45°	44°	43°	42°	41°	′

CO-SECANTS.

SECANTS.

′	49°	50°	51°	52°	53°	54°	55°	′
0	1·5242531	1·5557238	1·5890157	1·6242692	1·6616401	1·7013016	1·7434468	60
1	1·5247634	1·5562634	1·5895868	1·6248743	1·6622819	1·7019831	1·7441715	59
2	1·5252741	1·5568035	1·5901584	1·6254799	1·6629243	1·7026653	1·7448969	58
3	1·5257854	1·5573441	1·5907306	1·6260861	1·6635673	1·7033482	1·7456230	57
4	1·5262971	1·5578852	1·5913033	1·6266929	1·6642110	1·7040318	1·7463499	56
5	1·5268093	1·5584268	1·5918766	1·6273003	1·6648553	1·7047160	1·7470776	55
6	1·5273219	1·5589689	1·5924504	1·6279083	1·6655002	1·7054010	1·7478060	54
7	1·5278351	1·5595115	1·5930247	1·6285169	1·6661458	1·7060867	1·7485352	53
8	1·5283487	1·5600546	1·5935996	1·6291261	1·6667920	1·7067730	1·7492651	52
9	1·5288627	1·5605982	1·5941751	1·6297359	1·6674389	1·7074601	1·7499958	51
10	1·5293773	1·5611424	1·5947511	1·6303462	1·6680864	1·7081478	1·7507273	50
11	1·5298923	1·5616871	1·5953276	1·6309572	1·6687345	1·7088362	1·7514595	49
12	1·5304078	1·5622322	1·5959048	1·6315688	1·6693833	1·7095254	1·7521924	48
13	1·5309238	1·5627779	1·5964824	1·6321809	1·6700328	1·7102152	1·7529262	47
14	1·5314403	1·5633241	1·5970606	1·6327937	1·6706828	1·7109058	1·7536607	46
15	1·5319572	1·5638708	1·5976394	1·6334070	1·6713336	1·7115970	1·7543959	45
16	1·5324746	1·5644181	1·5982187	1·6340210	1·6719850	1·7122890	1·7551320	44
17	1·5329925	1·5649658	1·5987986	1·6346355	1·6726170	1·7129817	1·7558687	43
18	1·5335109	1·5655141	1·5993790	1·6352507	1·6732897	1·7136750	1·7566063	42
19	1·5340297	1·5660628	1·5999600	1·6358664	1·6739430	1·7143691	1·7573446	41
20	1·5345491	1·5666121	1·6005416	1·6364828	1·6745970	1·7150639	1·7580837	40
21	1·5350689	1·5671619	1·6011237	1·6370997	1·6752517	1·7157594	1·7588236	39
22	1·5355892	1·5677123	1·6017064	1·6377173	1·6759070	1·7164556	1·7595642	38
23	1·5361100	1·5682631	1·6022896	1·6383355	1·6765629	1·7171525	1·7603057	37
24	1·5366313	1·5688145	1·6028734	1·6389542	1·6772195	1·7178501	1·7610478	36
25	1·5371530	1·5693664	1·6034577	1·6395736	1·6778768	1·7185484	1·7617908	35
26	1·5376752	1·5699188	1·6040426	1·6401936	1·6785347	1·7192475	1·7625345	34
27	1·5381980	1·5704717	1·6046281	1·6408142	1·6791933	1·7199472	1·7632791	33
28	1·5387212	1·5710252	1·6052142	1·6414354	1·6798525	1·7206477	1·7640244	32
29	1·5392449	1·5715792	1·6058008	1·6420572	1·6805124	1·7213489	1·7647704	31
30	1·5397690	1·5721337	1·6063879	1·6426796	1·6811730	1·7220508	1·7655173	30
31	1·5402937	1·5726887	1·6069757	1·6433027	1·6818342	1·7227534	1·7662619	29
32	1·5408189	1·5732443	1·6075640	1·6439263	1·6824961	1·7234568	1·7670133	28
33	1·5413445	1·5738004	1·6081528	1·6415506	1·6831586	1·7241609	1·7677625	27
34	1·5418706	1·5743570	1·6087423	1·6451754	1·6838219	1·7248657	1·7685125	26
35	1·5423973	1·5749141	1·6093323	1·6458009	1·6844857	1·7255712	1·7692633	25
36	1·5429244	1·5754718	1·6099228	1·6464270	1·6851503	1·7262774	1·7700149	24
37	1·5434520	1·5760300	1·6105140	1·6470537	1·6858155	1·7269844	1·7707672	23
38	1·5439801	1·5765887	1·6111057	1·6476811	1·6864814	1·7276921	1·7715204	22
39	1·5445087	1·5771479	1·6116980	1·6483091	1·6871479	1·7284005	1·7722743	21
40	1·5450378	1·5777077	1·6122908	1·6489376	1·6878151	1·7291096	1·7730290	20
41	1·5455673	1·5782680	1·6128843	1·6495668	1·6884830	1·7298195	1·7737845	19
42	1·5460974	1·5788289	1·6134783	1·6501966	1·6891516	1·7305301	1·7745409	18
43	1·5466280	1·5793902	1·6140728	1·6508270	1·6898202	1·7312414	1·7752980	17
44	1·5471590	1·5799521	1·6146680	1·6514581	1·6904907	1·7319535	1·7760559	16
45	1·5476906	1·5805146	1·6152637	1·6520898	1·6911613	1·7326663	1·7768146	15
46	1·5482226	1·5810776	1·6158600	1·6527221	1·6918326	1·7333798	1·7775741	14
47	1·5487552	1·5816411	1·6164569	1·6533550	1·6925045	1·7340941	1·7783344	13
48	1·5492882	1·5822051	1·6170544	1·6539885	1·6931771	1·7348091	1·7790955	12
49	1·5498218	1·5827697	1·6176524	1·6546227	1·6938504	1·7355248	1·7798574	11
50	1·5503558	1·5833348	1·6182510	1·6552575	1·6945244	1·7362413	1·7806201	10
51	1·5508904	1·5839005	1·6188502	1·6558929	1·6951090	1·7369585	1·7813836	9
52	1·5514254	1·5844667	1·6194500	1·6565290	1·6958744	1·7376764	1·7821479	8
53	1·5519610	1·5850334	1·6200504	1·6571657	1·6965504	1·7383951	1·7829131	7
54	1·5524970	1·5856007	1·6206513	1·6578030	1·6972271	1·7391145	1·7836790	6
55	1·5530335	1·5861685	1·6212528	1·6584409	1·6979044	1·7398347	1·7844457	5
56	1·5535706	1·5867369	1·6218549	1·6590795	1·6985825	1·7405556	1·7852133	4
57	1·5541081	1·5873058	1·6224576	1·6597187	1·6992612	1·7412773	1·7859817	3
58	1·5546462	1·5878752	1·6230609	1·6603585	1·6999407	1·7419997	1·7867508	2
59	1·5551848	1·5884452	1·6236648	1·6609990	1·7006208	1·7427229	1·7875208	1
60	1·5557238	1·5890157	1·6242692	1·6616401	1·7013016	1·7434468	1·7882916	0
′	40°	39°	38°	37°	36°	35°	34°	′

CO-SECANTS.

SECANTS

′	56°	57°	58°	59°	60°	61°	62°	′
0	1·7882916	1·8360785	1·8870799	1·9416040	2·0000000	2·0626653	2·1300545	60
1	1·7890633	1·8369013	1·8879589	1·9425445	2·0010083	2·0637484	2·1312205	59
2	1·7898357	1·8377251	1·8888388	1·9434861	2·0020177	2·0648328	2·1323880	58
3	1·7906090	1·8385498	1·8897197	1·9444288	2·0030283	2·0659186	2·1335570	57
4	1·7913831	1·8393753	1·8906016	1·9453725	2·0040402	2·0670056	2·1347274	56
5	1·7921580	1·8402018	1·8914845	1·9463173	2·0050532	2·0680940	2·1358993	55
6	1·7929337	1·8410292	1·8923684	1·9472632	2·0060674	2·0691836	2·1370726	54
7	1·7937102	1·8418574	1·8932532	1·9482102	2·0070828	2·0702746	2·1382475	53
8	1·7944876	1·8426866	1·8941391	1·9491583	2·0080994	2·0713670	2·1394238	52
9	1·7952658	1·8435166	1·8950259	1·9501075	2·0091172	2·0724606	2·1406015	51
10	1·7960449	1·8443476	1·8959138	1·9510577	2·0101362	2·0735556	2·1417808	50
11	1·7968247	1·8451795	1·8968026	1·9520091	2·0111564	2·0746519	2·1429615	49
12	1·7976054	1·8460123	1·8976924	1·9529615	2·0121779	2·0757496	2·1441438	48
13	1·7983869	1·8468460	1·8985832	1·9539150	2·0132005	2·0768486	2·1453275	47
14	1·7991693	1·8476806	1·8994750	1·9548697	2·0142243	2·0779489	2·1465127	46
15	1·7999524	1·8485161	1·9003678	1·9558254	2·0152494	2·0790506	2·1476993	45
16	1·8007365	1·8493525	1·9012616	1·9567822	2·0162756	2·0801536	2·1488875	44
17	1·8015213	1·8501808	1·9021564	1·9577402	2·0173031	2·0812580	2·1500772	43
18	1·8023070	1·8510281	1·9030522	1·9586992	2·0183318	2·0823637	2·1512684	42
19	1·8030935	1·8518672	1·9039491	1·9596593	2·0193618	2·0834708	2·1524611	41
20	1·8038809	1·8527073	1·9048469	1·9606206	2·0203929	2·0845792	2·1536553	40
21	1·8046691	1·8535483	1·9057457	1·9615829	2·0214253	2·0856890	2·1548510	39
22	1·8054582	1·8543903	1·9066456	1·9625464	2·0224589	2·0868002	2·1560482	38
23	1·8062481	1·8552331	1·9075464	1·9635110	2·0234937	2·0879127	2·1572469	37
24	1·8070388	1·8560769	1·9084483	1·9644767	2·0245297	2·0890265	2·1584471	36
25	1·8078304	1·8569216	1·9093512	1·9654435	2·0255670	2·0901418	2·1596489	35
26	1·8086228	1·8577672	1·9102551	1·9664114	2·0266056	2·0912584	2·1608522	34
27	1·8094161	1·8586138	1·9111600	1·9673805	2·0276453	2·0923764	2·1620570	33
28	1·8102102	1·8594612	1·9120659	1·9683507	2·0286863	2·0934957	2·1632633	32
29	1·8110052	1·8603097	1·9129729	1·9693220	2·0297286	2·0946104	2·1644712	31
30	1·8118010	1·8611590	1·9138809	1·9702944	2·0307720	2·0957385	2·1656806	30
31	1·8125977	1·8620093	1·9147899	1·9712680	2.0318168	2·0968620	2·1668915	29
32	1·8133953	1·8628605	1·9156999	1·9722427	2·0328628	2·0979869	2·1681040	28
33	1·8141937	1·8637126	1·9166110	1·9732185	2·0339100	2·0991131	2·1693180	27
34	1·8149929	1·8645657	1·9175230	1·9741954	2·0349585	2·1002408	2·1705335	26
35	1·8157930	1·8654197	1·9184362	1·9751735	2·0360082	2·1013698	2·1717506	25
36	1·8165940	1·8662747	1·9193503	1·9761527	2·0370592	2·1025002	2·1729693	24
37	1·8173958	1·8671306	1·9202655	1·9771331	2·0381114	2·1026320	2·1741895	23
38	1·8181985	1·8679875	1·9211817	1·9781146	2·0391649	2·1047652	2·1754113	22
39	1·8190021	1·8688453	1·9220990	1·9790972	2·0402197	2·1058998	2·1766346	21
40	1·8198065	1·8699040	1·9230173	1·9800810	2·0412757	2·1070359	2·1778595	20
41	1·8206118	1·8705637	1·9239366	1·9810659	2·0423330	2·1081733	2·1790859	19
42	1·8214179	1·8714244	1·9248570	1·9820520	2·0433916	2·1093121	2·1803139	18
43	1·8222249	1·8722859	1·9257784	1·9830393	2·0444515	2·1104523	2·1815435	17
44	1·8230328	1·8731485	1·92670·9	1·9840276	2·0455126	2·1115940	2·1827746	16
45	1·8238416	1·8740120	1·9276244	1·9850172	2·0465750	2·1127371	2·1840074	15
46	1·8246512	1·8748764	1·9285490	1·9860080	2·0476386	2·1138815	2·1852417	14
47	1·8254617	1·8757419	1·9294746	1·9869997	2·0487036	2·1150274	2·1864775	13
48	1·8262731	1·8766082	1·9304013	1·9879927	2·0497698	2·1161748	2·1877150	12
49	1·8270854	1·8774755	1·9313290	1·9889869	2·0508373	2·1173235	2·1889541	11
50	1·8278985	1·8783438	1·9322578	1·9899822	2·0519061	2·1184737	2·1901947	10
51	1·8287125	1·8792131	1·9331876	1·9909787	2·0529762	2·1196253	2·1914370	9
52	1·8295274	1·8800833	1·9341185	1·9919764	2·0540476	2·1207783	2·1926808	8
53	1·8303432	1·8809545	1·9350505	1·9929752	2·0551203	2 1219328	2·1939262	7
54	1·8311599	1·8818266	1·9359835	1·9939753	2·0561942	2·1230887	2·1951733	6
55	1·8319774	1·8826998	1·9369176	1·9949764	2·0572695	2·1242460	2·1964219	5
56	1·8327959	1·8835738	1·9378527	1·9959788	2·0583460	2·1254048	2·1976721	4
57	1·8336152	1·8844489	1·9387889	1·9969823	2·0594239	2·1265651	2·1989240	3
58	1·8344354	1·8853249	1·9397262	1·9979870	2·0605031	2·1277267	2·2001775	2
59	1·8352565	1·8862019	1·9406646	1·9989929	2·0615836	2·1288899	2·2014326	1
60	1·8360785	1·8870799	1·9416040	2·0000000	2·0626653	2·1300545	2 2026893	0
′	33°	32°	31°	30°	29°	28°	27°	′

CO-SECANTS.

SECANTS.

′	63°	64°	65°	66°	67°	68°	69°	′
0	2·2026893	2·2811720	2·3662016	2·4585933	2·5593047	2·6694672	2·7904281	60
1	2·2039476	2·2825335	2·3676787	2·4602008	2·5610599	2·6713906	2·7925444	59
2	2·2052075	2·2838957	2·3691578	2·4618106	2·5628176	2·6733171	2·7946641	58
3	2·2064691	2·2852618	2·3706390	2·4634227	2·5645781	2·6752465	2·7967873	57
4	2·2077323	2·2866286	2·3721222	2·4650371	2·5663412	2 6771790	2·7989140	56
5	2·2089972	2·2879974	2.3736075	2·4666538	2·5681069	2·6791145	2·8010441	55
6	2·2102637	2·2893679	2·3750949	2·4682729	2·5698752	2·6810530	2·8031777	54
7	2·2115318	2·2907403	2·3765843	2·4698943	2·5716462	2·6829945	2·8053148	53
8	2·2128016	2·2921145	2·3780758	2·4715181	2·5734199	2·6849391	2·8074554	52
9	2·2140730	2·2934906	2·3795691	2·4731442	2·5751963	2·6868867	2·8095995	51
10	2·2153460	2·2948685	2·3810650	2·4747726	2·5769753	2·6888374	2·8117471	50
11	2·2166208	2·2962483	2·3825627	2·4764034	2·5787570	2·6907912	2·8138982	49
12	2·2178971	2·2976299	2·3840625	2·4780366	2·5805414	2·6927480	2·8160529	48
13	2·2191752	2·2990134	2·3855615	2·4796721	2·5823284	2·6947079	2·8182111	47
14	2·2204548	2·3003988	2·3870685	2·4813100	2·5841182	2·6966709	2·8203729	46
15	2·2217362	2·3017860	2·3885746	2·4829503	2·5859107	2·6986370	2·8225382	45
16	2 2230192	2·3031751	2·3900828	2·4845929	2·5877058	2·7006061	2·8247071	44
17	2·2243039	2·3045660	2·3915931	2·4862380	2·5895037	2·7025784	2·8268706	43
18	2·2255903	2·3059588	2·3931055	2·4878854	2·5913043	2·7045538	2·8290556	42
19	2·2268783	2·3073536	2·3946201	2·4895352	2·5931077	2·7065323	2·8312353	41
20	2·2281681	2·3087501	2·3961367	2·4911874	2·5949137	2·7085139	2·8334185	40
21	2·2294595	2·3101486	2·3976555	2·4928421	2·5967225	2·7104987	2·8356054	39
22	2·2307526	2·3115490	2·3991764	2·4944991	2·5985341	2·7124866	2·8377958	38
23	2·2320474	2·3129513	2·4006995	2·4961586	2·6003484	2·7144777	2·8399899	37
24	2·2333438	2·3143554	2·4022247	2·4978204	2·6021654	2·7164719	2·8421877	36
25	2·2346420	2·3157615	2·4037520	2·4994848	2·6039852	2·7184693	2·8443891	35
26	2·2359419	2·3171695	2·4052815	2·5011515	2·6058078	2·7204698	2·8465941	34
27	2·2372435	2·3185794	2·4068132	2·5028207	2·6076332	2·7224735	2·8488028	33
28	2·2385368	2·3199912	2·4083469	2·5044923	2·6094613	2·7244804	2·8510152	32
29	2·2398517	2·3214049	2·4098829	2·5061663	2·6112922	2·7264905	2·8532312	31
30	2·2411585	2·3228205	2·4114210	2·5078428	2·6131259	2·7285038	2·8554510	30
31	2·2424669	2·3242381	2·4129613	2·5095218	2·6149624	2·7305203	2·8576744	29
32	2·2437770	2·3256575	2·4145038	2·5112032	2·6168018	2·7325400	2·8599015	28
33	2·2450889	2·3270790	2·4160484	2·5128871	2·6186439	2·7345630	2·8621324	27
34	2·2464025	2·3285023	2·4175952	2·5145735	2·6204888	2·7365892	2·8643670	26
35	2·2477178	2·3299276	2·4191442	2·5162624	2·6223366	2·7386186	2·8666053	25
36	2·2490348	2·3313548	2·4206954	2·5179537	2·6241872	2·7406512	2·8688474	24
37	2·2503536	2·3327840	2·4222488	2·5196475	2·6260406	2·7426871	2·8710932	23
38	2·2516741	2·3342152	2·4238044	2·5213438	2·6278969	2·7447263	2·8733428	22
39	2·2529964	2·3356482	2·4253622	2·5230426	2·6297560	2·7467687	2·8755961	21
40	2·2543204	2·3370833	2·4269222	2·5247440	2·6316180	2·7488144	2·8778532	20
41	2·2556461	2·3385203	2·4284844	2·5264478	2·6334828	2·7508634	2·8801142	19
42	2·2569736	2·3399593	2·4300489	2·5281541	2·6353506	2·7529157	2·8823789	18
43	2·2583029	2·3414002	2·4316155	2·5298630	2·6372211	2·7549712	2·8846474	17
44	2·2596339	2·3428432	2·4331844	2·5315744	2·6390946	2·7570301	2·8869198	16
45	2·2609667	2·3442881	2·4347555	2·5332883	2·6409710	2·7590923	2·8891960	15
46	2·2623012	2·3457349	2·4363289	2·5350048	2·6428502	2·7611578	2·8914760	14
47	2 2636376	2·3471838	2·4379045	2·5367238	2·6447323	2·7632267	2·8937598	13
48	2·2649756	2·3486347	2·4394823	2·5384453	2·6466174	2·7652988	2·8960475	12
49	2·2663 55	2·3500875	2·4410624	2·5401694	2·6485054	2·7673744	2·8983391	11
50	2·2676571	2·3515424	2·4426448	2·5418961	2·6503963	2·7694532	2·9006346	10
51	2·2690005	2·3529992	2·4442294	2·5436253	2·6522901	2·7715355	2·9029339	9
52	2·2703457	2·3544581	2·4458163	2·5453571	2·6541868	2·7736211	2·9052372	8
53	2·2716927	2·3559189	2·4474054	2·5470915	2·6560865	2·7757100	2·90,5443	7
54	2·2730415	2·3573818	2·4489968	2·5488284	2·6579891	2·7778024	·2·9098553	6
55	2·2743921	2·3588467	2·4505905	2·5505680	2·6598947	2·7798982	2·9121703	5
56	2·2757445	2·3603136	2·4521865	2·5523101	2·6618033	2·7819973	2·9144892	4
57	2·2770987	2·3617826	2·4537848	2·5540548	2·6637148	2·7840999	2·9168121	3
58	2·2784546	2·3632535	2·4553853	2·5558022	2·6656292	2·7862059	2·9191389	2
59	2·2798124	2·3647265	2·4569882	2·5575521	2·6675467	2·7883153	2·9214697	1
60	2·2811720	2·3662016	2·4585933	2·5593047	2·6694672	2·7904281	2·9238044	0
′	26°	25°	24°	23°	22°	21°	20°	′

CO-SECANTS.

SECANTS.

′	70°	71°	72°	73°	74°	75°	76°	′
0	2·9238044	3·0715535	3·2360680	3·4203036	3·6279553	3·8637033	4·1335655	60
1	2·9261431	3·0741507	3·2389678	3·4235611	3·6316395	3·8679025	4·1383939	59
2	2·9284858	3·0767525	3·2418732	3·4268251	3·6353316	3·8721112	4·1432339	58
3	2·9308326	3·0793590	3·2447840	3·4300956	3·6390315	3·8763293	4·1480856	57
4	2·9331833	3·0819702	3·2477003	3·4333727	3·6427392	3·8805570	4·1529491	56
5	2·9355380	3·0845860	3·2506222	3·4366563	3·6464548	3·8847943	4·1578243	55
6	2·9378968	3·0872066	3·2535496	3·4399465	3·6501783	3·8890411	4·1627114	54
7	2·9402597	3·0898319	3·2564825	3·4432433	3·6539097	3·8932976	4·1676102	53
8	2·9426265	3·0924620	3·2594211	3·4465467	3·6576491	3·8975637	4·1725210	52
9	2·9449975	3·0950967	3·2623652	3·4498568	3·6613964	3·9018395	4·1774438	51
10	2·9473725	3·0977363	3·2653149	3·4531735	3·6651518	3·9061250	4·1823785	50
11	2·9497516	3·1003805	3·2682702	3·4564969	3·6689151	3·9104203	4·1873252	49
12	2·9521348	3·1030296	3·2712311	3·4598269	3·6726865	3·9147254	4·1922840	48
13	2·9545221	3·1056835	3·2741977	3·4631637	3·6764660	3·9190403	4·1972549	47
14	2·9569135	3·1083422	3·2771700	3·4665073	3·6802536	3·9233651	4·2022380	46
15	2·9593090	3·1110057	3·2801479	3·4698576	3·6840493	3·9276997	4·2072333	45
16	2·9617087	3·1136740	3·2831316	3·4732146	3·6878532	3·9320443	4·2122408	44
17	2·9641125	3·1163472	3·2861209	3·4765785	3·6916652	3·9363988	4·2172606	43
18	2·9665205	3·1190252	3·2891160	3·4799492	3·6954854	3·9407633	4·2222928	42
19	2·9689327	3·1217081	3·2921168	3·4833267	3·6993139	3·9451379	4·2273373	41
20	2·9713490	3·1243959	3·2951234	3·4867110	3·7031506	3·9495224	4·2323943	40
21	2·9737695	3·1270886	3·2981357	3·4901023	3·7069956	3·9539171	4·2374637	39
22	2·9761942	3·1297862	3·3011539	3·4935004	3·7108489	3·9583219	4·2425457	38
23	2·9786231	3·1324887	3·3041778	3·4969055	3·7147105	3·9627369	4·2476402	37
24	2·9810563	3·1351962	3·3072076	3·5003175	3·7185805	3·9671621	4·2527474	36
25	2·9834936	3·1379086	3·3102432	3·5037365	3·7224589	3·9715975	4·2578671	35
26	2·9859352	3·1406259	3·3132847	3·5071625	3·7263457	3·9760431	4·2629996	34
27	2·9883811	3·1433483	3·3163320	3·5105954	3·7302409	3·9804991	4·2681449	33
28	2·9908312	3·1460756	3·3193853	3·5140354	3·7341446	3·9849654	4·2733029	32
29	2·9932856	3·1488079	3·3224444	3·5174824	3·7380568	3·9894421	4·2784738	31
30	2·9957443	3·1515453	3·3255095	3·5209365	3·7419775	3·9939292	4·2836576	30
31	2·9982073	3·1542877	3·3285805	3·5243977	3·7459068	3·9984267	4·2888543	29
32	3·0006746	3·1570351	3·3316575	3·5278660	3·7498447	4·0029347	4·2940640	28
33	3·0031462	3·1597876	3·3347405	3·5313414	3·7537911	4·0074532	4·2992867	27
34	3·0056221	3·1625452	3·3378294	3·5348240	3·7577462	4·0119823	4·3045225	26
35	3·0081024	3·1653078	3·3409244	3·5383138	3·7617100	4·0165219	4·3097715	25
36	3·0105870	3·1680756	3·3440254	3·5418107	3·7656824	4·0210722	4·3150336	24
37	3·0130760	3·1708484	3·3471324	3·5453149	3·7696636	4·0256332	4·3203090	23
38	3·0155694	3·1736264	3·3502455	3·5488263	3·7736535	4·0302048	4·3255977	22
39	3·0180672	3·1764095	3·3533647	3·5523450	3·7776522	4·0347872	4·3308996	21
40	3·0205693	3·1791978	3·3564900	3·5558710	3·7816596	4·0393804	4·3362150	20
41	3·0230759	3·1819913	3·3596214	3·5594042	3·7856760	4·0439844	4·3415438	19
42	3·0255868	3·1847899	3·3627589	3·5629448	3·7897011	4·0485992	4·3468861	18
43	3·0281023	3·1875937	3·3659026	3·5664928	3·7937352	4·0532249	4·3522419	17
44	3·0306221	3·1904028	3·3690524	3·5700481	3·7977782	4·0578615	4·3576113	16
45	3·0331464	3·1932170	3·3722084	3·5736108	3·8018301	4·0625091	4·3629943	15
46	3·0356752	3·1960365	3·3753707	3·5771810	3·8058911	4·0671677	4·3683910	14
47	3·0382084	3·1988613	3·3785391	3·5807586	3·8099610	4·0718374	4·3738015	13
48	3·0107462	3·2016913	3·3817138	3·5843437	3·8140399	4·0765181	4·3792257	12
49	3·0432884	3·2045266	3·3848948	3·5879362	3·8181280	4·0812100	4·3846638	11
50	3·0458352	3·2073673	3·3880820	3·5915363	3·8222251	4·0859130	4·3901158	10
51	3·0483864	3·2102132	3·3912755	3·5951439	3·8263313	4·0906272	4·3955817	9
52	3·0509123	3·2130644	3·3944754	3·5987590	3·8304467	4·0953526	4·4010616	8
53	3·0535026	3·2159210	3·3976816	3·6023818	3·8345713	4·1000893	4·4065556	7
54	3·0560675	3·2187830	3·4008941	3·6060121	3·8387052	4·1048374	4·4120637	6
55	3·0586370	3·2216503	3·4041130	3·6096501	3·8428482	4·1095967	4·4175859	5
56	3·0612111	3·2245230	3·4073382	3·6133957	3·8470006	4·1143675	4·4231224	4
57	3·0637898	3·2274011	3·4105699	3·6169490	3·8511622	4·1191498	4·4286731	3
58	3·0663731	3·2302846	3·4138080	3·6206101	3·8553332	4·1239435	4·4342382	2
59	3·0689610	3·2331736	3·4170526	3·6242788	3·8595135	4·1287487	4·4398176	1
60	3·0715535	3·2360680	3·4203036	3·6279553	3·8637033	4·1335655	4·4454115	0
′	19°	18°	17°	16°	15°	14°	13°	′

CO-SECANTS.

SECANTS.

′	77°	78°	79°	80°	81°	82°	83°	′
0	4·4454115	4·8097343	5·2408431	5·7587705	6·3924532	7·1852965	8·2055090	60
1	4·4510108	4·8163258	5·2486979	5·7682867	6·4042154	7·2001996	8·2249952	59
2	4·4566428	4·8229357	5·2565768	5·7778350	6·4160216	7·2151653	8·2445748	58
3	4·4622803	4·8295643	5·2644798	5·7874153	6·4278719	7·2301940	8·2642485	57
4	4·4679324	4·8362114	5·2724070	5·7970280	6·4397666	7·2452859	8·2840171	56
5	4·4735993	4·8428774	5·2803587	5·8066732	6·4517059	7·2604117	8·3038812	55
6	4·4792810	4·8495621	5·2883347	5·8163510	6·4636901	7·2756616	8·3238415	54
7	4·4849775	4·8562657	5·2963354	5·8260617	6·4757195	7·2909460	8·3438986	53
8	4·4906889	4·8629883	5·3043608	5·8358053	6·4877944	7·3062954	8·3640534	52
9	4·4964152	4·8697299	5·3124109	5·8455820	6·4999148	7·3217102	8·3843065	51
10	4·5021565	4·8764907	5·3204860	5·8553921	6·5120812	7·3371909	8·4046586	50
11	4·5079129	4·8832707	5·3285861	5·8652356	6·5242938	7·3527377	8·4251105	49
12	4·5136844	4·8900700	5·3367114	5·8751128	6·5365528	7·3683512	8·4456629	48
13	4·5194711	4·8968886	5·3448620	5·8850238	6·5488586	7·3840318	8·4663165	47
14	4·5252730	4·9037267	5·3530379	5·8949688	6·5612113	7·3997798	8·4870721	46
15	4·5310903	4·9105844	5·3612393	5·9049479	6·5736112	7·4155959	8·5079304	45
16	4·5369229	4·9174616	5·3694664	5·9149614	6·5860587	7·4314803	8·5288923	44
17	4·5427709	4·9243586	5·3777192	5·9250095	6·5985540	7·4474335	8·5499584	43
18	4·5486344	4·9312754	5·3859979	5·9350922	6·6110973	7·4634560	8·5711295	42
19	4·5545134	4·9382120	5·3943026	5·9452098	6·6236890	7·4795482	8·5924065	41
20	4·5604080	4·9451687	5·4026333	5·9553625	6·6363293	7·4957106	8·6137901	40
21	4·5663183	4·9521453	5·4109903	5·9655504	6·6490184	7·5119437	8·6352812	39
22	4·5722444	4·9591421	5·4193737	5·9757737	6·6617568	7·5282478	8·6568805	38
23	4·5781862	4·9661591	5·4277835	5·9860326	6·6745446	7·5446236	8·6785889	37
24	4·5841439	4·9731964	5·4362199	5·9963274	6·6873822	7·5610713	8·7004071	36
25	4·5901174	4·9802541	5·4446831	6·0066581	6·7002699	7·5775916	8·7223361	35
26	4·5961070	4·9873323	5·4531731	6·0170250	6·7132079	7·5941849	8·7443766	34
27	4·6021126	4·9944311	5·4616901	6·0274282	6·7261965	7·6108516	8·7665295	33
28	4·6081343	5·0015505	5·4702342	6·0378680	6·7392360	7·6275923	8·7887957	32
29	4·6141722	5·0086907	5·4788056	6·0483445	6·7523268	7·6444075	8·8111761	31
30	4·6202263	5·0158517	5·4874043	6·0588580	6·7654691	7·6612976	8·8336715	30
31	4·6262967	5·0230337	5·4960305	6·0694085	6·7786632	7·6782631	8·8562828	29
32	4·6323835	5·0302367	5·5046843	6·0799964	6·7919095	7·6953047	8·8790109	28
33	4·6384867	5·0374607	5·5133659	6·0906219	6·8052082	7·7124227	8·9018567	27
34	4·6446064	5·0447060	5·5220754	6·1012850	6·8185597	7·7296176	8·9248211	26
35	4·6507427	5·0519726	5·5308129	6·1119861	6·8319642	7·7468901	8·9479051	25
36	4·6568956	5·0592606	5·5395786	6·1227253	6·8454222	7·7642406	8·9711095	24
37	4·6630652	5·0665701	5·5483726	6·1335028	6·8589338	7·7816697	8·9944354	23
38	4·6692516	5·0739012	5·5571951	6·1443189	6·8724995	7·7991778	9·0178837	22
39	4·6754548	5·0812539	5·5660460	6·1551736	6·8861195	7·8167656	9·0414553	21
40	4·6816748	5·0886284	5·5749258	6·1660674	6·8997942	7·8344335	9·0651512	20
41	4·6879119	5·0960248	5·5838343	6·1770003	6·9135239	7·8521821	9·0880725	19
42	4·6941660	5·1034431	5·5927719	6·1879725	6·9273089	7·8700120	9·1129200	18
43	4·7004372	5·1108835	5·6017386	6·1989843	6·9411496	7·8879238	9·1369940	17
44	4·7067256	5·1183461	5·6107345	6·2100359	6·9550464	7·9059179	9·1611980	16
45	4·7130313	5·1258309	5·6197599	6·2211275	6·9689994	7·9239950	9·1855305	15
46	4·7193542	5·1333381	5·6288148	6·2322504	6·9830092	7·9421556	9·2099934	14
47	4·7256915	5·1408677	5·6378995	6·2434316	6·9970760	7·9604003	9·2345877	13
48	4·7320524	5·1484199	5·6470140	6·2546446	7·0112001	7·9787208	9·2593145	12
49	4·7384277	5·1559948	5·6561584	6·2658984	7·0253820	7·9971445	9·2841749	11
50	4·7448206	5·1635924	5·6653331	6·2771933	7·0396220	8·0156450	9·3091699	10
51	4·7512312	5·1712128	5·6745380	6·2885295	7·0539205	8·0342321	9·3343006	9
52	4·7576596	5·1788563	5·6837734	6·2999073	7·0682777	8·0529062	9·3595682	8
53	4·7761058	5·1865228	5·6930393	6·3113269	7·0826941	8·0716681	9·3849738	7
54	4·7703699	5·1912125	5·7023360	6·3237884	7·0971700	8·0905182	9·4105184	6
55	4·7770519	5·2019254	5·7116636	6·3342923	7·1117059	8·1094573	9·4362033	5
56	4·7835520	5·2096618	5·7210223	6·3458386	7·1263019	8·1284860	9·4620296	4
57	4·7900702	5·2174216	5·7304121	6·3574276	7·1409587	8·1476048	9·4879984	3
58	4·7966066	5·2252050	5·7398333	6·3690595	7·1556764	8·1668145	9·5141110	2
59	4·8031613	5·2330121	5·7492861	6·3807347	7·1704556	8·1861157	9·5403686	1
60	4·8097343	5·2408431	5·7587705	6·3924532	7·1852965	8·2055090	9·5667722	0
′	12°	11°	10°	9°	8°	7°	6°	′

CO-SECANTS.

	SECANTS.						
′	**84°**	**85°**	**86°**	**87°**	**88°**	**89°**	′
0	9·5667722	11·473713	14·335587	19·107323	28·653708	57·298688	60
1	9·5933233	11·511990	14·395471	19·213970	28·894398	58·269755	59
2	9·6200229	11·550523	14·455859	19·321816	29·139169	59·274308	58
3	9·6468724	11·589316	14·516757	19·430882	29·388124	60·314110	57
4	9·6738730	11·628372	14·578172	19·541187	29·641373	61·391050	56
5	9·7010260	11·667693	14·640109	19 652754	29·899026	62·507153	55
6	9·7283327	11·707282	14·702576	19·765604	30·161201	63·664595	54
7	9·7557944	11·747141	14·765580	19·879758	30·428017	64·865716	53
8	9·7834124	11·787274	14·829128	19·995241	30·699598	66·113036	52
9	9·8111880	11·827683	14·893226	20·112075	30·976074	67·409272	51
10	9·8391227	11·868370	14·957882	20·230284	31·257577	68·757360	50
11	9·8672176	11·909340	15·021103	20·349893	31·544246	70·160474	49
12	9·8954744	11·950595	15·088896	20·470926	31·836225	71·622052	48
13	9·9238943	11·992137	15·155270	20·593409	32·133663	73·145827	47
14	9·9524787	12·033970	15·222231	20·717368	32·436713	74·735856	46
15	9·9812291	12·076098	15·289788	20·842830	32·745537	76·396554	45
16	10·010147	12·118522	15·357949	20·969824	33·060300	78·132742	44
17	10·039234	12·161246	15·426721	21·098376	33·381176	79·949684	43
18	10·068491	12·204274	15·496114	21·228515	33·708345	81·853150	42
19	10·097920	12·247608	15·566135	21·360272	34·041994	83·849470	41
20	10·127522	12·291252	15·636793	21·493676	34·382316	85·945609	40
21	10·157300	12·335210	15·708096	21·628759	34·729515	88·149244	39
22	10·187254	12·379484	15·780054	21·765553	35·083800	90·468853	38
23	10·217386	12·424078	15·852676	21·904090	35·445391	92·913869	37
24	10·247697	12·468995	15·925971	22·044403	35·814517	95·494711	36
25	10·278190	12·514240	15·999948	22·186528	36·191414	98·223033	35
26	10·308866	12·559815	16·074617	22·330499	36·576332	101·11185	34
27	10·339726	12·605724	16·149987	22·476353	36·969528	104·17574	33
28	10·370772	12·651971	16·226069	22·624126	37·371273	107·43114	32
29	10·402007	12·698560	16·302873	22·773857	37·781849	110·89656	31
30	10·433431	12·745495	16·380408	22·925586	38·201550	114·59301	30
31	10·465046	12·792779	16·458686	23·079351	38·630683	118·54440	29
32	10·496854	12·840416	16·537717	23·235196	39·069571	122·77803	28
33	10·528857	12·888410	16·617512	23·393161	39·518549	127·32526	27
34	10·561057	12·936765	16·698082	23·553291	39·977909	132·22229	26
35	10·593455	12·985486	16·779439	23·715630	40·448201	137·51108	25
36	10·626054	13·034576	16·861594	23·880224	40·929630	143·24061	24
37	10·658854	13·084040	16·944559	24·047121	41·422660	149·46837	23
38	10·691859	13·133882	17·028346	24·216370	41·927717	156·26228	22
39	10·725070	13·184106	17·112966	24·388020	42·445245	163·70325	21
40	10·758488	13·234717	17·198434	24·562123	42·975713	171·88831	20
41	10·792117	13·285719	17·284761	24·738731	43·519612	180·93496	19
42	10·825957	13·337116	17·371960	24·917900	44·077458	190·98680	18
43	10·860011	13·388914	17·460046	25·099685	44·649750	202·22122	17
44	10·894281	13·441118	17·549030	25·284144	45·237195	214·85995	16
45	10·928768	13·493731	17·638928	25·471337	45·840260	229·18385	15
46	10·963476	13·546758	17·729753	25·661324	46·459625	245·55440	14
47	10·998406	13·600205	17·821520	25·854169	47·095961	264·44269	13
48	11·033560	13·654077	17·914213	26·049937	47·749974	286·47948	12
49	11·068940	13·708379	18·007937	26·248694	48·422411	312·52297	11
50	11·104549	13·763115	18·102619	26·450510	49·114062	343·77516	10
51	11·140389	13·818291	18·198303	26·655455	49·825762	381·97230	9
52	11·176462	13·873913	18·295005	26·863603	50·558396	429·71873	8
53	11·212770	13·929985	18·392742	27·075030	51·312902	491·10702	7
54	11·249316	13·986514	18·491530	27·289814	52·090212	572·95809	6
55	11·286101	14·043504	18·591387	27·508035	52·891564	687·54960	5
56	11·323129	14·100963	18·692330	27·729777	53·717896	859.43689	4
57	11·360402	14·158894	18·794377	27·955125	54·570464	1145·9157	3
58	11·397922	14·217304	18·897545	28·184168	55·450534	1718·8735	2
59	11·435692	14·276200	19·001854	28·416997	56·359462	3437·7468	1
60	11·473715	14·335587	19·107323	28·653708	57·298688	Infinite.	0
′	**5°**	**4°**	**3°**	**2°**	**1°**	**0°**	′
	CO-SECANTS.						

BIBLIOGRAPHY

Baker, T.—Land and Engineering Surveying (London).
Birchal, H. F.—Modern Surveying for Civil Engineers (London).
Bonford, G.—Geodesy (Oxford).
Breed, C. B. and G. L.—The Principles and Practice of Surveying (London).
Chapman, R. W.—Elements of Astronomy for Surveyors (5th Edition) (London).
Clark, D.—Plane and Geodetric Surveying for Engineers, Vols. 1 and 2 (Fifth Edition) (London).
Clendinning, J.—Principles of Surveying (London and Glasgow).
Clendinning, J.—Principles and Use of Surveying Instruments (London and Glasgow).
Colonial Office Conference of British Commonwealth Survey Offices (London).
Davis, R. E.—Elementary Plane Surveying (New York and London).
Davis, R. E., and Foot, F. C.—Surveying: Theory and Practice (5th Edition) (New York and London).
Higgins, A. L.—Higher Surveying (London).
Hodgman, C. M.—The Building Society Surveyor (London).
Hunting Aerosurveys Ltd.—Photogrammetric Mapping (London).
Jameson, A. H., and Ormsby, M. J. M.—Elementary Surveying and Map Projection (London).
Kissam, P.—Surveying Instruments and Methods for Surveys of Limited Extent (New York and London).
Kissam, P.—Surveying for Civil Engineers (New York and London).
Knight, B. H.—Surveying and Levelling for Students (2nd Edition) (London).
McPherson, D. H.—Surveying (London).
Manton, B. G.—Highway Surveying and Setting-Out (London).
Malcolm, J.—Elementary Surveying (2nd Edition) (London).
Middleton, R. E., and Chadwick, O.—A Treatise on Surveying (6th Edition) (London).
Parry, R., and Jenkins, W. R.—Land Surveying (6th Edition) (London).
Perrott, S. W.—Surveying for Young Engineers (London).
Raynor, W. H., and Schmidt, M. O.—Surveying: Elementary and Advanced (New York).
Rainsford, H. F.—Uganda Surveying the Recomputation of the Uganda Main Triangulation (Entebbe).
Redmond, F. H.—Tacheometry (London).
Stewart, F. R., and Grassie, J. C.—Surveying for Agricultural Students and Planters (London).
Taylor, E. W.—Theodolites (London).
Threlfall, H.—A Textbook on Surveying and Levelling (London).
Whitelaw, J.—Surveying (9th Edition) (London).
Williamson, J.—Surveying and Field Work (London).
Willis, A. J.—To be a Surveyor (London).

INDEX

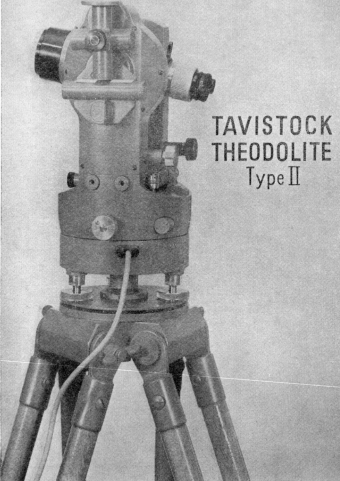

SURVEYING INSTRUMENTS

TAVISTOCK
THEODOLITE
Type II

Cooke Troughton & Simms LTD
YORK ENGLAND